Christian Hymns

NUMBER TWO

L. O. Sanderson, Editor

This compilation of Psalms, Hymns, and Spiritual Songs, including all of the best from the original Christian Hymns, with many additional standard compositions and a few high quality new ones, is sent forth with the hope that it will meet the need of the church and give honor and glory to our Father in heaven and his only begotten Son and our Saviour, Jesus Christ.

Published only in shaped notes, in durable cloth binding

PRICE $1.20 EACH

Delivery charges paid on cash orders only

Published by

GOSPEL ADVOCATE CO.

110 Seventh Avenue, North

NASHVILLE 1, TENNESSEE

Copyright, 1948, by the Gospel Advocate Company

PREFACE
A Song! A Beautiful Song!

L. O. S.

L. O. Sanderson

1. I would like to think when I'm near-er life's brink That I've writ-ten some
2. I would like to feel when the last time I kneel By my bed-side to
3. I would like to know when from earth I must go That the Christ was the

song that will live, And, liv-ing, im-part some help to some heart, And
pray my last prayer, That ev-er a-long my life was a song Whose
theme of my songs—In life or in hymn, the praise gave I Him, To

CHORUS

strength to the trav-el-er give.
mu-sic my heart set with care. And then, on-ly then! can I
whom all the glo-ry be-longs.

wel-come the end Of the path-way I've fol-lowed so long; And

rit.

leave be-hind, by truth re-fined, A song! A beau-ti-ful song!

1   Trust and Obey

J. H. Sammis   D. B. Towner

1. When we walk with the Lord In the light of His Word, What a glo-ry He
2. Not a bur-den we bear, Not a sor-row we share, But our toil He doth
3. But we nev-er can prove The de-lights of His love Un-til all on the
4. Then in fel-low-ship sweet We will sit at His feet, Or we'll walk by His

sheds on our way! While we do His good will, He a-bides with us still,
rich-ly re-pay; Not a grief nor a loss, Not a frown nor a cross,
al-tar we lay; For the fa-vor He shows, And the joy He be-stows,
side in the way; What He says we will do, Where He sends we will go—

CHORUS

And with all who will trust and o-bey.
But is blest if we trust and o-bey.   Trust and o-bey, for there's
Are for those who will trust and o-bey.
Nev-er fear, on-ly trust and o-bey.

no oth-er way To be hap-py in Je-sus, but to trust and o-bey.

2 I Know That My Redeemer Lives

Arr. by F. A. F.

Fred A. Fillmore

1. I know (I know) that my Re-deem-er lives, And ev-er
2. He wills (He wills) that I should ho-ly be, In word, in
3. I know (I know) that un-to sin-ful men His sav-ing
4. I know (I know) that o-ver yon-der stands A place pre-

prays (and ev-er prays) for me; I know (I know) e-ter-nal
tho't, (in word, in tho't,) in deed; Then I (then I) His ho-ly
grace (His sav-ing grace) is nigh; I know (I know) that He will
pared (a place pre-pared) for me; A home, (a home,) a house not

life He gives, From sin and sor-row free.
face may see, When from this earth-life freed.
come a-gain To take me home on high.
made with hands, Most won-der-ful to see.

CHORUS

I know, I know that
my Re-deem-er lives, I know, I know e-ter-nal life He gives;

I know, I know that my Re-deem-er lives.
I know that my Re-deem-er lives, that my

3

For Me He Careth

Horatius Bonar. Arr.

L. O. Sanderson

1. Yes, for me, for me He car-eth, With lov-ing, ten-der care;
2. Yes, for me, He stand-eth plead-ing At mer-cy's seat a-bove,
3. Yes, in me, in me He dwell-eth! In me and I in Him,

Yes, with me, with me He shar-eth Each bur-den and each fear.
Ev-er for me in-ter-ced-ing In love, un-tir-ing love.
And my soul with hope He fill-eth, Tho' fu-ture plans are dim.

REFRAIN

Yes, o'er me, o'er me He watch-eth, Cease-less watch-eth night and day;
Yes, in me a-broad He shed-deth Joys un-earth-ly, love and light;
Thus I wait for His re-turn-ing, Sing-ing all the way to heav'n;

Yes, e'en me, e'en me He snatch-eth From per-ils of the way.
And to cov-er me He spread-eth His lov-ing wings of might.
Such the joy-ful song of morn-ing, Such tran-quil song of ev'n.

4   No, Not One

Johnson Oatman, Jr.

Geo. C. Hugg

1. { There's not a friend like the low - ly Je - sus, No, not one! no, not one! }
{ None else could heal all our soul's dis - eas - es, No, not one! no, not one! }

2. { No friend like Him is so high and ho - ly, No, not one! no, not one! }
{ And yet no friend is so meek and low - ly, No, not one! no, not one! }

3. { There's not an hour that He is not near us, No, not one! no, not one! }
{ No night so dark but His love can cheer us, No, not one! no, not one! }

D.C.–*There's not a friend like the low - ly Je - sus, No, not one! no, not one!*

CHORUS   *D. C.*

Je - sus knows all a-bout our strug-gles; He will guide till the day is done;

5   There Is a Green Hill Far Away

Cecil F. Alexander

George C. Stebbins

1. There is a green hill far a - way, With-out a cit - y wall,
2. We may not know, we can - not tell What pains He had to bear;
3. There was no oth - er good e-nough To pay the price of sin;

Where the dear Lord was cru - ci - fied, Who died to save us all.
But we be - lieve it was for us He hung and suf - fered there.
He on - ly could un - lock the gate Of heaven and let us in.

There Is a Green Hill, Concluded

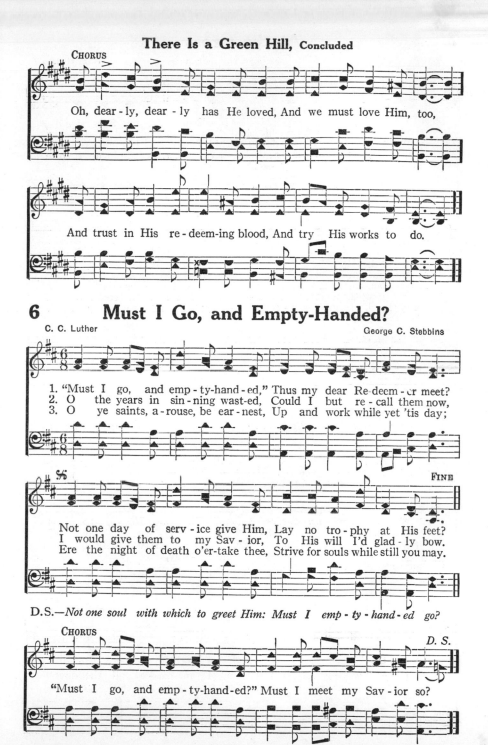

CHORUS

Oh, dear - ly, dear - ly has He loved, And we must love Him, too,

And trust in His re - deem-ing blood, And try His works to do.

6   Must I Go, and Empty-Handed?

C. C. Luther

George C. Stebbins

1. "Must I go, and emp - ty-hand - ed," Thus my dear Re-deem - er meet?
2. O the years in sin - ning wast-ed, Could I but re - call them now,
3. O ye saints, a - rouse, be ear - nest, Up and work while yet 'tis day;

FINE

Not one day of serv - ice give Him, Lay no tro - phy at His feet?
I would give them to my Sav - ior, To His will I'd glad - ly bow.
Ere the night of death o'er-take thee, Strive for souls while still you may.

D.S.—*Not one soul with which to greet Him: Must I emp - ty - hand - ed go?*

CHORUS

D. S.

"Must I go, and emp - ty-hand - ed?" Must I meet my Sav - ior so?

7   At the Cross

I. Watts

R. E. Hudson

1. A - las! and did my Sav - ior bleed? And did my Sov-'reign die?
2. Was it for crimes that I had done He groaned up - on the tree?
3. Well might the sun in dark-ness hide, And shut His glo - ries in,
4. But drops of grief can ne'er re - pay The debt of love I owe,

Would He de - vote that sa - cred head, For such a worm as I?
A - maz - ing pit - y! grace un-known! And love be - yond de - gree!
When Christ, the might - y Mak - er, died For man the crea-ture's sin.
Here, Lord, I give my - self a - way; 'Tis all that I can do.

CHORUS

At the cross, at the cross, where I first saw the light, And the

bur-den of my heart rolled a - way,
      rolled a - way,
It was there by faith

I re-ceived my sight, And now I am hap-py all the day.

8 We're Marching to Zion

Isaac Watts

Robert Lowry

9 Blest Be the Tie

John Fawcett

Hans G. Naegeli

1. Blest be the tie that binds Our hearts in Chris-tian love; The
2. Be - fore our Fa - ther's throne, We pour our ar - dent prayers; Our
3. We share our mu - tual woes; Our mu - tual bur - dens bear; And
4. When we a - sun - der part, It gives us in - ward pain; But

fel - low-ship of kin - dred minds Is like to that a - bove.
fears, our hopes, our aims are one, Our com - forts and our cares.
of - ten for each oth - er flows The sym - pa - thiz - ing tear.
we shall still be joined in heart, And hope to meet a - gain.

10 Praise the Lord, Ye Heavens Adore Him

J. Kempthorne

Lowell Mason

1. Praise the Lord, ye heav'ns, a-dore Him! Praise Him, an - gels, in the height;
2. Praise the Lord, for He hath spo-ken, Worlds His might-y voice o-beyed;
3. Praise the Lord, for He is glo-rious, Nev - er shall His prom-ise fail;
4. Praise the God of our sal - va-tion; Hosts on high, His pow'r pro-claim;

Sun and moon rejoice before Him;   Praise Him, all ye stars of light.
Laws which never shall be bro-ken,   For their guidance He hath made.
God hath made His saints victorious, Sin and death shall not prevail.
Heav'n and earth and all crea-tion,   Laud and mag-ni-fy His name.

(1) Sun   and moon rejoice before Him; Praise   Him, all ye stars of light.

REFRAIN

A - - - - men.

Hal - le - lu - jah! A - men, Hal - le - lu - jah! A - men, A - men, A - men.

11 Let Him In

J. B. Atchinson

E. O. Excell

1. There's a Stran-ger at the door, Let Him in;
2. O - pen now to Him your heart, Let Him in;
3. Hear you now His lov - ing voice? Let Him in;

Let the Savior in, Let the Savior in;

He has been there oft be - fore, Let Him in;
If you wait He will de - part, Let Him in;
Now, O now, make Him your choice, Let Him in;

Let the Savior in, Let the Savior in;

Let Him in, ere He is gone, Let Him in, the Ho - ly One,
Let Him in, He is your Friend, He your soul will sure de - fend,
He is stand-ing at your door, Joy to you He will re - store,

Je - sus Christ, the Fa-ther's Son, Let Him in.
He will keep you to the end, Let Him in.
And His name you will a - dore, Let Him in.

Let the Savior in, Let the Savior in.

12 Come to the Feast

Charlotte G. Homer

W. A. Ogden

1. "All things are read-y," come to the feast! Come, for the ta-ble now is
2. "All things are read-y," come to the feast! Come, for the door is o-pen
3. "All things are read-y," come to the feast! Come, while He waits to wel-come
4. "All things are read-y," come to the feast! Leave ev-'ry care and world-ly

spread; Ye fam-ish-ing, ye wea-ry, come, And thou shalt be rich-ly fed.
wide; A place of hon-or is re-served For you at the Mas-ter's side.
thee; De-lay not while this day is thine, To-mor-row may nev-er be.
strife; Come, feast up-on the love of God, And drink ev-er-last-ing life.

CHORUS

Hear.......... the in-vi-ta - - - tion, Come, "who - - - so-ev-er
Hear the in-vi-ta - tion, "Who-so-ev-er will," Hear the in-vi-ta - tion,

will;"................... Praise God.................... for full sal-
"Who-so-ev-er will;" Praise God for full sal-va - tion For

va - - - - tion For "who - so - ev - er will."
"Who-so-ev-er will,"

13 I Will Sing of My Redeemer

P. P. Bliss

James McGranahan

1. I will sing of my Re-deem-er, And His won-drous love to me;
2. I will tell the wondrous sto-ry, How my lost es-tate to save,
3. I will sing of my Re-deem-er, And His heav'n-ly love to me;

On the cru-el cross He suf-fered, From the curse to set me free.
In His bound-less love and mer-cy, He the ran-som free-ly gave.
He from death to life hath brought me, Son of God, with Him to be.

CHORUS

Sing, O sing............. of my Re-deem-er! With His
Sing, O sing of my Re-deem-er, Sing, O sing of my Re-deem-er;

blood........ He purchased me;........ On the cross........ He sealed my
blood He purchased me, With His blood He purchased me, On the cross He sealed my pardon, On the

par-don, Paid the debt.......... and made me free...........
cross He sealed my pardon, Paid the debt and made me free, and made me free, and made me free.

14 Consider the Lilies

Matthew 6: 28, 29

E. H. Packard

Con-sid-er the lil-ies of the field, Con-sid-er the lil-ies of the

how they grow;

field, They toil not, they toil not, they

how they grow; They toil not, they toil not,

toil not, nei-ther do they spin, do they spin: And yet I

nei-ther do they spin,

say un-to you, (un-to you,) And yet I say

And yet I say . . . . . . un-to

un-to you, That Sol-o-mon in all his glo-ry was not ar-

you, That e-ven Sol-o-mon.... in all his glo-ry

rayed,....... was not ar-rayed like one of these, like one of these.

was not ar-rayed, was not arrayed like one of these, like one of these.

15 The Home Up There

T. O. Chisholm Copyright, 1935, by L. O. Sanderson L. O. Sanderson

1. This is not our rest, this is not our home, We are trav-'lers bound
2. To the home up there oft we turn our eyes, When some joy de-parts,
3. Pre-cious home up there which the Lord pre-pares For the ones whose names

for a world to come; Comes full soon the end of life's lit-tle day,
when a dear one dies; Then we vi-sion here of a cit-y fair,
in His book ap-pears! How our fond hearts yearn for the Lord's re-turn,

D. S.—*Where we'll sigh no more 'Neath the loads we bear,*

FINE   CHORUS

And our place found emp-ty, for we fly a-way.
Where will end the part-ings—in the home up there.   O! it won't be long
When we'll meet to-geth-er in the home up there.

Be with Christ for-ev-er in the home up there.

D. S.

till we reach our home, Where no death in-vades, where no trou-ble comes;

16 The Precious Book Divine

Arr. by L. O. S. Copyright, 1935, by Gospel Advocate Company L. O. Sanderson

1. How pre-cious is the Book di-vine, By in-spi-ra-tion giv'n!
2. It sweet-ly cheers my droop-ing heart, In this dark vale of tears;
3. This lamp, thro' all the te-dious night Of life, shall guide my way,

Bright as a lamp its pre-cepts shine, To guide my soul to heav'n.
Light to my life it still im-parts, And quells my ris-ing fears.
Till I be-hold the clear-er light Of an e-ter-nal day.

CHORUS

Ho-ly Book di-vine!...... Pre-cious treas-ure mine!........
Ho-ly Bi-ble, Book di-vine! Pre-cious treas-ure, thou art mine!

Lamp to my feet and a light to my way To guide me safe-ly home.

17 More Love to Thee, O Christ

Elizabeth Prentiss W. H. Doane

1. More love to Thee, O Christ, More love to Thee! Hear Thou the
2. Once earth-ly joy I craved, Sought peace and rest; Now Thee a-
3. Then shall my lat-est breath Whis-per Thy praise; This be the

More Love to Thee, Concluded

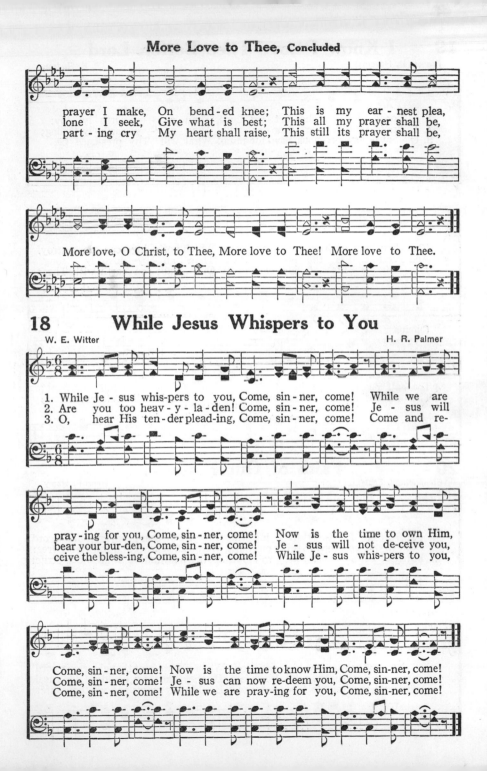

prayer I make, On bend-ed knee; This is my ear-nest plea,
lone I seek, Give what is best; This all my prayer shall be,
part-ing cry My heart shall raise, This still its prayer shall be,

More love, O Christ, to Thee, More love to Thee! More love to Thee.

18   While Jesus Whispers to You

W. E. Witter   H. R. Palmer

1. While Je-sus whis-pers to you, Come, sin-ner, come! While we are
2. Are you too heav-y-la-den! Come, sin-ner, come! Je-sus will
3. O, hear His ten-der plead-ing, Come, sin-ner, come! Come and re-

pray-ing for you, Come, sin-ner, come! Now is the time to own Him,
bear your bur-den, Come, sin-ner, come! Je-sus will not de-ceive you,
ceive the bless-ing, Come, sin-ner, come! While Je-sus whis-pers to you,

Come, sin-ner, come! Now is the time to know Him, Come, sin-ner, come!
Come, sin-ner, come! Je-sus can now re-deem you, Come, sin-ner, come!
Come, sin-ner, come! While we are pray-ing for you, Come, sin-ner, come!

19 I Know I Love Thee Better, Lord

Frances R. Havergal

R. E. Hudson

1. I know I love Thee bet-ter, Lord, Than an-y earth-ly joy;
2. I know that Thou art near-er still Than an-y earth-ly throng;
3. O Sav-ior, pre-cious Sav-ior mine! What will Thy pres-ence be,

For Thou hast giv-en me the peace Which noth-ing can de-stroy.
And sweet-er is the tho't of Thee Than an-y love-ly song.
If such a life of joy can crown Our walk on earth with Thee?

CHORUS

{ The half has nev-er yet been told,   Of love so full and free! }
{ The half has nev-er yet been told,   The blood—it cleanseth me! }
(yet been told,)

20 Faith of Our Fathers!

Frederick W. Faber

Henri F. Hemy

1. Faith of our fa-thers! liv-ing still In spite of dun-geon, fire, and sword:
2. Our fa-thers, chained in pris-ons dark, Were still in heart and conscience free:
3. Faith of our fa-thers! we will love Both friend and foe in all our strife:

O how our hearts beat high with joy When-e'er we hear that glo-rious word!
How sweet would be their chil-dren's fate, If they, like them, could die for thee!
And preach thee, too, as love knows how, By kind-ly words and vir-tuous life:

Faith of Our Fathers, Concluded

Faith of our fa-thers, ho - ly faith! We will be true to thee till death!
Faith of our fa-thers, ho - ly faith! We will be true to thee till death!
Faith of our fa-thers, ho - ly faith! We will be true to thee till death!

21 Be with Me, Lord

T. O. Chisholm

L. O. Sanderson

1. Be with me, Lord— I can-not live with-out Thee, I dare not
2. Be with me, Lord, and then if dan-gers threat-en, If storms of
3. Be with me, Lord! No oth - er gift or bless - ing Thou couldst be-
4. Be with me, Lord, when lone - li - ness o'er-takes me, When I must

try to take one step a - lone, I can-not bear the loads of
tri - al burst a - bove my head, If lash-ing seas leap ev - 'ry-
stow could with this one com-pare— A con-stant sense of Thy a-
weep a - mid the fires of pain, And when shall come the hour of

life, un - aid - ed, I need Thy strength to lean my - self up - on.
where a - bout me, They can - not harm, or make my heart a - fraid.
bid - ing pres - ence, Wher-e'er I am, to feel that Thou art near.
"my de - part - ure" For "worlds un-known," O Lord, be with me then.

22 Sing On, Ye Joyful Pilgrims

Carrie M. Wilson

Jno. R. Sweney

1. Sing on, ye joy-ful pil-grims, Nor think the moments long; My faith is heav'nward
2. Sing on, ye joy-ful pil-grims, While here on earth we stay; Let songs of home and
3. Sing on, ye joy-ful pil-grims, The time will not be long, Till in our Fa-ther's

ris - ing With ev - 'ry tune - ful song; Lo! on the mount of bless - ing, The
Je - sus Be - guile each fleet-ing day; Sing on the grand old sto - ry Of
king - dom We swell a no - bler song, Where those we love are wait - ing To

glorious mount, I stand; And look-ing o - ver Jor-dan, I see the promised land.
His re-deem-ing love, The ev - er - last-ing cho-rus That fills the realms a-bove.
greet us on the shore, We'll meet beyond the riv-er, Where surges roll no more.

CHORUS

Sing on, O bliss-ful mu - sic! With ev - 'ry note you raise My heart is filled with

rap - ture, My soul is lost in praise; Sing on, O bliss-ful mu - sic!
Sing on, bliss ful, bliss-ful mu - sic!

With ev-'ry note you raise My heart is filled with rapture, My soul is lost in praise.

23   There's a Great Day Coming

W. L. T.   Will L. Thompson

1. There's a great day com-ing, A great day com-ing, There's a great day
2. There's a bright day com-ing, A bright day com-ing, There's a bright day
3. There's a sad day com-ing, A sad day com-ing, There's a sad day

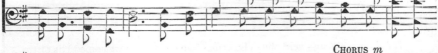

com-ing by and by; When the saints and the sin-ners shall be part-ed
com-ing by and by; But its bright-ness shall on-ly come to them that
com-ing by and by; When the sin-ner shall hear his doom,"De-part, I

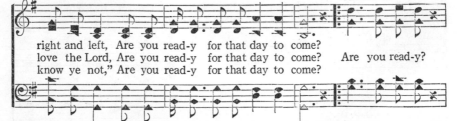

CHORUS *m*

right and left, Are you read-y for that day to come?
love the Lord, Are you read-y for that day to come?   Are you read-y?
know ye not," Are you read-y for that day to come?

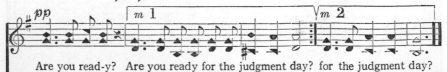

pp   *m 1*   *m 2*

Are you read-y? Are you ready for the judgment day? for the judgment day?

24 Tell Me the Story of Jesus

Fanny J. Crosby

Jno. R. Sweney

1. Tell me the sto-ry of Je-sus, Write on my heart ev-'ry word;
2. Fast-ing a-lone in the des-ert, Tell of the days that are passed,
3. Tell of the cross where they nailed Him, Writh-ing in an-guish and pain;

Cho.—Tell me the sto-ry of Je-sus, Write on my heart ev-'ry word;

Fine

Tell me the sto-ry most pre-cious, Sweet-est that ev-er was heard.
How for our sins He was tempt-ed, Yet was tri-um-phant at last.
Tell of the grave where they laid Him, Tell how He liv-eth a-gain.

Tell me the sto-ry most pre-cious, Sweet-est that ev-er was heard.

Tell how the an-gels in cho-rus, Sang as they welcomed His birth,
Tell of the years of His la-bor, Tell of the sor-row He bore,
Love in that sto-ry so ten-der, Clear-er than ev-er I see;

D. C. for Chorus

"Glo-ry to God in the high-est, Peace and good ti-dings to earth."
He was de-spised and af-flict-ed, Home-less, re-ject-ed, and poor.
Stay, let me weep while you whis-per, Love paid the ran-som for me.

25 Worthy Art Thou!

T. S. T.

Tillit S. Teddlie

1. Wor-thy of praise is Christ our Re-deem-er; Wor-thy of glo-ry,
2. Lift up the voice in praise and de-vo-tion, Saints of all earth be-
3. Lord, may we come be-fore Thee with sing-ing, Filled with Thy Spir-it,

hon-or and pow'r! Wor-thy of all our soul's ad-o-ra-tion,
fore Him should bow; An-gels in heav-en wor-ship Him, say-ing,
wis-dom and pow'r; May we as-cribe Thee glo-ry and hon-or,

CHORUS

Wor-thy art Thou!.... Wor-thy art Thou! Wor-thy of rich-es, blessings and
Worthy art Thou!

hon-or, Wor-thy of wis-dom, glo-ry and pow'r! Wor-thy of earth and

heav-en's thanks-giv-ing, Wor-thy art Thou!..... Wor-thy art Thou!......
Worthy art Thou! art Thou!

26 O Why Not To-night?

Elizabeth Reed

J. Calvin Bushey

1. O do not let the word de-part, And close thine eyes a-gainst the light;
2. To-mor-row's sun may nev-er rise To bless thy long-de-lud-ed sight;
3. Our bless-ed Lord re-fus-es none Who would to Him their souls u-nite;

Poor sin-ner, hard-en not thy heart, Be saved, O to-night.
This is the time, O then be wise, Be saved, O to-night.
Be-lieve, o-bey, the work is done, Be saved, O to-night.

CHORUS

O why not to-night? O why not to-night?
O why not tonight? why not tonight? Why not tonight? why not tonight?

Wilt thou be saved? Then why not to-night?
Wilt thou be saved, wilt thou be saved? Then why not, O why not to-night?

27 Cast Thy Burden On the Lord

John Cennick. George Rawson

Arr. from L. M. Gottschalk

1. Cast thy bur-den on the Lord, On-ly lean up-on His word;
2. Ev-er in the rag-ing storm Thou shalt see His cheer-ing form,
3. He will gird thee by His pow'r, In thy wea-ry faint-ing hour;

Cast Thy Burden, Concluded

Thou shalt soon have cause to bless His e - ter - nal faith - ful - ness.
Hear His pledge of com - ing aid: "It is I, be not a - fraid."
Lean then, lov - ing, on His word; Cast thy bur - den on the Lord.

28 There Is a Habitation

L. H. Jameson

J. H. Rosecrans

1. There is a hab - i - ta - tion, Built by the liv - ing God,
2. No night is there, no sor - row, No death, and no de - cay;
3. With - in its pearl - y por - tals, An - gel - ic ar - mies sing,

For all of ev - 'ry na - tion Who seek that grand a - bode.
No yes - ter - day, no mor - row— But one e - ter - nal day.
With glo - ri - fied im - mor - tals, The prais - es of its King.

CHORUS

O Zi - on, Zi - on, I long thy gates to see; O
O Zi - on, love - ly Zi - on, O love - ly

Zi - - on, Zi - on, When shall I dwell in thee?
Zi - on, love - ly Zi - on,

29 There Shall Be Showers of Blessing

El Nathan

James McGranahan

1. "There shall be show-ers of bless-ing:" This is the prom-ise of love;
2. "There shall be show-ers of bless-ing"—Pre-cious re-viv-ing a-gain;
2. "There shall be show-ers of bless-ing:" O, that to-day they might fall,

There shall be sea-sons re-fresh-ing, Sent from the Sav-ior a-bove.
O - ver the hills and the val - leys, Sound of a - bun-dance of rain.
Now as to God we're con-fess-ing, Now as on Je - sus we call!

CHORUS

Show - - - ers of bless-ing, Show-ers of bless-ing we need:
Show - ers, show-ers of bless-ing,

Mer - cy-drops round us are fall-ing, But for the show-ers we plead.

30 Must Jesus Bear the Cross Alone?

Thos. Shepherd

Geo. N. Allen

1. Must Je - sus bear the cross a - lone, And all the world go free?—
2. The con - se - crat - ed cross I'll bear, Till death shall set me free,
3. O pre-cious cross! O glo-rious crown! O res - ur - rec - tion day!

Must Jesus Bear the Cross, Concluded

No, there's a cross for ev-'ry one, And there's a cross for me.
And then go home my crown to wear, For there's a crown for me.
Ye an-gels, from the stars come down, And bear my soul a-way.

31 God Is Love

Anon.

E. S. Lorenz

1. Come, let us all u-nite to sing, God is love; Let heav'n and earth their
2. O, tell to earth's re-mot-est bound, God is love; In Christ we have re-
3. How hap-py is our por-tion here, God is love; His prom-is-es our

prais-es bring, God is love; Let ev-'ry soul from sin a-wake,
demp-tion found, God is love; His blood has washed our sins a-way,
spir-its cheer, God is love; He is our sun and shield by day,

Each in his heart sweet mu-sic make, And sing with us for Je-sus' sake,
His Spir-it turned our night to day, And now we can re-joice to say,
Our help, our hope, our strength and stay, He will be with us all the way,

D. S.—Come, let us all u-nite to sing

FINE   REFRAIN

D. S.

For God is love. God is love! God is love!
That God is love.
Our God is love. God is love! God is love!

That God is love.

32 A New Creature

T. O. Chisholm

L. O. Sanderson

1. Bur - ied with Christ, my bless - ed Re - deem - er, Dead to the
2. Dead un - to sin, a - live through the Spir - it, Ris - en with
3. Sin hath no more its cru - el do - min - ion, Walk - ing "in

old life of fol - ly and sin; Sa - tan may call, the world may en-
Him from the gloom of the grave, All things are new, and I am re-
new - ness of life," I am free—Glo - ri - ous life of Christ, my Re-

CHORUS

treat me, There is no voice that an - swers with - in.
joic - ing In His great love, His pow - er to save. Dead to the world, to
deem - er, Which He so rich - ly shar - eth with me.

voic - es that call me, Liv - ing a - new, o - be - dient but free; Dead to the

joys that once did en - thrall me—Yet 'tis not I, Christ liv - eth in me.

33 In the Shadow of His Wings

J. B. Atchinson

E. O. Excell

1. In the shad-ow of His wings There is rest, sweet rest; There is
2. In the shad-ow of His wings There is peace, sweet peace, Peace that
3. In the shad-ow of His wings There is joy, glad joy; There is

rest from care and la-bor, There is rest for friend and neigh-bor; In the
pass-eth un-der-stand-ing, Peace, sweet peace that knows no end-ing; In the
joy to tell the sto-ry, Joy ex-ceed-ing, full of glo-ry; In the

shad-ow of His wings There is rest, sweet rest, In the shad-ow of His wings
shad-ow of His wings There is peace, sweet peace, In the shad-ow of His wings
shad-ow of His wings There is joy, glad joy, In the shad-ow of His wings

Chorus

There is rest (sweet rest). There is rest, There is peace, There is
There is peace (sweet peace).
There is joy (glad joy). sweet rest, sweet peace,

joy, In the shad-ow of His wings; shad-ow of His wings.
glad joy,

34 Why Did My Savior Come to Earth?

J. G. D.   J. G. Dailey

1. Why did my Sav-ior come to earth, And to the hum-ble go?
2. Why did He drink the bit-ter cup Of sor-row, pain and woe?
3. Till Je-sus comes I'll sing His praise, And then to glo-ry go,

Why did He choose a low-ly birth? Be-cause He loved me so!
Why on the cross be lift-ed up? Be-cause He loved me so!
And live with Him thro' end-less days, Be-cause He loved me so.

CHORUS

He loved...... me so, He loved...... me so;
He loved, He loved me so, He loved, He loved me so;

He gave His pre-cious life for me, for me, Be-cause He loved me so.

35 Savior, More Than Life

Fanny J. Crosby   W. H. Doane

1. Sav-ior, more than life to me, I am cling-ing, cling-ing close to Thee;
2. Thro' this chang-ing world be-low, Lead me gen-tly, gen-tly, as I go;
3. Let me love Thee more and more, Till this fleet-ing, fleet-ing life is o'er;

Savior, More Than Life, Concluded

FINE

Let Thy pre-cious blood ap-plied, Keep me ev - er, ev - er near Thy side.
Trust-ing Thee, I can - not stray, I can nev - er, nev - er lose my way.
Till my soul is lost in love, In a brighter, brighter world a - bove.

D. S.—*May Thy ten - der love to me Bind me clos - er, clos - er, Lord, to Thee.*

REFRAIN

D. S.

Ev - 'ry day, ev - 'ry hour, Let me feel Thy cleansing pow'r;
Ev - 'ry day and hour, ev - 'ry day and hour.

36 Sweet Hour of Prayer

W. W. Walford

Wm. B. Bradbury

1. Sweet hour of prayer, sweet hour of prayer! That calls me from a world of care,
2. Sweet hour of prayer, sweet hour of prayer! The joy I feel, the bliss I share,
3. Sweet hour of prayer, sweet hour of prayer! Thy wings shall my pe - ti - tion bear

FINE

And bids me, at my Fa-ther's throne, Make all my wants and wish-es known.
Of those whose anx-ious spir - its burn With strong de-sires for thy re-turn.
To Him whose truth and faith-ful - ness En - gage the wait - ing soul to bless.

D.S.—And oft es - caped the tempt-er's snare, By thy re-turn, sweet hour of prayer.
D.S.—And glad-ly take my sta - tion there, And wait for thee, sweet hour of prayer.
D.S.—I'll cast on Him my ev - 'ry care, And wait for thee, sweet hour of prayer.

D. S.

In sea-sons of dis-tress and grief My soul has of - ten found re - lief,
With such I has-ten to the place Where God, my Sav-ior, shows His face,
And since He bids me seek His face, Be - lieve His word, and trust His grace,

37 When We All Get to Heaven

E. E. Hewitt

Mrs. J. G. Wilson

1. Sing the won-drous love of Je - sus, Sing His mer - cy and His grace:
2. While we walk the pil-grim path-way, Clouds will o - ver-spread the sky;
3. Let us then be true and faith-ful, Trust-ing, serv-ing ev - 'ry day;

In the man-sions bright and bless-ed, He'll pre-pare for us a place.
But when trav-'ling days are o - ver, Not a shad-ow, not a sigh.
Just one glimpse of Him in glo - ry Will the toils of life re - pay.

1. for us a place.

CHORUS

When we all get to heaven, What a day of rejoicing that will be!
When we all What a day of re-joic-ing that will be!

When we all see Je-sus, We'll sing and shout the vic-to-ry............
When we all and shout the vic-to-ry.

38 He Leadeth Me

Joseph H. Gillmore

William B. Bradbury

1. He lead-eth me! O bless-ed tho't! O words with heav'n-ly com-fort fraught!
2. Sometimes 'mid scenes of deepest gloom, Sometimes where E-den's bow-ers bloom,
3. And when my task on earth is done, When, by Thy grace, the vic-t'ry's won,

He Leadeth Me, Concluded

What-e'er I do, wher-e'er I be, Still 'tis God's hand that lead-eth me.
By wa-ters still, o'er trou-bled sea,—Still 'tis God's hand that lead-eth me.
E'en death's cold waves I will not flee, Since God thro' Jor-dan lead-eth me.

REFRAIN

{ He lead-eth me, He lead-eth me, By His own hand He leadeth me:
His faithful fol-l'wer I would be, For by His hand He (*Omit. . . .*) leadeth me.

39 Did You Think to Pray?

Mrs. M. A. Kidder

W. O. Perkins

1. Ere you left your room this morning, Did you think to pray? In the name of
2. When your heart was filled with an-ger, Did you think to pray? Did you plead for
3. When sore tri-als came up-on you, Did you think to pray? When your soul was

FINE

Christ, our Sav-ior, Did you sue for lov-ing fa-vor, As a shield to-day?
grace, my broth-er, That you might for-give an-oth-er Who had crossed your way?
bowed in sor-row, Balm of Gil-ead did you bor-row At the gates of day?

D. S.—*So when life seems dark and drear-y, Don't for-get to pray.*

CHORUS

D. S.

O how pray-ing rests the wea-ry! Prayer will change the night to day;

40 To the Work

Fanny J. Crosby

W. H. Doane

1. To the work! to the work! We are serv-ants of God, Let us fol-low the
2. To the work! to the work! Let the hun-gry be fed; To the foun-tain of
3. To the work! to the work! In the strength of the Lord, And a robe and a

path that our Mas-ter has trod; With the balm of His coun-sel our
life let the wea-ry be led; In the cross and its ban-ner our
crown shall our la-bor re-ward; When the home of the faith-ful our

strength to re-new, Let us do with our might what our hands find to do.
glo-ry shall be, While we her-ald the ti-dings, Sal-va-tion is free!
dwell-ing shall be, And we shout with the ransomed, "Sal-va-tion is free."

CHORUS

Toil-ing on, toil-ing on, Toil-ing on, toil-ing on;
Toil-ing on, toil-ing on, Toil-ing on, toil-ing on;

Let us hope, let us watch, And la-bor till the Mas-ter comes.
and trust, and pray,

41 Nearer, My God, to Thee

Sarah F. Adams

Lowell Mason

1. Near - er, my God, to Thee, Near - er to Thee! E'en tho' it be a cross
2. Tho' like a wan-der-er, The sun gone down, Dark-ness be o - ver me,
3. There let the way ap-pear Steps un - to heav'n; All that Thou send-est me,
4. Or, if on joy - ful wing, Cleav-ing the sky, Sun, moon, and stars for-got,

D. S.—*Near - er, my God, to Thee,*

FINE.

D. S.

That rais-eth me; Still all my song shall be, Near - er, my God, to Thee,
My rest a stone; Yet in my dreams I'd be Near - er, my God, to Thee,
In mer - cy giv'n; An - gels to beck - on me Near - er, my God, to Thee,
Up - ward I fly; Still all my song shall be, Near - er, my God, to Thee,

Near - er to Thee!

42 My Soul, Be On Thy Guard

George Heath

Lowell Mason

1. My soul, be on thy guard; Ten thou - sand foes a - rise;
2. O watch, and fight, and pray; The bat - tle ne'er give o'er;
3. Ne'er think the vic - t'ry won, Nor lay thine ar - mor down;
4. Fight on, my soul, till death Shall bring thee to thy God;

The hosts of sin are press - ing hard To draw thee from the skies.
Re - new it bold - ly ev - 'ry day, And help di - vine im - plore.
The work of faith will not be done, Till thou ob - tain the crown.
He'll take thee, at thy part - ing breath, To His di - vine a - bode.

43 Heavenly Sunlight

H. J. Zelley

G. H. Cook

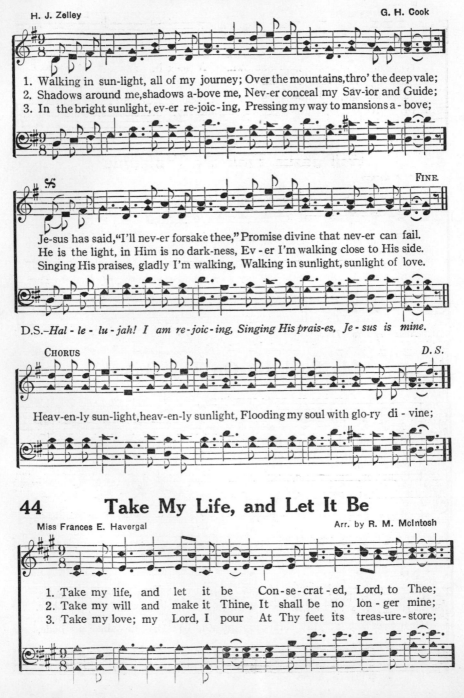

1. Walking in sun-light, all of my journey; Over the mountains, thro' the deep vale;
2. Shadows around me, shadows a-bove me, Nev-er conceal my Sav-ior and Guide;
3. In the bright sunlight, ev-er re-joic-ing, Pressing my way to mansions a-bove;

FINE.

Je-sus has said, "I'll nev-er forsake thee," Promise divine that nev-er can fail.
He is the light, in Him is no dark-ness, Ev-er I'm walking close to His side.
Singing His praises, gladly I'm walking, Walking in sunlight, sunlight of love.

D.S.—*Hal-le-lu-jah! I am re-joic-ing, Singing His prais-es, Je-sus is mine.*

CHORUS

D. S.

Heav-en-ly sun-light, heav-en-ly sunlight, Flooding my soul with glo-ry di-vine;

44 Take My Life, and Let It Be

Miss Frances E. Havergal

Arr. by R. M. McIntosh

1. Take my life, and let it be Con-se-crat-ed, Lord, to Thee;
2. Take my will and make it Thine, It shall be no lon-ger mine;
3. Take my love; my Lord, I pour At Thy feet its treas-ure-store;

Take My Life, Concluded

Take my hands, and let them move At the im-pulse of Thy love.
Take my heart, it is Thine own, It shall be Thy roy-al throne.
Take my-self, and I will be Ev - er, on - ly, all for Thee.

45   Will Jesus Find Us Watching?

Fanny J. Crosby   W. H. Doane

1. When Je - sus comes to re-ward His serv-ants, Whether it be noon or night,
2. If, at the dawn of the ear - ly morn-ing, He shall call us one by one,
3. Bless - ed are those whom the Lord finds watching, In His glo-ry they shall share;

rit.

Faith-ful to Him will He find us watching, With our lamps all trimmed and bright?
When to the Lord we re-store our tal-ents, Will He an-swer thee—Well done?
If He shall come at the dawn or midnight, Will He find us watch-ing there?

Chorus

O can we say we are read-y, broth-er? Read-y for the soul's bright home?

Say, will He find you and me still watching, Waiting, waiting when the Lord shall come?

46 Wonderful Love of Jesus

E. D. Mund

E. S. Lorenz

1. In vain in high and ho-ly lays My soul her grate-ful voice would raise; For
2. A joy by day, a peace by night, In storms a calm, in dark-ness light; In
3. My hope for par-don when I call, My trust for lift-ing when I fall; In

who can sing the wor-thy praise Of the won-der-ful love of Je-sus!
pain a balm, in weakness might Is the won-der-ful love of Je-sus.
life, in death, my all in all, Is the won-der-ful love of Je-sus.

REFRAIN

Won-der-ful love! won-der-ful love! Won-der-ful love of Je-sus!

Won-der-ful love! won-der-ful love! Won-der-ful love of Je-sus!

47 How Sweet the Name of Jesus Sounds

John Newton

Thomas Hastings

1. How sweet the name of Je-sus sounds In a be-liev-er's ear! It soothes his
2. It makes the wounded spirit whole, And calms the troubled breast; 'Tis man-na
3. Weak is the ef-fort of my heart, And cold my warmest tho't; But when I
4. Till then, I would Thy love proclaim With ev-'ry fleet-ing breath; And may the

sorrows, heals his wounds, And drives away his fear, And drives away his fear.
to the hun-gry soul, And to the wea-ry, rest, And to the wea-ry, rest.
see Thee as Thou art, I'll praise Thee as I ought, I'll praise Thee as I ought.
mu - sic of Thy name Re-fresh my soul in death, Re-fresh my soul in death.

48 **O How I Love Jesus**

F. Whitfield

1. There is a name I love to hear, I love to sing its worth;
2. It tells me of a Sav-ior's love, Who died to set me free;
3. It tells of One whose lov - ing heart Can feel my deep-est woe;

It sounds like mu - sic in mine ear, The sweet-est name on earth.
It tells me of His pre-cious blood, The sin - ner's per - fect plea.
Who in each sor - row bears a part, That none can bear be - low.

CHORUS

O how I love Je - sus, O how I love Je - sus,

O how I love Je - sus, Be - cause He first loved me.

49 Rock of Ages

Augustus M. Toplady

Thomas Hastings

1. Rock of A - ges, cleft for me, Let me hide my - self in Thee;
2. Could my tears for - ev - er flow, Could my zeal no lan-guor know,
3. While I draw this fleet-ing breath, When my eyes shall close in death,

Let the wa - ter and the blood, From Thy wound-ed side which flowed,
These for sin could not a - tone; Thou must save, and Thou a - lone:
When I rise to worlds un-known, And be - hold Thee on Thy throne,

Be of sin the dou - ble cure, Save from wrath and make me pure.
In my hand no price I bring, Sim - ply to Thy cross I cling.
Rock of A - ges, cleft for me, Let me hide my - self in Thee.

50 Just As I Am

Charlotte Elliott

Wm. Bradbury

1. Just as I am, with - out one plea, But that Thy blood was shed for me,
2. Just as I am, and wait - ing not To rid my soul of one dark blot,
3. Just as I am, tho' tossed a-bout With man-y a con-flict, man-y a doubt,
4. Just as I am, Thou wilt re-ceive, Wilt welcome, par-don, cleanse, re-lieve;

Just As I Am, Concluded

And that Thou bidd'st me come to Thee, O Lamb of God, I come, I come!
To Thee whose blood can cleanse each spot, O Lamb of God, I come, I come!
Fightings with-in, and fears with-out, O Lamb of God, I come, I come!
Be-cause Thy prom-ise I be-lieve, O Lamb of God, I come, I come!

51 Seeking for Me

E. E. Hasty

1. Je-sus, my Sav-ior, to Beth-le-hem came, Born in a man-ger to sor-row and
2. Je-sus, my Sav-ior, on Cal-va-ry's tree, Paid the great debt and my soul He set
3. Je-sus, my Sav-ior, shall come from on high: Sweet is the promise as wea-ry years

FINE.

shame; O it was won-der-ful, blest be His name! Seek-ing for me, for me!
free; O it was won-der-ful, how could it be? Dy-ing for me, for me!
fly; O I shall see Him de-scend-ing the sky, Com-ing for me, for me!

D. S.—O it was won-der-ful, blest be His name! Seek-ing for me, for me!
D. S.—O it was won-der-ful, how could it be? Dy-ing for me, for me!
D. S.—O I shall see Him de-scend-ing the sky, Com-ing for me, for me!

For me!......... For me!.........

REFRAIN D. S.

Seek-ing for me! Seek-ing for me! Seek-ing for me! Seek-ing for me!
Dy-ing for me! Dy-ing for me! Dy-ing for me! Dy-ing for me!
Com-ing for me! Com-ing for me! Com-ing for me! Com-ing for me!

52 I'll Never Forsake My Lord

Mrs. Damon Canter Snoddy. Arr. by L. O. S.

L. O. Sanderson

1. Though my cross may be hard to bear, Though my life may be filled with care;
2. Though the tempt-er in ef-forts bold, Or in sub-tle-ty as of old,
3. Though so help-less I can-not see What the fu-ture may hold for me;

Though mis-for-tune be mine to share—I'll nev-er for-sake my Lord.
Should es-say to al-lure my soul—I'll nev-er for-sake my Lord.
Je - sus knows and my guide will be— I'll nev-er for-sake my Lord.

Chorus

I'll nev-er for-sake the Sav - ior, He has nev-er for-sak-en me! 'Neath His

shel-ter-ing arm I am safe from all harm—I'll nev-er for - sake my Lord.

53 Immortal Love, Forever Full

John G. Whittier

E. L. Jorgenson

1. Im - mor - tal Love, for - ev - er full, For - ev - er flow-ing free,
2. We may not climb the heav'n-ly steeps To bring the Lord Christ down;
3. But warm, sweet, ten-der, e - ven yet A pres-ent help is He;
4. Thro' Him the first fond prayers are said Our lips of child-hood frame;

For - ev - er shared, for - ev - er whole, A nev - er - ebb - ing sea!
In vain we search the low - est deeps, For Him no depths can drown.
And faith has still its Ol - i - vet, And love its Gal - i - lee.
The last low whis-pers of our dead Are bur-dened with His name.

54 'Tis the Blessed Hour of Prayer

Fanny J. Crosby

W. H. Doane

1. 'Tis the bless - ed hour of prayer, when our hearts low - ly bend, And we
2. 'Tis the bless - ed hour of prayer, when the Sav - ior draws near, With a
3. At the bless - ed hour of prayer, trust-ing Him, we be - lieve That the

gath - er to Je - sus, our Sav - ior and Friend; If we come to Him in
ten - der com - pas-sion His chil - dren to hear; When He tells us we may
bless-ing we're need-ing we'll sure - ly re - ceive; In the full - ness of this

faith, His pro - tec - tion to share, What a balm for the wea - ry!
cast at His feet ev - 'ry care, What a balm for the wea - ry!
trust we shall lose ev - 'ry care, What a balm for the wea - ry!

FINE. CHORUS

D. S.

O how sweet to be there! Bless-ed hour of prayer, bless-ed hour of prayer,

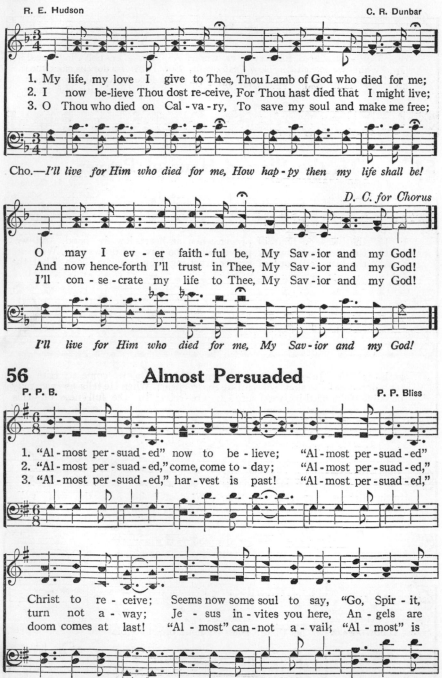

55 I'll Live for Him

R. E. Hudson

C. R. Dunbar

1. My life, my love I give to Thee, Thou Lamb of God who died for me;
2. I now be-lieve Thou dost re-ceive, For Thou hast died that I might live;
3. O Thou who died on Cal-va-ry, To save my soul and make me free;

Cho.—*I'll live for Him who died for me, How hap-py then my life shall be!*

D. C. for Chorus

O may I ev-er faith-ful be, My Sav-ior and my God!
And now hence-forth I'll trust in Thee, My Sav-ior and my God!
I'll con-se-crate my life to Thee, My Sav-ior and my God!

I'll live for Him who died for me, My Sav-ior and my God!

56 Almost Persuaded

P. P. B.

P. P. Bliss

1. "Al-most per-suad-ed" now to be-lieve; "Al-most per-suad-ed"
2. "Al-most per-suad-ed," come, come to-day; "Al-most per-suad-ed,"
3. "Al-most per-suad-ed," har-vest is past! "Al-most per-suad-ed,"

Christ to re-ceive; Seems now some soul to say, "Go, Spir-it,
turn not a-way; Je-sus in-vites you here, An-gels are
doom comes at last! "Al-most" can-not a-vail; "Al-most" is

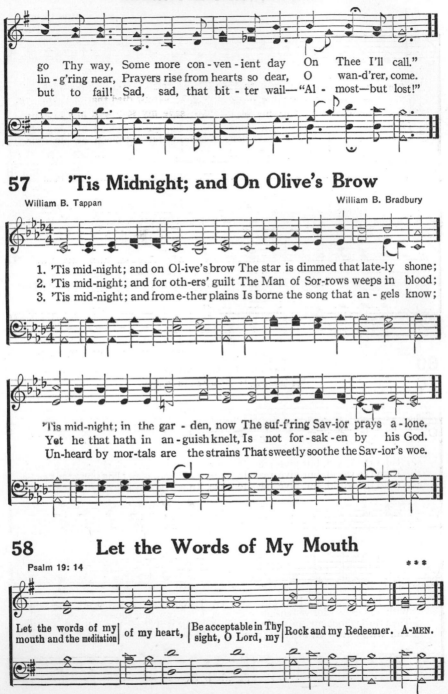

go Thy way, Some more con-ven-ient day On Thee I'll call."
lin-g'ring near, Prayers rise from hearts so dear, O wan-d'rer, come.
but to fail! Sad, sad, that bit-ter wail—"Al-most—but lost!"

57 'Tis Midnight; and On Olive's Brow

William B. Tappan

William B. Bradbury

1. 'Tis mid-night; and on Ol-ive's brow The star is dimmed that late-ly shone;
2. 'Tis mid-night; and for oth-ers' guilt The Man of Sor-rows weeps in blood;
3. 'Tis mid-night; and from e-ther plains Is borne the song that an - gels know;

'Tis mid-night; in the gar - den, now The suf-f'ring Sav-ior prays a - lone.
Yet he that hath in an-guish knelt, Is not for-sak-en by his God.
Un-heard by mor-tals are the strains That sweetly soothe the Sav-ior's woe.

58 Let the Words of My Mouth

Psalm 19: 14

Let the words of my | of my heart, | Be acceptable in Thy | Rock and my Redeemer. A-MEN.
mouth and the meditation | | sight, O Lord, my |

59 Nothing But the Blood

R. L.

Robert Lowry

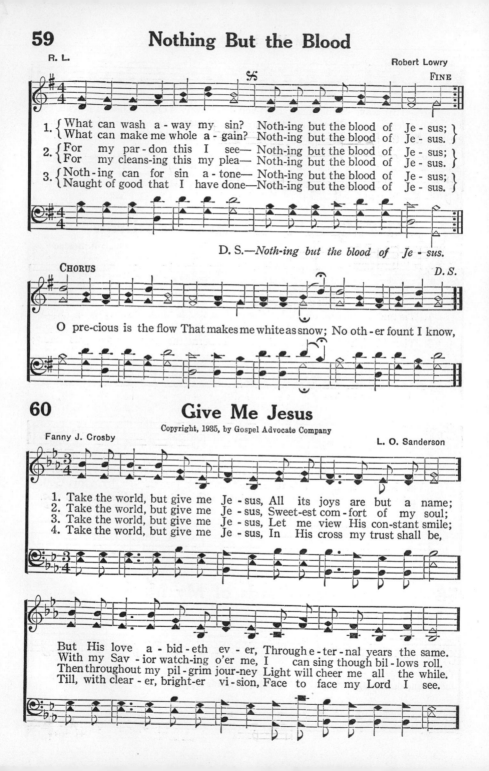

1. { What can wash a-way my sin? Noth-ing but the blood of Je - sus;
   { What can make me whole a - gain? Noth-ing but the blood of Je - sus. }
2. { For my par-don this I see— Noth-ing but the blood of Je - sus;
   { For my cleans-ing this my plea— Noth-ing but the blood of Je - sus. }
3. { Noth-ing can for sin a-tone— Noth-ing but the blood of Je - sus;
   { Naught of good that I have done—Noth-ing but the blood of Je - sus. }

D. S.—*Noth-ing but the blood of Je - sus.*

CHORUS

O pre-cious is the flow That makes me white as snow; No oth-er fount I know,

60 Give Me Jesus

Copyright, 1935, by Gospel Advocate Company

Fanny J. Crosby

L. O. Sanderson

1. Take the world, but give me Je - sus, All its joys are but a name;
2. Take the world, but give me Je - sus, Sweet-est com - fort of my soul;
3. Take the world, but give me Je - sus, Let me view His con-stant smile;
4. Take the world, but give me Je - sus, In His cross my trust shall be,

But His love a - bid - eth ev - er, Through e - ter - nal years the same.
With my Sav - ior watch-ing o'er me, I can sing though bil - lows roll.
Then throughout my pil - grim jour-ney Light will cheer me all the while.
Till, with clear - er, bright - er vi - sion, Face to face my Lord I see.

Give Me Jesus, Concluded

CHORUS

O the height and depth of mer - cy! O the length and breadth of love!

O the ful - ness of re-demp-tion, Pledge of end-less life a - bove.

61   The Gospel Is for All

J. M. McCaleb   Arr. R. M. McIntosh

1. Of one the Lord has made the race, Thro' one has come the fall;
2. Say not the hea-then are at home, Be - yond we have no call,
3. Re-ceived ye free - ly, free - ly give, From ev - 'ry land they call;

FINE

Where sin has gone must go His grace: The Gos - pel is for all.
For why should we be blest a - lone? The Gos - pel is for all.
Un - less they hear they can - not live: The Gos - pel is for all.

D.S.—*Where sin has gone must go His grace: The Gos - pel is for all.*

CHORUS   D. S.

The bless - ed Gos - pel is for all, The Gos - pel is for all;

62 My Precious Bible

H. B. H.

E. S. Lorenz

1. Like a Star of the morn-ing in its beau-ty, Like a
2. 'Tis a Light in the wil-der-ness of sor-row, And a
3. It shall stand in its beau-ty and its glo-ry, When the

Sun is the Bi-ble to my soul, Shin-ing clear on the way of
Lamp on the wea-ry pil-grim way, And it guides to the bright, e-
earth and the heav-ens pass a-way; Ev-er tell-ing the bless-ed,

D S.—*I will cling to the dear, old*

FINE

love and du-ty, As I has-ten on my jour-ney to the goal.
ter-nal mor-row, Shin-ing more and more un-to the per-fect day.
won-drous sto-ry Of the lov-ing Lamb, the on-ly Liv-ing Way.

Ho-ly Bi-ble, As I has-ten to the Cit-y of the King.

CHORUS

Ho-ly Bi-ble! my pre-cious Bi-ble!
Ho-ly Bi-ble! Ho-ly Bi-ble! pre-cious Bi-ble, book di-vine!

D. S.

Gift of God and Lamp of life, My Beau-ti-ful Bi-ble!
Bi-ble, thou art mine!

63 Come Unto Me

F. E. B.

F. E. Belden

1. O heart bowed down with sor - row! O eyes that long for sight!
2. Earth's fleet - ing gain and pleas - ure Can nev - er sat - is - fy:
3. His peace is like a riv - er, His love is like a song;

There's glad - ness in be - liev - ing; In Je - sus there is light.
'Tis love our joy doth meas - ure, For love can nev - er die.
His yoke's a bur - den nev - er; 'Tis eas - y all day long.

CHORUS

"Come...... un - to Me,........ all ye........ that la - - bor
"Come, O come, come un - to Me, Come, O come, all ye that la - bor;
Take... My yoke up - on..... you, and learn...... of Me;........ for
Come, O come, Come, take My yoke, come, O come, come, learn of Me;

[1]

and....... are heav - y - la - den, and I........ will give you rest.......
Come, O come, heav - y - la - den souls, I........ will give you rest,

I will give you rest,......

[2]

I...... am meek and lowly in heart: and ye shall find rest un - to your souls."
I am meek and low - ly in heart:

64 God's Hand Is In It All

R. C. W.

R. C. Ward

1. When skies are clear and friends are dear, When joys pos-sess the soul—'Mid
2. When storm and cloud the earth enshroud, Or sor - row casts her pall, When
3. When life is o'er and on that shore We an - swer to the call, At

FINE CHORUS

for-tune's day we free-ly say: "God's hand is in it all." God's hand is
dark the way we're loath to say: "God's hand is in it all." God's hand is
home with Thee, we'll clearly see Thy hand was in it all. God's hand is

D.S.—faith se-rene 'tis plain-ly seen, God's hand is in it all.

D. S.

in it all, God's hand..... is in it all; With

65 Jesus, Keep Me Near the Cross

Fanny J. Crosby

W. H. Doane

1. Je - sus, keep me near the cross: There a pre-cious foun-tain, Free to all, a
2. Near the cross, a trembling soul, Love and mer-cy found me; There the Bright and
3. Near the cross! O Lamb of God, Bring its scenes be-fore me; Help me walk from

CHORUS

healing stream, Flows from Calv'ry's mountain.
Morn-ing Star Sheds its beams a-round me. In the cross, in the cross, Be my
day to day With its shad-ow o'er me.

glo-ry ev - er, Till my rap-tured soul shall find Rest be-yond the riv - er.

66 I've Found a Friend

James Gridley Small
George C. Stebbins

1. I've found a Friend, O such a Friend! He loved me ere I knew Him;
2. I've found a Friend, O such a Friend! He bled, He died to save me;
3. I've found a Friend, O such a Friend! So kind, and true, and ten-der,

He drew me with the cords of love, And thus He bound me to Him.
And not a-lone the gift of life, But His own self He gave me.
So wise a Coun-sel-lor and Guide, So might-y a De-fend-er!

And round my heart still close-ly twine Those ties which naught can sev - er,
Naught that I have my own I call: I hold it for the Giv-er;
From Him who loves me now so well, What pow'r my soul can sev-er?

For I am His, and He is mine, For-ev - er and for - ev - er.

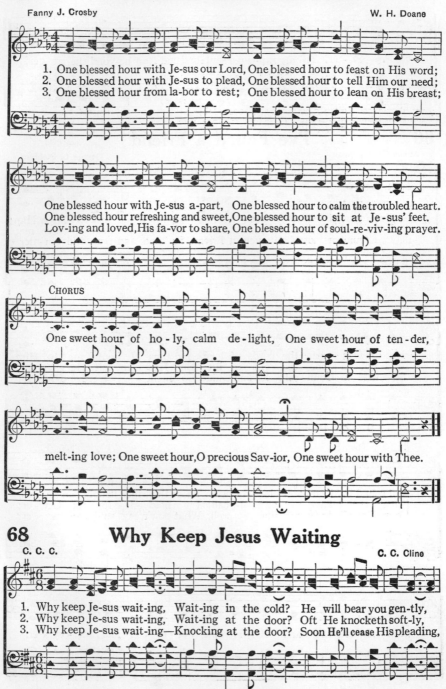

67 **One Blessed Hour with Jesus**

Fanny J. Crosby

W. H. Doane

1. One blessed hour with Je-sus our Lord, One blessed hour to feast on His word;
2. One blessed hour with Je-sus to plead, One blessed hour to tell Him our need;
3. One blessed hour from la-bor to rest; One blessed hour to lean on His breast;

One blessed hour with Je-sus a-part, One blessed hour to calm the troubled heart.
One blessed hour refreshing and sweet, One blessed hour to sit at Je-sus' feet.
Lov-ing and loved, His fa-vor to share, One blessed hour of soul-re-viv-ing prayer.

CHORUS

One sweet hour of ho-ly, calm de-light, One sweet hour of ten-der,

melt-ing love; One sweet hour, O precious Sav-ior, One sweet hour with Thee.

68 **Why Keep Jesus Waiting**

C. C. C.

C. C. Cline

1. Why keep Je-sus wait-ing, Wait-ing in the cold? He will bear you gen-tly,
2. Why keep Je-sus wait-ing, Wait-ing at the door? Oft He knocketh soft-ly,
3. Why keep Je-sus wait-ing—Knocking at the door? Soon He'll cease His pleading,

Why Keep Jesus Waiting, Concluded

rit. I im - plore.

Gen-tly to His fold; See Him, soul, and o-pen, O-pen, I im-plore.
Soft-ly, o'er and o'er; Hear Him, soul, and o-pen, O-pen, I im-plore.
Yes, for-ev-er-more; Come, poor soul, o-bey Him, O-pen, I im-plore.

69 To Christ Be True

Elisha A. Hoffman

D. M. Wilson

1. To Christ be loy - al and be true; His ban-ner be un - furled,
2. To Christ be loy - al and be true; He needs brave vol - un - teers
3. To Christ be loy - al and be true; In no - ble serv - ice prove

And borne a - loft till is se-cured The con-quest of the world.
To stand a-gainst the pow'rs of sin, Moved not by frowns or fears.
Your faith and your fi - del - i - ty, The fer - vor of your love.

Chorus

To Christ the Lord be true, For He will go with you,
ev-er true, For He will ev - er go with you,

And help you all your con - flicts thro'; To Christ the Lord be true.

70 O Thou Fount of Every Blessing

Robert Robinson

A. Nettleton

FINE

1. { O Thou Fount of ev-'ry bless-ing, Tune my heart to sing Thy grace; }
   { Streams of mer - cy, nev-er ceas-ing, Call for songs of loud-est praise. }

D.C.—While the hope of end-less glo-ry Fills my heart with joy and love.

2. { O to grace how great a debt-or Dai-ly I'm constrained to be! }
   { Let Thy good-ness like a fet-ter Bind my wan-d'ring heart to Thee. }

D.C.—Here's my heart, O take and seal it, Seal it for Thy courts a-bove.

D. C.

Teach me ev - er to a-dore Thee; May I still Thy good-ness prove;
Nev - er let me wan-der from Thee, Nev-er leave the God I love;

71 Purer In Heart, O God

Mrs. A. L. Davison

J. H. Fillmore

1. Pur - er in heart, O God, Help me to be; May I de-
2. Pur - er in heart, O God, Help me to be; Teach me to
3. Pur - er in heart, O God, Help me to be; That I Thy

vote my life Whol-ly to Thee. Watch Thou my way-ward feet,
do Thy will Most lov-ing-ly. Be Thou my Friend and Guide,
ho - ly face One day may see. Keep me from se-cret sin,

Guide me with coun - sel sweet; Pur - er in heart, Help me to be.
Let me with Thee a-bide; Pur - er in heart, Help me to be.
Reign Thou my soul with-in; Pur - er in heart, Help me to be.

72 Wonderful Story of Love

J. M. D.

J. M. Driver

1. Won-der-ful sto-ry of love: Tell it to me a-gain; Won-der-ful sto-ry of
2. Won-der-ful sto-ry of love: Tho' you are far a-way; Won-der-ful sto-ry of
3. Won-der-ful sto-ry of love: Je-sus pro-vides a rest; Won-der-ful sto-ry of

love: Wake the im-mor-tal strain! An-gels with rap-ture an-nounce it,
love: Still He doth call to-day; Call-ing from Cal-va-ry's moun-tain,
love: For all the pure and blest; Rest in those man-sions a-bove us,

Shep-herds with won-der re-ceive it; Sin-ner, O won't you be-lieve it?
Down from the crys-tal bright foun-tain, E'en from the dawn of cre-a-tion,
With those who've gone on be-fore us, Sing-ing the rap-tur-ous cho-rus,

CHORUS

Won-der-ful sto-ry of love. Won - - der - - ful! Won - -
Won-der-ful sto-ry of love! Won-der-ful

der - - ful! Won - der - - ful! Won-der-ful sto-ry of love!
sto-ry of love! Won-der-ful sto-ry of love!

73 Hark! The Gentle Voice

Mrs. M. B. C. Slade

A. B. Everett

1. Hark! the gen-tle voice of Je-sus fall-eth Ten-der-ly up-on your ear;
2. Take His yoke, for He is meek and low-ly, Bear His bur-den, to Him turn;
3. Then, His lov-ing, ten-der voice o-bey-ing, Bear His yoke, His bur-den take;

FINE.

Sweet His cry of love and pit-y call-eth; Turn and lis-ten, stay and hear.
He who call-eth is the Mas-ter ho-ly, He will teach if you will learn.
Find the yoke His hand is on you lay-ing, Light and eas-y for His sake.

D.S.—*Ye that la-bor and are heav-y-la-den, Come, and I will give you rest.*

CHORUS

D. S.

Ye that la-bor and are heav-y-la-den, Lean up-on your dear Lord's breast;

74 I Am Coming, Lord

L. H.

L. Hartsough

1. I hear Thy welcome voice, That calls me, Lord, to Thee, For cleans-ing
2. Tho' com-ing weak and vile, Thou dost my strength as-sure; Thou dost my
3. 'Tis Je-sus calls me on To per-fect faith and love, To per-fect

CHORUS

in Thy pre-cious blood That flowed on Cal-va-ry.
vile-ness ful-ly cleanse, Till spot-less all and pure.
hope, and peace and trust, For earth and heav'n a-bove.

I am com-ing, Lord!

Com-ing now to Thee! Wash me, cleanse me in the blood That flowed on Cal-va-ry!

75   What a Friend We Have in Jesus

Geo. Scriven   C. C. Converse

1. What a Friend we have in Je - sus, All our sins and griefs to bear;
2. Have we tri - als and temp-ta - tions? Is there trou-ble an - y-where?
3. Are we weak and heav-y - la - den, Cum-bered with a load of care?

What a priv-i-lege to car - ry Ev - 'ry-thing to God in prayer.
We should nev-er be dis-cour-aged, Take it to the Lord in prayer.
Pre-cious Sav-ior, still our ref - uge,— Take it to the Lord in prayer.

O what peace we of - ten for - feit, O what need-less pain we bear,
Can we find a friend so faith - ful, Who will all our sor-rows share?
Do thy friends de-spise, for-sake thee? Take it to the Lord in prayer;

All be-cause we do not car - ry Ev - 'ry-thing to God in prayer.
Je - sus knows our ev - 'ry weak-ness: Take it to the Lord in prayer.
In His arms He'll take and shield thee, Thou wilt find a sol-ace there.

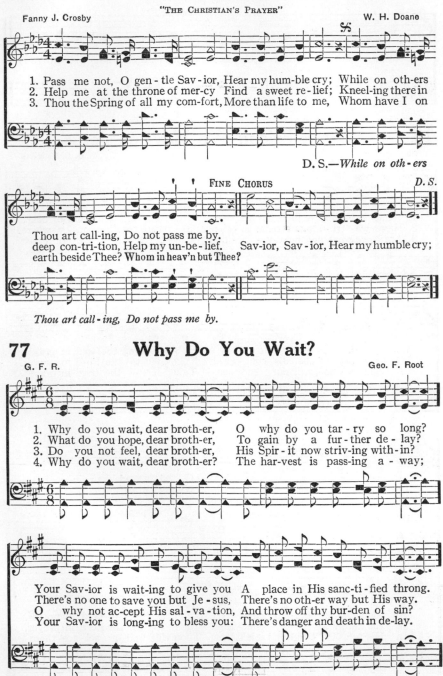

76 Pass Me Not

"The Christian's Prayer"

Fanny J. Crosby

W. H. Doane

1. Pass me not, O gen-tle Sav-ior, Hear my hum-ble cry; While on oth-ers
2. Help me at the throne of mer-cy Find a sweet re-lief; Kneel-ing there in
3. Thou the Spring of all my com-fort, More than life to me, Whom have I on

D. S.—*While on oth-ers*

FINE CHORUS
D. S.

Thou art call-ing, Do not pass me by.
deep con-tri-tion, Help my un-be-lief.   Sav-ior, Sav-ior, Hear my humble cry;
earth beside Thee? Whom in heav'n but Thee?

Thou art call-ing, Do not pass me by.

77 Why Do You Wait?

G. F. R.

Geo. F. Root

1. Why do you wait, dear broth-er, O why do you tar-ry so long?
2. What do you hope, dear broth-er, To gain by a fur-ther de-lay?
3. Do you not feel, dear broth-er, His Spir-it now striv-ing with-in?
4. Why do you wait, dear broth-er? The har-vest is pass-ing a-way;

Your Sav-ior is wait-ing to give you A place in His sanc-ti-fied throng.
There's no one to save you but Je-sus, There's no oth-er way but His way.
O why not ac-cept His sal-va-tion, And throw off thy bur-den of sin?
Your Sav-ior is long-ing to bless you: There's danger and death in de-lay.

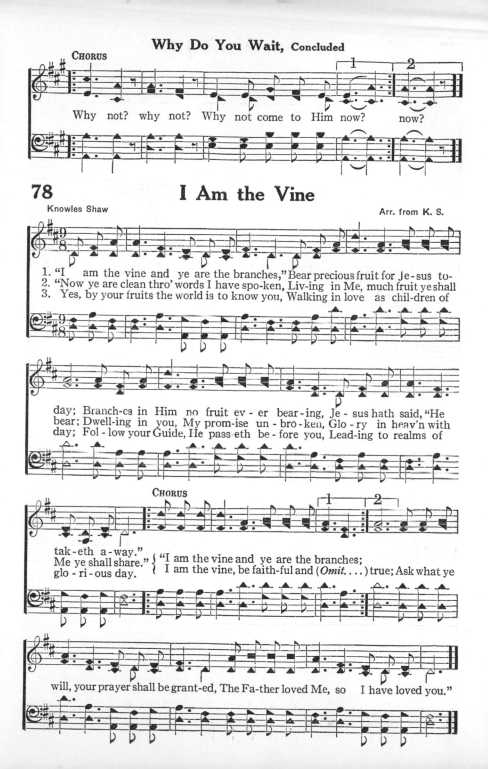

Why Do You Wait, Concluded

CHORUS

Why not? why not? Why not come to Him now? now?

78   I Am the Vine

Knowles Shaw

Arr. from K. S.

1. "I am the vine and ye are the branches," Bear precious fruit for Je-sus to-
2. "Now ye are clean thro' words I have spo-ken, Liv-ing in Me, much fruit ye shall
3. Yes, by your fruits the world is to know you, Walking in love as chil-dren of

day; Branch-es in Him no fruit ev - er bear-ing, Je - sus hath said, "He
bear; Dwell-ing in you, My prom-ise un - bro - ken, Glo - ry in heav'n with
day; Fol - low your Guide, He pass-eth be - fore you, Lead-ing to realms of

CHORUS

tak - eth a - way."
Me ye shall share." ⎰ "I am the vine and ye are the branches;
glo - ri - ous day. ⎱ I am the vine, be faith-ful and (*Omit....*) true; Ask what ye

will, your prayer shall be grant-ed, The Fa-ther loved Me, so   I have loved you."

There Is a Fountain

William Cowper

Lowell Mason

1. There is a foun-tain filled with blood, Drawn from Im-man-uel's veins;
2. Dear dy-ing Lamb, Thy pre-cious blood Shall nev-er lose its pow'r,
3. E'er since by faith I saw the stream Thy flow-ing wounds sup-ply,

FINE

And sin-ners, plunged be-neath that flood, Lose all their guilt-y stains.
Till all the ran-somed Church of God Be saved to sin no more.
Re-deem-ing love has been my theme, And shall be till I die.

D. S.

Lose all their guilt-y stains,..... Lose all their guilt-y stains;
Be saved to sin no more,...... Be saved to sin no more;
And shall be till I die,....... And shall be till I die;

80 Bringing in the Sheaves

Knowles Shaw

George A. Minor

1. Sow-ing in the morn-ing, sow-ing seeds of kind-ness, Sow-ing in the noon-tide
2. Sow-ing in the sun-shine, sow-ing in the shad-ows, Fearing nei-ther clouds nor
3. Go then, e-ven weep-ing, sow-ing for the Mas-ter, Tho' the loss sustained our

and the dew'-y eve; Wait-ing for the har-vest, and the time of reap-ing,
win-ter's chilling breeze; By and by the har-vest, and the la-bor end-ed,
spir-it of-ten grieves; When our weeping's o-ver, He will bid us wel-come,

Bringing in the Sheaves, Concluded

CHORUS

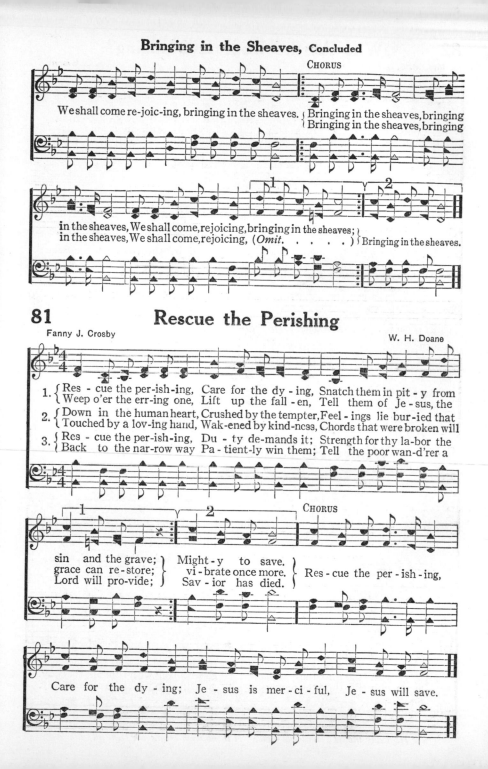

We shall come re-joic-ing, bringing in the sheaves. Bringing in the sheaves, bringing
Bringing in the sheaves, bringing

in the sheaves, We shall come, rejoicing, bringing in the sheaves;
in the sheaves, We shall come, rejoicing, (*Omit* . . . . .) Bringing in the sheaves.

81 Rescue the Perishing

Fanny J. Crosby

W. H. Doane

1. Res - cue the per-ish-ing, Care for the dy - ing, Snatch them in pit - y from
   Weep o'er the err-ing one, Lift up the fall - en, Tell them of Je - sus, the

2. Down in the human heart, Crushed by the tempter, Feel - ings lie bur-ied that
   Touched by a lov-ing hand, Wak-ened by kind-ness, Chords that were broken will

3. Res - cue the per-ish-ing, Du - ty de-mands it; Strength for thy la-bor the
   Back to the nar-row way Pa - tient-ly win them; Tell the poor wan-d'rer a

CHORUS

sin and the grave; } Might - y to save.
grace can re-store; } vi - brate once more. } Res - cue the per - ish - ing,
Lord will pro-vide; }   Sav - ior has died.

Care for the dy - ing; Je - sus is mer - ci - ful, Je - sus will save.

82 Who At the Door Is Standing?

Mrs. M. B. C. Slade

A. B. Everett

1. Who at the door is stand-ing, Pa-tient-ly draw-ing near,
2. Lone-ly with-out He's stay-ing: Lone-ly with-in am I;
3. Door of my heart, I has-ten! Thee will I o-pen wide;

FINE

En-trance with-in de-mand-ing? Whose is the voice I hear?
While I am still de-lay-ing, Will He not pass me by?
Though He re-buke and chas-ten, He shall with me a-bide.

D.S.—*If thou wilt heed My call-ing I will a-bide with thee."*

REFRAIN

D. S.

Sweet-ly the tones are fall-ing: "O-pen the door for Me!

83 Where He Leads Me I Will Follow

E. W. Blandly

J. S. Norris

1. I can hear my Sav-ior call-ing, I can hear my Sav-ior call-ing,
2. I'll go with Him thro' the gar-den, I'll go with Him thro' the gar-den,
3. I'll go with Him thro' the judg-ment, I'll go with Him thro' the judg-ment,

Ref.—*Where He leads me I will fol-low, Where He leads me I will fol-low,*

D. C. for Refrain.

I can hear my Sav-ior call-ing, "Take thy cross and fol-low, fol-low Me."
I'll go with Him thro' the gar-den, I'll go with Him, with Him all the way.
I'll go with Him thro' the judgment, I'll go with Him, with Him all the way.

Where He leads me I will fol-low, I'll go with Him, with Him all the way.

84   Let Him Have His Way with Thee

C. S. N.

Cyrus S. Nusbaum

1. Would you live for Je - sus and be al-ways pure and good? Would you walk with
2. Would you have Him make you free, and fol - low at His call? Would you know the
3. Would you in His king-dom find a place of constant rest? Would you prove Him

Him with - in the nar - row road? Would you have Him bear your bur - den,
peace that comes by giv - ing all? Would you have Him save you, so that
true each prov - i - den - tial test? Would you in His serv - ice la - bor

Chorus

car - ry all your load? Let Him have His way with thee.
you need nev-er fall? Let Him have His way with thee. His pow'r can make you
al - ways at your best? Let Him have His way with thee.

what you ought to be; His blood can cleanse your heart and make you free; His

love can fill your soul, and you will see 'Twas best for Him to have His way with thee.

85   I Need Thee Every Hour

Annie S. Hawks   Robert Lowry

1. I need Thee ev-'ry hour, Most gra - cious Lord; No ten - der voice like
2. I need Thee ev-'ry hour, Stay Thou near by; Temp-ta-tions lose their
3. I need Thee ev-'ry hour, In joy or pain; Come quick-ly and a-
4. I need Thee ev-'ry hour, Most Ho - ly One; O make me Thine in-

CHORUS

Thine Can peace af - ford.
pow'r When Thou art nigh
bide, Or life is vain
deed, Thou bless - ed Son!

I need Thee, O I need Thee;

Ev - 'ry hour I need Thee! O bless me now, my Sav-ior, I come to Thee!

86   We'll Work Till Jesus Comes

Mrs. Elizabeth Mills   Wm. Miller

1. O land of rest, for thee I sigh; When will the mo-ment come,
2. No tran-quil joys on earth I know, No peace-ful, shel-t'ring dome,
3. To Je - sus Christ I fled for rest; He bade me cease to roam,

When I shall lay my ar - mor by, And dwell in peace at home?
This world's a wil - der - ness of woe, This world is not my home.
And lean for suc - cor on His breast, Till He con-duct me home.

We'll Work Till Jesus Comes, Concluded

CHORUS

We'll work   till Je - sus comes, We'll work   till Je - sus comes,
We'll work,   We'll work

We'll work   till Je - sus comes, And we'll be gath-ered home.
We'll work

87 Tarry with Me, O My Savior

Mrs. C. S. Smith

Knowles Shaw

1. Tar - ry with me, O my Sav - ior, For the day is pass-ing by;
2. Man - y friends were gath-ered round me In the bright days of the past;
3. Deep-er, deep - er grow the shad - ows, Pal - er now the glow-ing west;

FINE.

See, the shades of eve - ning gath - er, And the night is draw-ing nigh.
But the grave has closed a-bove them, And I lin - ger here the last.
Swift the night of death ad-vanc - es: Shall it be the night of rest?

D.S.—*For I'm lone - ly here with-out Thee: Tar - ry with me through the night.*

CHORUS

D. S.

Tar - ry with me, bless-ed Sav - ior; Leave me not till morn-ing light:

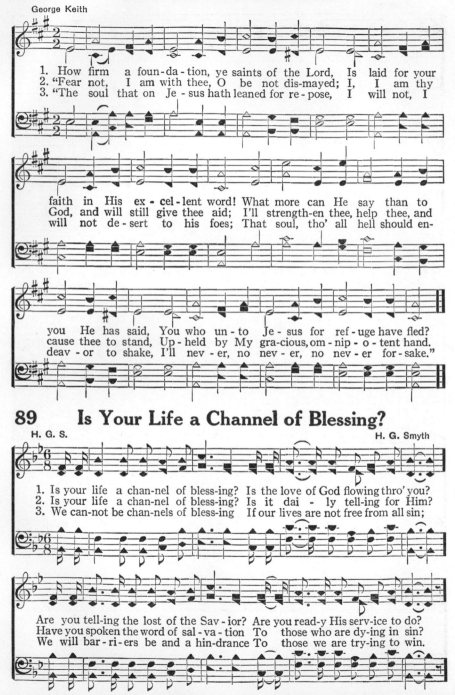

88 How Firm a Foundation

George Keith

1. How firm a foun-da-tion, ye saints of the Lord, Is laid for your
2. "Fear not, I am with thee, O be not dis-mayed; I, I am thy
3. "The soul that on Je-sus hath leaned for re-pose, I will not, I

faith in His ex-cel-lent word! What more can He say than to
God, and will still give thee aid; I'll strength-en thee, help thee, and
will not de-sert to his foes; That soul, tho' all hell should en-

you He has said, You who un-to Je-sus for ref-uge have fled?
cause thee to stand, Up-held by My gra-cious, om-nip-o-tent hand.
deav-or to shake, I'll nev-er, no nev-er, no nev-er for-sake."

89 Is Your Life a Channel of Blessing?

H. G. S.   H. G. Smyth

1. Is your life a chan-nel of bless-ing? Is the love of God flowing thro' you?
2. Is your life a chan-nel of bless-ing? Is it dai-ly tell-ing for Him?
3. We can-not be chan-nels of bless-ing If our lives are not free from all sin;

Are you tell-ing the lost of the Sav-ior? Are you read-y His serv-ice to do?
Have you spoken the word of sal-va-tion To those who are dy-ing in sin?
We will bar-ri-ers be and a hin-drance To those we are try-ing to win.

Is Your Life a Channel, Concluded

CHORUS

Make me a channel of blessing to-day, Make me a chan-nel of bless-ing, I pray;

My life pos-sess-ing, My service blessing, Make me a chan-nel of bless-ing to-day.

90 Jesus Will Give You Rest

Fanny J. Crosby

Jno. R. Sweney

1. Will you come, will you come, with your poor broken heart, Burdened and sin - op-
2. Will you come, will you come? There is mer - cy for you, Balm for your ach-ing
3. Will you come, will you come? How He pleads with you now! Fly to His lov - ing

prest? Lay it down at the feet of your Sav - ior and Lord: Je-sus will give you rest.
breast; On-ly come as you are and be-lieve on His name: Je-sus will give you rest.
breast, And whatever your sin or your sor - row may be, Je-sus will give you rest.

D. S.—*O why won't you come in simple, trusting faith? Je-sus will give you rest.*

REFRAIN

D. S.

O hap-py rest, sweet, hap-py rest! Je - sus will give you rest; hap-py rest;

91

Softly and Tenderly

W. L. T.

Will L. Thompson

Very slow

1. Soft-ly and ten-der-ly Je-sus is call-ing, Call-ing for you and for me;
2. Why should we tarry when Jesus is pleading, Pleading for you and for me?
3. Time is now fleeting, the moments are passing, Passing from you and from me;

See, on the por-tals He's waiting and watching, Watching for you and for me.
Why should we linger and heed not His mer-cies, Mer-cies for you and for me?
Shad-ows are gath-er-ing, death warnings coming, Com-ing for you and for me.

FINE.

D. S.—Ear-nest-ly, ten-der-ly, Je-sus is call-ing, Call-ing, O sin-ner, come home!

D. S. pp

CHORUS   *cres.*

Come home,.... come home,.... Ye who are wea-ry, come home;....
Come home,   come home,

92

Peace, Perfect Peace

Edward H. Bickersteth

George T. Caldbeck

1. Peace, per - fect peace, in this dark world of sin:....
2. Peace, per - fect peace, by throng - ing du - ties pressed:
3. Peace, per - fect peace, with sor - rows surg - ing round:
4. Peace, per - fect peace, our fu - ture all un - known:

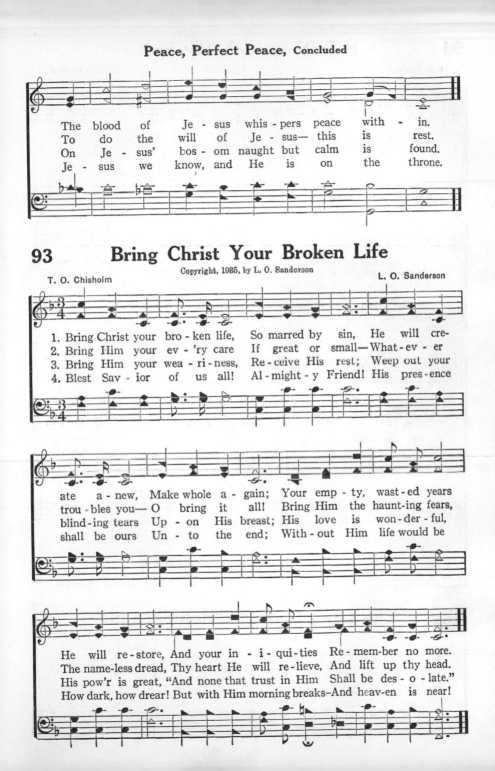

The blood of Je - sus whis - pers peace with - in.
To do the will of Je - sus— this is rest.
On Je - sus' bos - om naught but calm is found.
Je - sus we know, and He is on the throne.

93 Bring Christ Your Broken Life

Copyright, 1935, by L. O. Sanderson

T. O. Chisholm   L. O. Sanderson

1. Bring Christ your bro - ken life, So marred by sin, He will cre-
2. Bring Him your ev - 'ry care If great or small—What - ev - er
3. Bring Him your wea - ri - ness, Re - ceive His rest; Weep out your
4. Blest Sav - ior of us all! Al - might - y Friend! His pres - ence

ate a - new, Make whole a - gain; Your emp - ty, wast - ed years
trou - bles you— O bring it all! Bring Him the haunt - ing fears,
blind - ing tears Up - on His breast; His love is won - der - ful,
shall be ours Un - to the end; With - out Him life would be

He will re - store, And your in - i - qui - ties Re - mem - ber no more.
The name - less dread, Thy heart He will re - lieve, And lift up thy head.
His pow'r is great, "And none that trust in Him Shall be des - o - late."
How dark, how drear! But with Him morning breaks–And heav - en is near!

94 It Is Well with My Soul

H. G. Spafford

P. P. Bliss

1. When peace like a riv-er at-tend-eth my way, When sor-rows like
2. My sin— O the bliss of this glo-ri-ous tho't—My sin, not in
3. And, Lord, haste the day when the faith shall be sight, The clouds be rolled

sea-bil-lows roll; What-ev-er my lot, Thou hast taught me to say,
part but the whole, Is nailed to the cross and I bear it no more:
back as a scroll, The trump shall re-sound and the Lord shall de-scend,

CHORUS

"It is well, it is well with my soul." It is well..........
Praise the Lord, praise the Lord, O my soul!
"E-ven so"— it is well with my soul. It is well

with my soul (with my soul), It is well, it is well with my soul.

95 The Lord Is in His Holy Temple

Habakkuk 2: 20

Wm. J. Kirkpatrick

The Lord is in His ho-ly tem-ple: Let all the earth keep si-lence be-

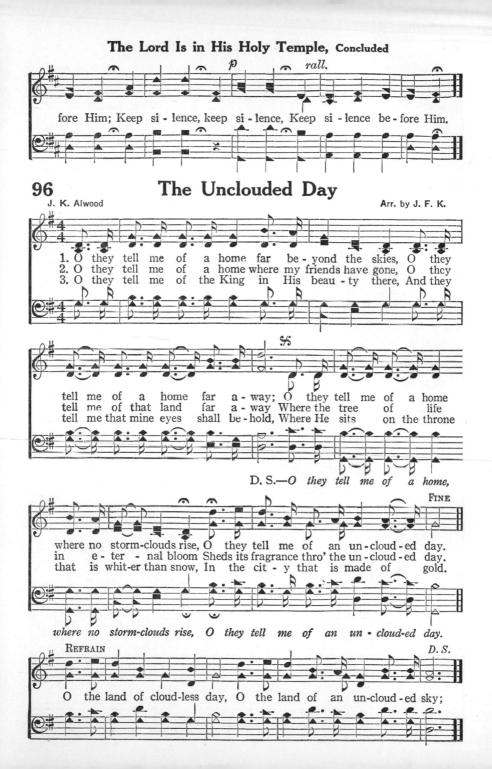

fore Him; Keep si - lence, keep si - lence, Keep si - lence be - fore Him.

96 The Unclouded Day

J. K. Alwood

Arr. by J. F. K.

1. O they tell me of a home far be - yond the skies, O they
2. O they tell me of a home where my friends have gone, O they
3. O they tell me of the King in His beau - ty there, And they

tell me of a home far a - way; O they tell me of a home
tell me of that land far a - way Where the tree of life
tell me that mine eyes shall be - hold, Where He sits on the throne

D. S.—*O they tell me of a home,*

where no storm-clouds rise, O they tell me of an un - cloud - ed day.
in e - ter - nal bloom Sheds its fragrance thro' the un - cloud - ed day.
that is whit-er than snow, In the cit - y that is made of gold.

FINE

where no storm-clouds rise, O they tell me of an un - cloud-ed day.

REFRAIN   D. S.

O the land of cloud-less day, O the land of an un-cloud - ed sky;

97 Tell It to Jesus Alone

J. B. Rankin

E. S. Lorenz

1. Are you wea-ry, are you heav-y-heart-ed? Tell it to Je-sus,
2. Do the tears flow down your cheeks un-bid-den? Tell it to Je-sus,
3. Do you fear the gath-'ring clouds of sor-row? Tell it to Je-sus,

Tell it to Je-sus; Are you griev-ing o-ver joys de-part-ed?
Tell it to Je-sus; Have you sins that to man's eyes are hid-den?
Tell it to Je-sus; Are you anx-ious what will be to-mor-row?

FINE. CHORUS

Tell it to Je-sus a-lone. Tell it to Je-sus, Tell it to Je-sus,

D.S.—*Tell it to Je-sus a-lone.*

D. S.

He is a friend that's well known; You have no oth-er such a friend or broth-er;

98 Savior, Breathe an Evening Blessing

James Edmeston

George C. Stebbins

1. Sav-ior, breathe an eve-ning bless-ing Ere re-pose our spir-its seal;
2. Tho' the night be dark and drear-y, Darkness can-not hide from Thee;
3. Should swift death this night o'ertake us, And our couch be-come our tomb,

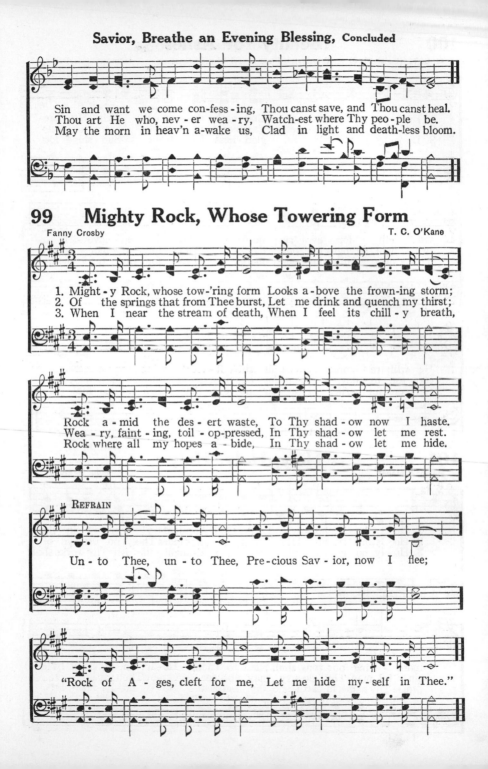

Sin and want we come con-fess-ing, Thou canst save, and Thou canst heal.
Thou art He who, nev-er wea-ry, Watch-est where Thy peo-ple be.
May the morn in heav'n a-wake us, Clad in light and death-less bloom.

99   Mighty Rock, Whose Towering Form

Fanny Crosby   T. C. O'Kane

1. Might-y Rock, whose tow-'ring form Looks a-bove the frown-ing storm;
2. Of   the springs that from Thee burst, Let me drink and quench my thirst;
3. When I near the stream of death, When I feel its chill-y breath,

Rock a-mid the des-ert waste, To Thy shad-ow now I haste.
Wea-ry, faint-ing, toil-op-pressed, In Thy shad-ow let me rest.
Rock where all my hopes a-bide, In Thy shad-ow let me hide.

REFRAIN

Un-to Thee, un-to Thee, Pre-cious Sav-ior, now I flee;

"Rock of A-ges, cleft for me, Let me hide my-self in Thee."

100 Beauty for Ashes

G. C. T. (Isaiah 61:3)   Copyright, 1948, by Gospel Advocate Company   Grant Colfax Tullar

1. Beau-ty for ash-es God hath de-cr..ed! Help He pro-
2. God gives for sad-ness "gar-ments of praise;" Stars for our
3. Beau-ty for ash-es, glad-ness for tears, Sun-shine for

vid-eth for ev-'ry need; What is un-love-ly
twi-light, strength for our days; Hope for to-mor-row,
dark-ness, faith for our fears; Peace for our tur-moil,

He will re-store; Grace all suf-fi-cient:—what need we more?
care for to-day, Light for our foot-steps all of life's way.
con-cord for strife, Heav-en at eve-ning— then end-less life!

101 Holy, Holy, Holy

Reginald Heber   John B. Dykes

1. Ho-ly, ho-ly, ho-ly! Lord God Al-might-y! Ear-ly in the
2. Ho-ly, ho-ly, ho-ly! Tho' the darkness hides Thee, Tho' the eye of
3. Ho-ly, ho-ly, ho-ly! Lord God Al-might-y! All Thy works shall

morn-ing our song shall rise to Thee; Ho-ly, ho-ly, ho-ly!
sin-ful man Thy glo-ry may not see, On-ly Thou art ho-ly;
praise Thy name, in earth, and sky, and sea; Ho-ly, ho-ly, ho-ly!

mer - ci - ful and might - y! God in Three Per-sons, bless-ed Trin - i - ty!
there is none be - side Thee Per - fect in pow'r, in love, and pu - ri - ty.
mer - ci - ful and might - y! God in Three Per-sons, bless-ed Trin - i - ty!

102 Savior, Lead Me, Lest I Stray

F. M. D.

Frank M. Davis

1. Sav - ior, lead me, lest I stray, Gen - tly lead me all the way;
2. Thou the ref-uge of my soul When life's stormy billows roll;
3. Sav - ior, lead me, then at last, When the storm of life is past,

I am safe when by Thy side, I would in Thy love a-bide.
I am safe when Thou art nigh, All my hopes on Thee re-ly.
To the land of end-less day, Where all tears are wiped away.

CHORUS

Lead me, lead me, Sav - ior, lead me, lest I stray;

Gen-tly down the stream of time, Lead me, Sav-ior, all the way.

Seeking the Lost

W. A. O.

W. A. Ogden

1. Seek - ing the lost, yes, kind - ly en - treat - ing, Wan - der - ers
2. Seek - ing the lost, and point - ing to Je - sus, Souls that are
3. Thus I would go on mis - sions of mer - cy, Fol - low - ing

on the moun - tain a - stray; "Come un - to Me," His mes - sage re-
weak and hearts that are sore; Lead - ing them forth in ways of sal-
Christ from day un - to day; Cheer - ing the faint, and rais - ing the

peat - ing, Words of the Mas - ter speak - ing to - day.
va - tion, Show - ing the path to life ev - er - more.
fall - en; Point - ing the lost to Je - sus, the Way.

CHORUS

{ Go - ing a - far up - on the mountain,
{ In - to the fold of my Re - deem - er,

{ Go - ing a - far............ up - on the moun - tain,..... Bringing the
{ In - to the fold.......... of my Re - deem - er,....... Je - sus the

1. 2.

Bringing the wand'rer back a - gain, back a - gain, }
Je - sus the Lamb for sin - ners (*Omit.* . . . .) } slain, for sin - ners slain.

wan - - - - d'rer back a - gain........... }
Lamb.............. for sin - ners (*Omit.* . . . .)} slain..............

104 Standing on the Promises

R. K. C.

R. Kelso Carter

1. Stand-ing on the prom-is-es of Christ my King, Thro' e-ter-nal a-ges
2. Stand-ing on the prom-is-es that can-not fail, When the howling storms of
3. Stand-ing on the prom-is-es of Christ the Lord, Bound to Him e-ter-nal-

let His prais-es ring; Glo-ry in the high-est, I will shout and sing,
doubt and fear as-sail, By the liv-ing word of God I shall pre-vail,
ly by love's strong cord, O-ver-com-ing dai-ly with the Spir-it's sword,

CHORUS

Stand-ing on the prom-is-es of God. Stand - ing, stand - ing,
Standing on the promises, standing on the promises,

Stand-ing on the prom-is-es of God my Sav-ior; Stand - - ing,
Standing on the prom-is-es,

stand - - - ing, I'm stand-ing on the prom-is-es of God.
stand-ing on the prom-is-es,

105 Sweet Peace, the Gift of God's Love

P. P. B.

P. P. Bilhorn

1. There comes to my heart one sweet strain, A glad and a joy-ous re-frain;...
2. Thro' Christ on the cross peace was made; My debt by His death was all paid;..
3. In Je-sus for peace I a-bide,.... And as I keep close to His side,...

(1) sweet strain,   refrain,

I   sing it a-gain and a-gain: Sweet peace, the gift of God's love.
No   oth-er foun-da-tion is laid   For peace, the gift of God's love.
There's noth-ing but peace doth be-tide,   Sweet peace, the gift of God's love.

CHORUS

Peace, peace, sweet peace! Won-der-ful gift from a-bove (a-bove)!

O won-der-ful, won-der-ful peace! Sweet peace, the gift of God's love.

106   'Tis Set, the Feast Divine

Vana R. Raye

Copyright, 1948, by Gospel Advocate Company

L. O. Sanderson

1. 'Tis set, the   feast   di-vine— The bread, the fruit of the vine—
2. May we   the   Lord dis-cern, His death our ho-ly con-cern;

And saints com-mune be - fore the shrine, In the sup - per of the Lord.
We feast in faith, His com - ing yearn, In the sup - per of the Lord.

107   'Tis the Bible

Tom C. Neal

1. There's a book which sur-pass-es the sag - es, A vol-ume of wis-dom di-vine;
2. 'Tis the light which will guide us to glo - ry, The Sword of the Spir - it of might;
3. It re-veals where a foun-tain is flow-ing, Which washes the soul from its stain;

And the glo-ry that gleams from its pag-es, No splen-dor of earth can out-shine.
And to dwell on its beau-ti-ful sto - ry Is of heav-en the sweet-est de-light.
Age and sor-row are com-fort-ed, knowing With earth they shall part with all pain.

CHORUS

{ 'Tis the Bi - - ble! the Bi - - ble! Our
{ 'Tis the bless-ed, bless-ed Bi - ble! the bless-ed, bless-ed Bi - ble! Our
{ The Bi - - ble! the Bi - - ble! We
{ The bless-ed, bless-ed Bi - ble! the bless-ed, bless-ed Bi - ble! We

guid-ing star that leads from earth to heav'n, love the precious Book of Truth which God has giv'n.

108   Anywhere with Jesus

Jessie Brown Pounds
V. 3 by Mrs. C. M. A.

D. B. Towner

1. An - y - where with Je - sus I can safe - ly go, An - y - where He
2. An - y - where with Je - sus I am not a - lone; Oth - er friends may
3. An - y - where with Je - sus, o - ver land and sea, Tell - ing souls in

leads me in this world be - low; An - y - where with-out Him dear - est
fail me, He is still my own; Tho' His hand may lead me o - ver
dark - ness of sal - va - tion free; Read - y as He sum-mons me to

joys would fade; An - y - where with Je - sus I am not a - fraid.
drear - est ways, An - y - where with Je - sus is a house of praise.
go or stay, An - y - where with Je - sus when He points the way.

Chorus

An - y - where, an - y - where! Fear I can - not know;

An - y - where with Je - sus I can safe - ly go.

109 Will You Not Tell It Today

Jessie Brown Pounds

J. H. Fillmore

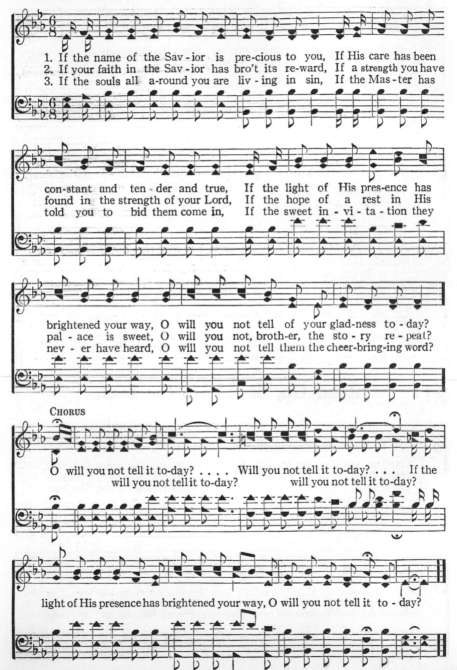

1. If the name of the Sav-ior is pre-cious to you, If His care has been
con-stant and ten-der and true, If the light of His pres-ence has
brightened your way, O will you not tell of your glad-ness to-day?

2. If your faith in the Sav-ior has bro't its re-ward, If a strength you have
found in the strength of your Lord, If the hope of a rest in His
pal-ace is sweet, O will you not, broth-er, the sto-ry re-peat?

3. If the souls all a-round you are liv-ing in sin, If the Mas-ter has
told you to bid them come in, If the sweet in-vi-ta-tion they
nev-er have heard, O will you not tell them the cheer-bring-ing word?

CHORUS

O will you not tell it to-day? .... Will you not tell it to-day? ... If the
will you not tell it to-day? will you not tell it to-day?

light of His presence has brightened your way, O will you not tell it to-day?

110 Let the Lower Lights Be Burning

P. P. B.

P. P. Bliss

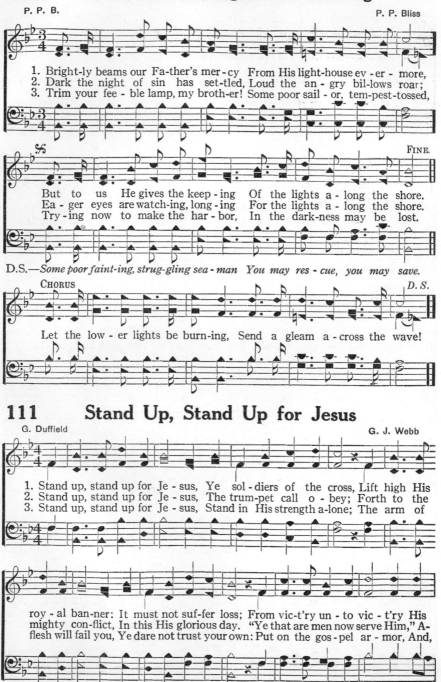

1. Bright-ly beams our Fa-ther's mer-cy From His light-house ev-er-more,
2. Dark the night of sin has set-tled, Loud the an-gry bil-lows roar;
3. Trim your fee-ble lamp, my broth-er! Some poor sail-or, tem-pest-tossed,

But to us He gives the keep-ing Of the lights a-long the shore.
Ea-ger eyes are watch-ing, long-ing For the lights a-long the shore.
Try-ing now to make the har-bor, In the dark-ness may be lost.

D.S.—*Some poor faint-ing, strug-gling sea-man You may res-cue, you may save.*

Chorus

D. S.

Let the low-er lights be burn-ing, Send a gleam a-cross the wave!

111 Stand Up, Stand Up for Jesus

G. Duffield

G. J. Webb

1. Stand up, stand up for Je-sus, Ye sol-diers of the cross, Lift high His
2. Stand up, stand up for Je-sus, The trum-pet call o-bey; Forth to the
3. Stand up, stand up for Je-sus, Stand in His strength a-lone; The arm of

roy-al ban-ner: It must not suf-fer loss; From vic-t'ry un-to vic-t'ry His
mighty con-flict, In this His glorious day. "Ye that are men now serve Him," A-
flesh will fail you, Ye dare not trust your own: Put on the gos-pel ar-mor, And,

Stand Up, Stand Up for Jesus, Concluded

ar - my shall He lead, Till ev - 'ry foe is vanquished, And Christ is Lord in-deed.
gainst unnumbered foes, Let courage rise with danger, And strength to strength oppose.
watching un - to prayer, Where duty calls or dan-ger, Be nev - er wanting there.

112 Are You Coming to Jesus Tonight?

Jessie H. Brown   J. E. Hawes

1. The voice of the Sav-ior says "Come," The cross where He died is in sight,
2. The voice of the Fa-ther im-plores, From mer-cy's most wonderful height,
3. O who to him-self will be true, Of all whom these voic-es in - vite?

E'en now at the cross there is room, Are you com-ing to Je - sus to-night?
His love in that call He out-pours, Are you com-ing to Je - sus to-night?
Who an-swers, my broth-er, do you? I am com-ing to Je - sus to-night?

CHORUS

Are you com-ing to Je - sus to-night? Are you com-ing to Je - sus to-night?

The Bride and the Spir-it in - vite, Are you com-ing to Je - sus to-night?

113 Whosoever Will May Come

P. P. B.

P. P. Bliss

1. Who-so-ev-er heareth, shout, shout the sound! Spread the blessed tidings all the world a-
2. Who-so-ev-er com-eth need not de-lay; Now the door is o-pen, en-ter while you
3. "Who-so-ev-er will"—the promise secure—"Who-so-ev-er will" for-ev-er must en-

round; Spread the joyful news wherever man is found: "Who-so-ev-er will may come."
may; Je-sus is the true, the on-ly Liv-ing Way: "Who-so-ev-er will may come."
dure; "Who-so-ev-er will"—'tis life for-ev-er-more: "Who-so-ev-er will may come."

CHORUS

"Who-so-ev-er will, who-so-ev-er will!" Send the proclamation o-ver vale and hill;

'Tis a lov-ing Fa-ther calls the wand'rer home: "Who-so-ev-er will may come."

114 We May Not Climb the Heavenly Steeps

John G. Whittier

William V. Wallace

1. We may not climb the heav'n-ly steeps To bring the Lord Christ down;
2. But warm, sweet, ten-der, e-ven yet A pres-ent help is He;
3. Thro' Him the first fond prayers are said Our lips of child-hood frame;

In vain we search the low - est deeps, For Him no depths can drown.
And faith has still its Ol - i - vet, And love its Gal - i - lee.
The last low whis-pers of our dead Are bur-dened with His name.

115 It Came Upon the Midnight Clear

E. H. Sears

R. S. Willis

1. It came up - on the mid-night clear, That glo-rious song of old,
2. Still thro' the clo - ven skies they come With peace-ful wings un - furled,
3. Yet with the woes of sin and strife The world has suf - fered long;

From an - gels bend-ing near the earth To touch their harps of gold:
And still their heav'n-ly mu - sic floats O'er all the wea - ry world;
Be - neath the an - gel-strain have rolled Two thou-sand years of wrong;

"Peace on the earth, good-will to men, From heav'n's all-gra-cious King;"
A - bove its sad and low - ly plains They bend on hov-'ring wing,
And men, at war with men, hear not The love-song which they bring:

The world in sol - emn still - ness lay To hear the an - gels sing.
And ev - er, o'er its Ba - bel sounds, The bless - ed an - gels sing.
O hush the noise, ye men of strife, And hear the an - gels sing.

116 Beyond This Land of Parting

Mrs. M. B. C. Slade

Dr. A. B. Everett

1. Be-yond this land of part-ing, los-ing and leav-ing, Far be-yond the
2. Be-yond this land of toil-ing, sow-ing and reap-ing, Far be-yond the
3. Be-yond this land of wait-ing, seek-ing and sigh-ing, Far be-yond the

loss-es dark-en-ing this, And far be-yond the tak-ing and the be-reav-ing
shad-ows dark-en-ing this, And far be-yond the sigh-ing, moaning and weep-ing,
sor-rows dark-en-ing this, And far be-yond the pain and sick-ness and dy-ing.

FINE   REFRAIN

Lies the sum-mer-land of bliss. Land be-yond,.... so fair and bright! Land be-
Land be-yond, so fair and bright!

D.S.—hap-py sum-mer-land of bliss!

yond..... where is no night! Sum-mer-land,..... God is its Light, O
Land be-yond, where is no night!   Sum-mer-land,

D. S.

117 I Will Pray

A. Cummings

J. H. Tenney

1. Fa-ther, in the morn-ing Un-to Thee   I pray; Let Thy lov-ing-
2. At the bus-y noon-tide, Pressed with work   and care, Then I'll wait with
3. When the eve-ning shad-ows Chase a-way   the light, Fa-ther, then I'll
4. Thus in life's glad morn-ing, In its bright   noon-day, In the shadowy
(1) Un-to Thee I pray;

I Will Pray, Concluded

CHORUS

kind-ness Keep me through this day.
Je - sus, Till He hear my prayer. I will pray, I will pray,
pray Thee, Bless Thy child to - night.
eve - ning, Ev - er will I pray.

Keep me through this day.   I will pray,   I will pray,

Ev - er will.... I pray; Morning, noon and evening Un-to Thee I'll pray.

Ev - er will I pray;   Un-to Thee I'll pray.

---

118 Some Blessed Day

G. C. T.

Grant Colfax Tullar

1. Some day in Je - sus' name, The sun will shine a - gain, Hope on, nor
2. Some day we'll need no sun, 'Twill mean that heav'n's begun, With all earth's
3. Per - haps it soon may be That shad-ows dark shall flee, And from earth's

hope in vain, 'Twill come some day!........ Grief then shall change to joy,
bat - tles won, When dawns that day......... With shad-ows past, and woe,
fet - ters free, We'll greet that day!........ Thro' grace from heaven's throne,

God's will our pow'rs employ, And sin no more destroy, Some bless-ed day!
All dark things clearer grow, And we great joy shall know Some bless-ed day!
Not mer - it of our own, We'll find a better home Some bless-ed day!

119 Low in the Grave He Lay

R. L.

Robert Lowry

Slowly

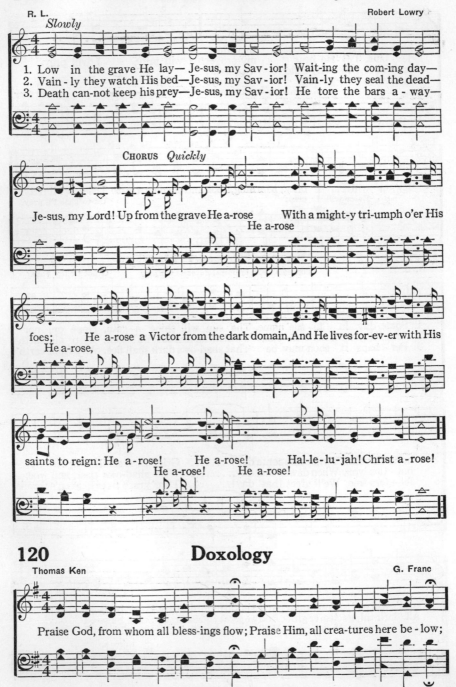

1. Low in the grave He lay— Je-sus, my Sav-ior! Wait-ing the com-ing day—
2. Vain - ly they watch His bed— Je-sus, my Sav-ior! Vain-ly they seal the dead—
3. Death can-not keep his prey— Je-sus, my Sav-ior! He tore the bars a-way—

CHORUS *Quickly*

Je-sus, my Lord! Up from the grave He a-rose   With a might-y tri-umph o'er His
He a-rose

foes;   He a-rose a Victor from the dark domain, And He lives for-ev-er with His
He a-rose,

saints to reign: He a-rose!   He a-rose!   Hal-le-lu-jah! Christ a-rose!
He a-rose!   He a-rose!

120 Doxology

Thomas Ken

G. Franc

Praise God, from whom all bless-ings flow; Praise Him, all crea-tures here be-low;

Doxology, Concluded

Praise Him a-bove, ye heav'n-ly host; Praise Fa-ther, Son, and Ho-ly Ghost!

121   Jesus, I Come

W. T. Sleeper

Geo. C. Stebbins

1. Out of my bond-age, sor-row and night, Je-sus, I come, Je-sus, I come;
2. Out of my shame-ful fail-ure and loss, Je-sus, I come, Je-sus, I come;
3. Out of the fear and dread of the tomb, Je-sus, I come, Je-sus, I come;

In-to Thy free-dom, glad-ness and light, Je-sus, I come to Thee;
In-to the glo-rious gain of Thy cross, Je-sus, I come to Thee;
In-to the joy and light of Thy home, Je-sus, I come to Thee;

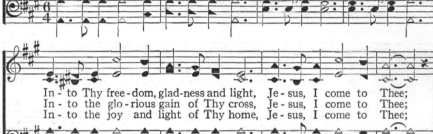

Out of my sick-ness, in-to Thy health, Out of my want and in-to Thy wealth,
Out of earth's sorrows, in-to Thy balm, Out of life's storms and in-to Thy calm,
Out of the depths of ru-in un-told, In-to the peace of Thy shel-ter-ing fold,

Out of my sin and in-to Thy-self, Je-sus, I come to Thee.
Out of dis-tress to ju-bi-lant psalm, Je-sus, I come to Thee.
Ev-er Thy glo-rious face to be-hold, Je-sus, I come to Thee.

122 There Is Sunshine in My Soul

E. E. Hewitt

John R. Sweney

1. There is sun-shine in my soul to-day, More glo - ri - ous and bright
2. There is mu - sic in my soul to-day, A car - ol to my King,
3. There is glad-ness in my soul to-day, And hope and praise and love,

Than glows in an - y earth-ly sky, For Je - sus is my light.
And Je - sus, lis - ten-ing, can hear The songs I can - not sing.
For bless-ings which He gives me now, For joys laid up a - bove.

REFRAIN

O there's sun - - - - shine, bless - ed sun - - - shine,
O there's sun-shine in my soul, bless - ed sun-shine in my soul,

While the peace-ful, hap - py mo-ments roll; When
hap - py mo-ments roll;

Je - sus shows His smil-ing face, There is sun-shine in my soul.

123   Heaven Holds All to Me

T. S. T.

Tillit S. Teddlie

1. Earth holds no treas-ures but per-ish with us-ing, How-ev-er
2. Out on the hill of that won-der-ful coun-try, Hap-py, con-
3. Why should I long for the world with its sor-rows, When in that

pre-cious they be; Yet there's a coun-try to which I am go-ing,
tent-ed and free, Loved ones are wait-ing and watch-ing my com-ing,
home o'er the sea, Mil-lions are sing-ing the won-der-ful sto-ry,

CHORUS

Heav-en holds all to me. Heav-en holds all to me, . . .
to me,

Bright-er its glo-ry will be; Joy with-out meas-ure

will be my treas-ure, Heav-en holds all to me.

124   Ho! Reapers of Life's Harvest

I. B. W.

I. B. Woodbury

1. Ho! reap-ers of life's har-vest, Why stand with rust-ed blade,
2. Thrust in your sharp-ened sick-le, And gath-er in the grain,
3 Mount up the heights of Wis-dom, And crush each er-ror low;

Un - til the night draws round thee, And day be-gins to fade?
The night is fast ap-proach-ing, And soon will come a-gain.
Keep back no words of knowl-edge That hu-man hearts should know.

D.S.–The gold-en morn is pass-ing, Why sit ye i-dle, dumb?
D.S.–Shall sheaves lie there un-gath-ered, And waste up-on the plain?
D.S.–And then a gold-en chap-let Shall be Thy just re-ward.

FINE

Why stand ye i-dle, wait-ing For reap-ers more to come?
The Mas-ter calls for reap-ers, And shall He call in vain?
Be faith-ful to thy mis-sion, In serv-ice of thy Lord,

D. S.

125   My Faith Looks Up to Thee

Ray Palmer

Lowell Mason

1. My faith looks up to Thee, Thou Lamb of Cal-va-ry, Sav-ior di-vine:
2. May Thy rich grace im-part Strength to my fainting heart, My zeal in-spire;
3. When life's dark maze I tread, And griefs a-round me spread, Be Thou my guide;
4. When ends life's transient dream, When death's cold, sullen stream Shall o'er me roll;

127 Only a Step

C. H. G.
Chas. H. Gabriel

1. Hear the sweet voice of Je-sus say, "Come un-to Me, I am the way;"
2. Cast-ing your heav-y bur-den down, Come to the cross, the world may frown;
3. O-pen, for you, the pearl-y gate; Loved ones for you now watch and wait;

FINE.

Heark-en, the lov-ing call o-bey; Come, for He loves you so.
Yet you shall wear a glo-rious crown, When He makes up His own.
Ter-ri-ble tho't, to cry "too late"—"Je-sus, I come to Thee."

D.S.—He's the same lov-ing Sav-ior yet, Je-sus the Cru-ci-fied.

CHORUS
D.S.

On-ly a step, on-ly a step: Come, for He bled for you and died;

128 We Assemble Here to Worship

Copyright, 1948, by Gospel Advocate Company

Vana R. Raye
L. O. Sanderson

1. We as-sem-ble here to wor-ship With the church of God Most High;
   In the name of Christ we gath-er, Know-ing He is (*Omit.* . . .) ev-er nigh.

2. Praise and hon-or to the Fa-ther; Love and glo-ry to the Son;
   By the Spir-it Christians worship, As at Zion it (*Omit.* . . .) was be-gun.

In the spir-it, un-der-standing, Praising on-ly God's own way:
Teaching, giv-ing, and communing, Praying, singing (*Omit . . .*) on this day.

129 Throw Out the Life-Line

E. S. Ufford

Arr. Geo. C. Stebbins

1. Throw out the Life-Line a-cross the dark wave; There is a broth-er whom
2. Throw out the Life-Line to dan-ger-fraught men, Sink-ing in an-guish where
3. Soon will the sea-son of res-cue be o'er, Soon will they drift to e-

some one should save; Some-bod-y's broth-er! O who then will dare To
you've nev-er been; Winds of temp-ta-tion and bil-lows of woe Will
ter-ni-ty's shore; Haste then, my broth-er, no time for de-lay, But

CHORUS

throw out the Life-Line, his per-il to share?
soon hurl them out where the dark wa-ters flow.   Throw out the Life-Line!
throw out the Life-Line and save them to-day.

Throw out the Life-Line! Some one is drifting a-way; Some one is sink-ing to-day.

130 Some Sweet Day

S. H. C.

S. H. Chord

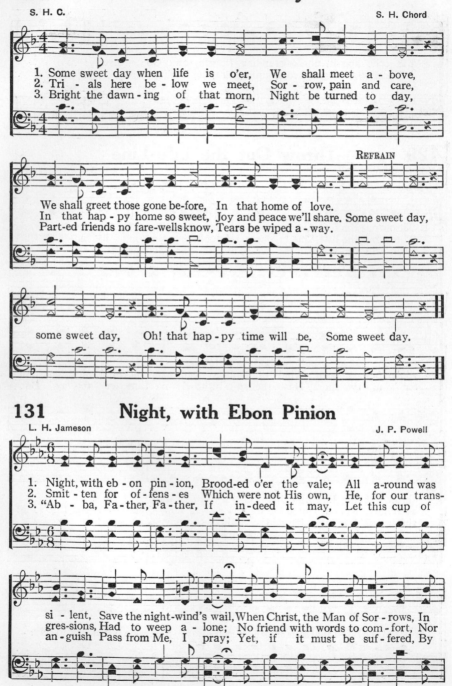

1. Some sweet day when life is o'er, We shall meet a - bove,
2. Tri - als here be - low we meet, Sor - row, pain and care,
3. Bright the dawn - ing of that morn, Night be turned to day,

We shall greet those gone be-fore, In that home of love.
In that hap - py home so sweet, Joy and peace we'll share. Some sweet day,
Part-ed friends no fare-wells know, Tears be wiped a - way.

some sweet day, Oh! that hap-py time will be, Some sweet day.

131 Night, with Ebon Pinion

L. H. Jameson

J. P. Powell

1. Night, with eb - on pin - ion, Brood-ed o'er the vale; All a-round was
2. Smit - ten for of - fens - es Which were not His own, He, for our trans-
3. "Ab - ba, Fa - ther, Fa - ther, If in-deed it may, Let this cup of

si - lent, Save the night-wind's wail, When Christ, the Man of Sor - rows, In
gres-sions, Had to weep a - lone; No friend with words to com - fort, Nor
an - guish Pass from Me, I pray; Yet, if it must be suf - fered, By

tears and sweat and blood, Pros-trate in the gar-den, Raised His voice to God.
hand to help was there, When the Meek and Low-ly Hum-bly bowed in prayer.
Me, Thine on-ly Son, Ab-ba, Fa-ther, Fa-ther, Let Thy will be done."

132   I Know Whom I Have Believed

El Nathan

James McGranahan

1. I know not why God's won-drous grace To me He hath made known,
2. I know not what of good or ill May be re-served for me,
3. I know not when my Lord may come, At night or noon-day fair,

Nor why, un-wor-thy, Christ in love Re-deemed me for His own.
Of wea-ry ways or gold-en days, Be-fore His face I see.
Nor if I'll walk the vale with Him, Or "meet Him in the air."

CHORUS

But "I know whom I have be-liev-ed, And am per-suad-ed that He is

a-ble To keep that which I've com-mit-ted Un-to Him a-gainst that day."

133   Is That Somebody You?

Vana R. Raye   Copyright, 1948, by Gospel Advocate Company   L. O. Sanderson

1. Someone by faith has been born a-gain; Someone is faith-ful in Je-sus' name;
2. Someone is drift-ing in care-less-ness; Someone has cru-ci-fied Christ a-fresh;
3. Someone has lift-ed a soul distress d; Someone has pointed to right-eous-ness;
4. Some to the end will the Mas-ter own; Some will not struggle in death a-lone;

Some-one thro' faith-ful-ness life will gain; Is that some-bod-y you?
Some-one is lost in his fool-ish-ness; Is that some-bod-y you?
Some-one has sweetened life's bit-ter-ness; Is that some-bod-y you?
Some will have en-trance to that blest home; Is that some-bod-y you?

134   Leaning on the Everlasting Arms

E. A. Hoffman   A. J. Showalter

1. What a fel-low-ship, what a joy di-vine, Lean-ing on the ev-er-last-ing arms;
2. O how sweet to walk in this pilgrim way, Lean-ing on the ev-er-last-ing arms;
3. What have I to dread, what have I to fear, Lean-ing on the ev-er-last-ing arms?

What a bless-ed-ness, what a peace is mine, Leaning on the ev-er-last-ing arms.
O how bright the path grows from day to day, Leaning on the ev-er-last-ing arms.
I have bless-ed peace with my Lord so near, Leaning on the ev-er-last-ing arms.

REFRAIN

Lean - ing, lean - ing, Safe and se-cure from all a-larms;
Lean-ing on Je-sus, lean-ing on Je-sus,

Leaning on the Everlasting Arms, Concluded

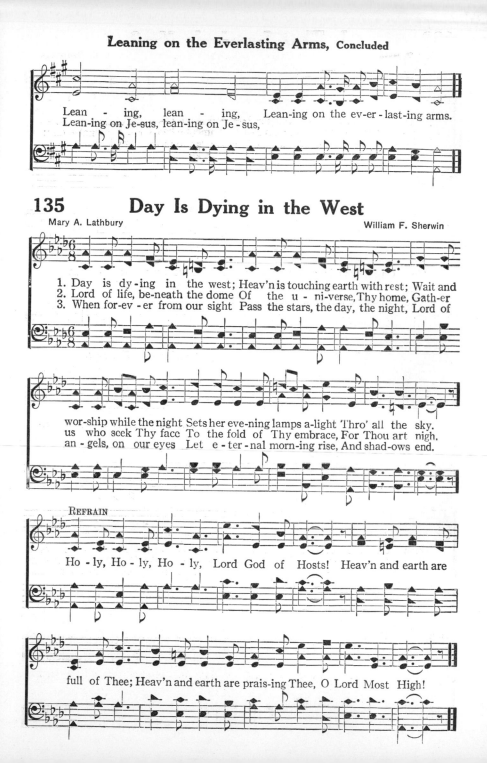

Lean - ing, lean - ing, Lean-ing on the ev-er-last-ing arms.
Lean-ing on Je-sus, lean-ing on Je-sus,

135 Day Is Dying in the West

Mary A. Lathbury

William F. Sherwin

1. Day is dy-ing in the west; Heav'n is touching earth with rest; Wait and
2. Lord of life, be-neath the dome Of the u - ni-verse, Thy home, Gath-er
3. When for-ev - er from our sight Pass the stars, the day, the night, Lord of

wor-ship while the night Sets her eve-ning lamps a-light 'Thro' all the sky.
us who seek Thy face To the fold of Thy embrace, For Thou art nigh.
an - gels, on our eyes Let e - ter-nal morn-ing rise, And shad-ows end.

REFRAIN

Ho - ly, Ho - ly, Ho - ly, Lord God of Hosts! Heav'n and earth are

full of Thee; Heav'n and earth are prais-ing Thee, O Lord Most High!

136 On Jordan's Stormy Banks

Samuel Stennett

T. C. O'Kane

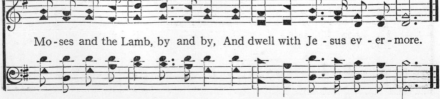

1. On   Jor-dan's storm-y banks I stand, And cast a wish-ful eye
2. O'er   all those wide-ex-tend-ed plains Shines one e-ter-nal day;
3. Filled with de-light, my rap-tured soul Would here no lon-ger stay;

To Ca-naan's fair and hap-py land, Where my pos-ses-sions lie.
There God, the Sun, for-ev-er reigns, And scat-ters night a-way.
Tho' Jor-dan's waves a-round me roll, Fear-less I'd launch a-way.

CHORUS

We will rest in the fair and hap-py land, by and by, Just a-

cross on the ev-er-green shore,............ Sing the song of
ev-er-green shore,

Mo-ses and the Lamb, by and by, And dwell with Je-sus ev-er-more.

137 I Am Bound for the Promised Land

Samuel Stennett

Arr. by R. M. McIntosh

1. On Jor-dan's storm-y banks I stand, And cast a wish-ful eye,
2. O'er all those wide-ex-tend-ed plains Shines one e-ter-nal day,
3. When shall I reach that hap-py place, And be for-ev-er blest?

Cho.—*I am bound for the prom-ised land,........ I am bound for the promised land;*
promised land,

FINE

D. C. for Cho.

To Ca-naan's fair and hap-py land, Where my pos-ses-sions lie.
There God the Son for-ev-er reigns And scat-ters night a-way.
When shall I see the Fa-ther's face, And in His bos-om rest?

O who will come and go with me? I am bound for the prom-ised land.

138 When I Can Read My Title Clear

Isaac Watts

J. C. Lowry

1. When I can read my ti-tle clear To man-sions in the skies,.....
2. Should earth a-gainst my soul en-gage, And fier-y darts be hurled,....
3. Let cares like a wild del-uge come, And storms of sorrow fall,......
4. There I can bathe my wea-ry soul In seas of heav'n-ly rest,......

I'll bid fare-well to ev-'ry fear, And wipe my weep-ing eyes.
Then I can smile at Sa-tan's rage, And face a frown-ing world.
I know I'll safe-ly reach my home, My God, my heav'n, my all.
And not a wave of trou-ble roll A-cross my peace-ful breast.

139 The Lily of the Valley

English Melody

1. I have found a friend in Je-sus, He's ev-'ry-thing to me, He's the
2. O He all my griefs has tak-en, and all my sor-rows borne; In temp-
3. He will nev-er, nev-er leave me, nor yet for-sake me here, While I

fair-est of ten-thou-sand to my soul; The Lil-y of the Val-ley, in
ta-tion He's my strong and mighty tow'r; I have all for Him for-sak-en, and
live by faith and do His bless-ed will; A wall of fire a-bout me, I've

Him a-lone I see All I need to cleanse and make me ful-ly whole.
all my i-dols torn From my heart, and now He keeps me by His pow'r.
noth-ing now to fear, With His man-na He my hun-gry soul shall fill.

D.S.—*Bright and Morning Star, He's the fair-est of ten-thou-sand to my soul.*

In sor-row He's my com-fort, in trou-ble He's my stay, He
Tho' all the world for-sake me, and Sa-tan tempt me sore, Thro'
Then sweep-ing up to glo-ry to see His bless-ed face, Where

tells me ev-'ry care on Him to roll. He's the Lil-y of the Val-ley, the
Je-sus I shall safe-ly reach the goal. He's the Lil-y of the Val-ley, the
riv-ers of de-light shall ev-er roll. He's the Lil-y of the Val-ley, the

140 In the Desert of Sorrow and Sin

H. R. Trickett

Fred A. Fillmore

1. In the des-ert of sor-row and sin, Lo! I faint as I
2. In my weak-ness I turn to the fount, From the Rock that was
3. O Thou God of com-pas-sion, I pray, Let me ev-er a-

jour-ney a-long; With the war-fare with-out and with-in, See my
smit-ten for me; And I drink, and I joy-ful-ly count All my
bide in Thy sight; Let me drink of the fount day by day, Till I

CHORUS

strength and my hope near-ly gone. I thirst, let me drink,
tri-als a bless-ing to be.
join Thee in man-sions of light. I thirst, let me drink,

Of the life-giv-ing stream let me drink; 'Tis the Rock,
let me drink; 'Tis the Rock,

cleft for me, 'Tis the wa-ter, the wa-ter of life.
cleft for me,

141 Harvest Time

Mary Brown Copyright, 1931, by Gospel Advocate Company Chas. H. Gabriel

1. A - rise! the Mas-ter calls for thee, The har-vest days are here! No lon-ger
2. Go seek the lost and err - ing ones, Who nev-er knew the Lord; Go, lead them
3. The mes-sage bear to dis-tant lands Be-yond the roll - ing sea; Go tell them

sit with fold - ed hands, But gath-er, far and near. The no - ble ranks of
from the ways of sin, And thou shalt have re - ward. Go out in - to the
of a Sav-ior's love—The Lamb of Cal - va - ry. A - rise! the Mas-ter

A - rise!..................
A - rise!.......... A-

vol - un-teers Are dai - ly grow-ing ev - 'ry-where, But still there's work for
hedg-es,where The care-less drift up - on the tide, And from the high-ways
calls for thee! Sal - va - tion full and free pro-claim, Till ev - 'ry kin-dred,

.... A - rise,.......... A - rise!..........

rise!..........
Chorus

mil-lions more! Then for the field pre - pare. A - rise!.... A - rise!.... The
bring them in— Let no one be de - nied.
tribe and tongue Ex - alt the Sav-ior's name! A-rise! A - rise!

Mas - ter calls for thee, A - rise! A - rise! A faith - ful
A - rise!........ A - rise!..........

reap - er be, A - rise! The field...... is white,.... and days are go - ing

The field   is white.

by,...... A - wake,..... a - wake..... And an - swer: "Here am I!"

A - rise!   A - wake,   a - wake

142   Glory to His Name

E. A. Hoffman   J. H. Stockton

1. Down at the cross where my Sav - ior died, Down where for cleans - ing from
2. I   am so won - drous - ly saved from sin, Je - sus so sweet - ly a -
3. O   pre - cious foun - tain that saves from sin, I   am so glad I have

sin   I cried, There to my heart was the blood ap - plied; Glo - ry to His
bides with - in, There at the cross where He took me in; Glo - ry to His
en - tered in; There Je - sus saves me and keeps me clean; Glo - ry to His

D. S.—*There to my heart was the blood ap - plied; Glo - ry to His*

FINE   CHORUS   D. S.

name.   Glo - ry to His name,   Glo - ry to His name;

name.

143   Hallelujah, Praise Jehovah!

Psalm 148

Wm. J. Kirkpatrick

1. Hal - le - lu - jah, praise Je - ho - vah! From the heav-ens praise His name;
2. Let them prais-es give Je - ho - vah! They were made at His com-mand;
3. All ye fruit - ful trees and ce - dars, All ye hills and moun-tains high,

Praise Je - ho - vah in the high - est; All His an-gels praise pro-claim.
Them for - ev - er He es - tab-lished: His de-cree shall ev - er stand.
Creep-ing things and beasts and cat - tle, Birds that in the heav-ens fly,

All His hosts to - geth - er praise Him, Sun and moon and stars on high;
From the earth, O praise Je - ho - vah, All ye floods, ye drag-ons all,
Kings of earth, and all ye peo - ple, Princ-es great, earth's judg-es all;

Praise Him, O ye heav'n of heav - ens, And ye floods a - bove the sky.
Fire and hail and snow and va - pors, Storm-y winds that hear Him call.
Praise His name, young men and maid - ens, A - ged men, and chil-dren small.

CHORUS

Let them prais - - - es give Je - ho - vah, For His name a - lone is high,
Let them prais-es

And His glo - - - ry is ex-alt-ed, And His glo - - ry is ex-alt-ed,
And His glo-ry   And His glo-ry

pp   *p*

ff

And His glo - - - ry is ex-alt-ed Far a-bove the earth and sky.
And His glo - ry

144 Bring Them In

Alexcenah Thomas   William A. Ogden

1. Hark! 'tis the Shepherd's voice I hear, Out in the des-ert dark and drear,
2. Who'll go and help this Shepherd kind, Help Him the wand'ring ones to find?
3. Out in the des-ert hear their cry Out on the mountains wild and high;

Call-ing the sheep who've gone a-stray Far from the Shepherd's fold a-way.
Who'll bring the lost ones to the fold, Where they'll be sheltered from the cold?
Hark! 'tis the Mas-ter speaks to thee, "Go find my sheep wher-e'er they be."

CHORUS

{ Bring them in, bring them in, Bring them in from the fields of sin;
{ Bring them in, bring them in, Bring the wand'ring ones to (*Omit* . . . .) Je-sus.

145 Jesus, Lover of My Soul

Charles Wesley   (MARTYN)   S. B. Marsh

1. Je - sus, Lov - er of my soul, Let me to Thy bos - om fly,
2. Oth - er ref - uge have I none, Hangs my help-less soul on Thee;
3. Plen-teous grace with Thee is found, Grace to cov - er all my sin;

While the near - er wa - ters roll, While the tem - pest still is high;
Leave, O leave me not a - lone, Still sup-port and com - fort me;
Let the heal - ing streams a-bound, Make and keep me pure with-in;

Hide me, O my Sav - ior, hide, Till the storm of life is past;
All my trust on Thee is stayed; All my help from Thee I bring;
Thou of life the foun - tain art; Free - ly let me take of Thee;

Safe in - to the ha - ven guide, O re-ceive my soul at last.
Cov - er my de - fense-less head With the shad-ow of Thy wing.
Spring Thou up with-in my heart, Rise to all e - ter - ni - ty.

146 Jesus, Lover of My Soul

Charles Wesley   (REFUGE)   J. P. Holbrook

1. Je - sus, Lov - er of my soul, Let me to Thy bos - om fly,
2. Oth - er ref - uge have I none; Hangs my help-less soul on Thee;
3. Plenteous grace with Thee is found, Grace to cov - er all my sin;

While the near - er wa - ters roll, While the tem - pest still is high.
Leave, O leave me not a - lone, Still sup - port and com-fort me.
Let the heal - ing streams a-bound; Make and keep me pure with-in.

{ Hide me, O my Sav-ior, hide, Till the storm of life is past;
{ Safe in-to the ha-ven guide; O re-ceive (*Omit.* . . . .) my soul at last.
{ All my trust on Thee is stayed, All my help from Thee I bring;
{ Cov - er my de-fense-less head With the shad - - - - ow of Thy wing.
{ Thou of life the foun-tain art, Free-ly let me take of Thee;
{ Spring Thou up with-in my heart, Rise to all (*Omit.* . . . .) e - ter - ni - ty.

147 Lord, We Come Before Thee Now

W. Hammond   C. H. A. Malan

Slowly

1. Lord, we come be-fore Thee now; At Thy feet we hum-bly bow: O do not our
2. Lord, on Thee our souls de-pend; In com-pas-sion now de-scend; Fill our hearts with
3. In Thine own ap-point-ed way, Now we seek Thee, here we stay; Lord, we know not
4. Grant that all may seek and find Thee a God su-preme-ly kind; Heal the sick, the

suit dis - dain; Shall we seek Thee, Lord, in vain? Shall we seek Thee, Lord, in vain?
Thy rich grace, Tune our lips to sing Thy praise, Tune our lips to sing Thy praise.
how to go, Till a bless-ing Thou be-stow, Till a bless-ing Thou be-stow.
cap-tive free; Let us all re-joice in Thee, Let us all re-joice in Thee.

148   Christ Receiveth Sinful Men

Arr. from Neumaster

James McGranahan

1. Sin - ners Je - sus will re - ceive; Sound this word of grace to all
2. Come, and He will give you rest; Trust Him, for His word is plain;
3. Christ re - ceiv - eth sin - ful men, E - ven me with all my sin;

Who the heav'n - ly path - way leave, All who lin - ger, all who fall.
He will take the sin - ful - est; Christ re - ceiv - eth sin - ful men.
Purged from ev - 'ry spot and stain, Heav'n with Him I en - ter in.

REFRAIN

Sing it o'er.............. and o'er a - gain;............ Christ re-
Sing it o'er a - gain,   sing it o'er a - gain; Christ re-

ceiv - - - eth sin - ful men;......... Make the mes - - sage
ceiv-eth sin - ful men, Christ re - ceiv-eth sin - ful men;   Make the message plain,

clear and plain:............. Christ re - ceiv - eth sin - ful men.
make the mes - sage plain:

149   He Is Able to Deliver Thee

W. A. O.

Walter A. Ogden

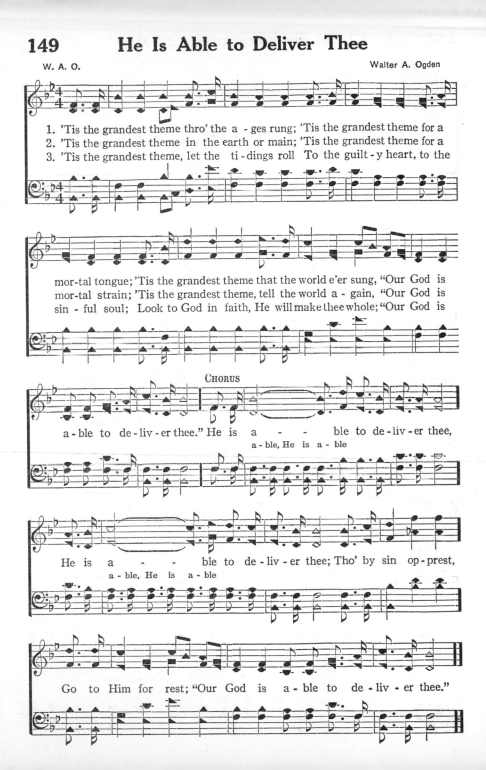

1. 'Tis the grandest theme thro' the a - ges rung; 'Tis the grandest theme for a
2. 'Tis the grandest theme in the earth or main; 'Tis the grandest theme for a
3. 'Tis the grandest theme, let the ti - dings roll To the guilt - y heart, to the

mor - tal tongue; 'Tis the grandest theme that the world e'er sung, "Our God is
mor - tal strain; 'Tis the grandest theme, tell the world a - gain, "Our God is
sin - ful soul; Look to God in faith, He will make thee whole; "Our God is

CHORUS

a - ble to de - liv - er thee." He is a - - ble to de - liv - er thee,
a - ble, He is a - ble

He is a - - ble to de - liv - er thee; Tho' by sin op - prest,
a - ble, He is a - ble

Go to Him for rest; "Our God is a - ble to de - liv - er thee."

150

Abide with Me

Henry F. Lyte

Wm. H. Monk

1. A - bide with me: fast falls the e - ven - tide; The dark-ness
2. Swift to its close ebbs out life's lit - tle day; Earth's joys grow
3. Hold Thou Thy cross be - fore my clos-ing eyes; Shine through the

deep - ens: Lord, with me a - bide! When oth - er help - ers
dim, its glo - ries pass a - way; Change and de - cay in
gloom, and point me to the skies; Heav'n's morn-ing breaks, and

fail, and com-forts flee, Help of the help-less, O a - bide with me!
all a - round I see; O Thou who chang-est not, a - bide with me!
earth's vain shad-ows flee; In life, in death, O Lord, a - bide with me!

151

The Great Physician

William Hunter

J. H. Stockton

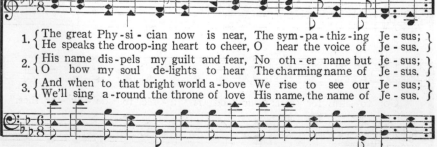

1. { The great Phy-si - cian now is near, The sym - pa - thiz-ing Je - sus; }
   { He speaks the droop-ing heart to cheer, O hear the voice of Je - sus. }

2. { His name dis-pels my guilt and fear, No oth - er name but Je - sus; }
   { O how my soul de-lights to hear The charming name of Je - sus. }

3. { And when to that bright world a-bove We rise to see our Je - sus; }
   { We'll sing a-round the throne of love His name, the name of Je - sus. }

The Great Physician, Concluded

CHORUS

{ Sweetest note in ser-aph song, }
{ Sweetest name on mortal tongue, } Sweetest carol ev-er sung, Jesus, blessed Je-sus.

152   More About Jesus

E. E. Hewitt

Jno. R. Sweney

1. More a-bout Je-sus would I know, More of His grace to oth-ers show;
2. More a-bout Je-sus let me learn, More of His ho-ly will dis-cern;
3. More a-bout Je-sus in His Word, Hold-ing com-mun-ion with my Lord;
4. More a-bout Je-sus on His throne, Rich-es in glo-ry all His own;

More of His sav-ing ful-ness see, More of His love who died for me.
Spir-it of God, my teach-er be, Show-ing the things of Christ to me.
Hear-ing His voice in ev-'ry line, Mak-ing each faith-ful say-ing mine.
More of His kingdom's sure in-crease; More of His com-ing, Prince of Peace.

REFRAIN

More, more a-bout Je-sus, More, more a-bout Je-sus;

More of His sav-ing ful-ness see, More of His love who died for me.

153 Blessed Assurance

Fanny J. Crosby

Mrs. Joseph F. Knapp

1. Bless - ed as - sur - ance, Je - sus is mine! O what a
2. Per - fect sub - mis - sion, per - fect de - light, Vi - sions of
3. Per - fect sub - mis - sion, all is at rest, I in my

fore - taste of glo - ry di - vine! Heir of sal - va - tion, pur-chase of
rap - ture now burst on my sight; An - gels de - scend-ing, bring from a-
Sav - ior am hap-py and blest; Watch-ing and wait - ing, look-ing a-

God; Born of His Spir - it, washed in His blood.
bove Ech - oes of mer - cy, whis-pers of love. This is my sto - ry,
bove, Filled with His good-ness, lost in His love.

REFRAIN

this is my song, Prais-ing my Sav - ior all the day long; This is my

sto - ry, this is my song, Prais-ing my Sav - ior all the day long.

154 Sweet By and By

S. Fillmore Bennett

Jos. P. Webster

1. There's a land that is fair - er than day, And by faith we can see
2. We shall sing on that beau - ti - ful shore The me - lo - di - ous songs
3. To our boun - ti - ful Fa - ther a - bove We will of - fer our trib-

it a - far; For the Fa - ther waits o - ver the way, To pre-
of the blest; And our spir - its shall sor - row no more— Not a
ute of praise For the glo - ri - ous gift of His love, And the

Chorus

pare us a dwell - ing place there. In the sweet by and
sigh for the bless - ing of rest.
bless - ings that hal - low our days. In the sweet

by, We shall meet on that beau - ti - ful shore; In the
by and by, by and by;

sweet by and by, We shall meet on that beau - ti - ful shore.
In the sweet by and by, by and by,

155   Guide Me, O Thou Great Jehovah

W. Williams

Thomas Hastings

1. Guide me, O Thou great Je - ho - vah, Pil-grim thro' this bar-ren land; I am
2. O - pen now the crys-tal foun-tain, Whence the healing wa-ters flow; Let the
3. When I tread the verge of Jor - dan, Bid my anx-ious fears sub-side; Bear me

weak, but Thou art might-y, Hold me with Thy pow'r-ful hand; Bread of heav - en,
fier - y, cloud - y pil - lar, Lead me all my jour-ney thro'; Strong De-liv-'rer,
thro' the swell-ing cur-rent, Land me safe on Ca-naan's side; Songs of prais-es

Feed me till I want no more: Bread of heaven, Feed me till I want no more.
Be Thou still my strength and shield: Strong Deliv'rer, Be Thou still my strength and shield.
I will ev - er give to Thee; Songs of prais-es I will ev - er give to Thee.

156   My Jesus, I Love Thee

W. R. Featherston

A. J. Gordon

1. My Je - sus, I love Thee, I know Thou art mine; For Thee all the fol - lies
2. I love Thee, be-cause Thou hast first lov-ed me, And purchased my par - don
3. In man-sions of glo - ry and end-less de-light, I'll ev - er a - dore Thee

of sin I re-sign; My gra-cious Re - deem - er, my Sav - ior art Thou:
on Cal - va-ry's tree; I love Thee for wear-ing the thorns on Thy brow:
in heav - en so bright; I'll sing with the glit - ter-ing crown on my brow:

REFRAIN

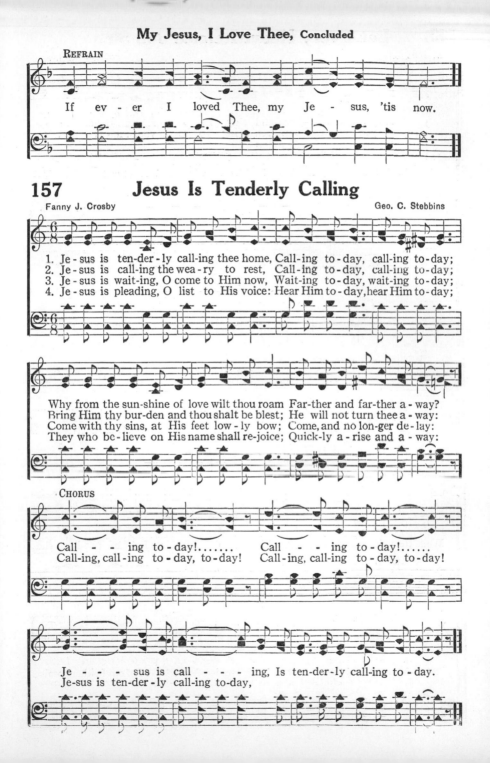

If ev-er I loved Thee, my Je - sus, 'tis now.

157   Jesus Is Tenderly Calling

Fanny J. Crosby   Geo. C. Stebbins

1. Je - sus is ten-der - ly call-ing thee home, Call-ing to - day, call-ing to - day;
2. Je - sus is call-ing the wea - ry to rest, Call-ing to - day, call-ing to - day;
3. Je - sus is wait-ing, O come to Him now, Wait-ing to - day, wait-ing to - day;
4. Je - sus is pleading, O list to His voice: Hear Him to - day, hear Him to - day;

Why from the sun-shine of love wilt thou roam Far-ther and far-ther a - way?
Bring Him thy bur-den and thou shalt be blest; He will not turn thee a - way:
Come with thy sins, at His feet low - ly bow; Come, and no lon-ger de - lay:
They who be-lieve on His name shall re-joice; Quick-ly a - rise and a - way:

CHORUS

Call - - ing to - day!....... Call - - ing to - day!......
Call-ing, call-ing to - day, to - day! Call-ing, call-ing to - day, to - day!

Je - - - sus is call - - - ing, Is ten-der-ly call-ing to - day.
Je-sus is ten-der - ly call-ing to-day,

158 Let Every Heart Rejoice and Sing

Henry S. Washburne

Geo. J. Webb

1. { Let ev-'ry heart re-joice and sing, Let cho-ral an-thems rise;
   Ye a-ged men, and chil-dren, bring To God your sac-ri-fice.

2. { He bids the sun to rise and set; In heav'n His pow'r is known;
   And earth sub-dued to Him, shall yet Bow low be-fore His throne.

CHORUS

For He is good, the Lord is good, And kind are all His ways; With songs and hon-ors sound-ing loud, The Lord Je-ho-vah praise. While the rocks and the rills, While the vales and the hills, A glo-rious an-them raise; Let each pro-long the

rit.

grate-ful song, And the God of our fathers praise, And the God of our fa-thers praise.

159 Sweet Is the Promise

C. H. G.

Chas. H. Gabriel

1. Sweet is the prom-ise "I will not for-get thee," Nothing can mo-lest or
2. Trust-ing the prom-ise "I will not for-get thee," On-ward will I go with
3. When at the gold-en por-tals I am stand-ing, All my trib-u-la-tions,

turn my soul a-way; E'en tho' the night be dark with-in the val-ley,
songs of joy and love, Tho' earth de-spise me, tho' my friends for-sake me,
all my sor-rows past, How sweet to hear the bless-ed proc-la-ma-tion,

CHORUS

Just be-yond is shin-ing an e-ter-nal day. I............ will not for-
I shall be re-mem-bered in my home a-bove.
"En-ter faith-ful serv-ant, welcome home at last." I will not for-get thee;

get thee or leave thee, In my hands I'll hold thee, In my arms I'll fold thee, I........
I will never leave thee, I will not for-

.... will not for-get thee or leave thee; I am thy Re-deem-er, I will care for thee.
get thee, for-get

Live for Jesus

E. R. Latta

Frank M. Davis

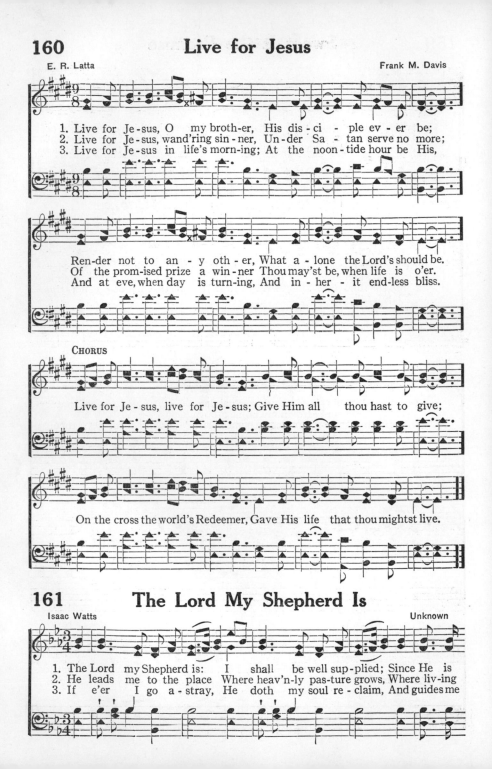

1. Live for Je-sus, O my broth-er, His dis-ci-ple ev-er be;
2. Live for Je-sus, wand'ring sin-ner, Un-der Sa-tan serve no more;
3. Live for Je-sus in life's morn-ing; At the noon-tide hour be His,

Ren-der not to an-y oth-er, What a-lone the Lord's should be.
Of the prom-ised prize a win-ner Thou may'st be, when life is o'er.
And at eve, when day is turn-ing, And in-her-it end-less bliss.

CHORUS

Live for Je-sus, live for Je-sus; Give Him all thou hast to give;

On the cross the world's Redeemer, Gave His life that thou mightst live.

161 The Lord My Shepherd Is

Isaac Watts

Unknown

1. The Lord my Shepherd is: I shall be well sup-plied; Since He is
2. He leads me to the place Where heav'n-ly pas-ture grows, Where liv-ing
3. If e'er I go a-stray, He doth my soul re-claim, And guides me

The Lord My Shepherd Is, Concluded

mine, and I am His, What can I want be-side? What can I want be-side?
wa - ters gen-tly pass, And full sal-va-tion flows, And full sal-va-tion flows.
in His own right way, For His most ho - ly name, For His most ho-ly name.

162 Take the Name of Jesus with You

Mrs. Lydia Baxter

W. H. Doane

1. Take the name of Je - sus with you, Child of sor-row and of woe;
2. Take the name of Je - sus ev - er As a shield from ev-'ry snare;
3. O the pre-cious name of Je - sus! How it thrills our souls with joy.

It will joy and com-fort give you, Take it then, wher-e'er you go.
If temp - ta-tions round you gath - er, Breathe that ho - ly name in prayer.
When His lov - ing arms re - ceive us, And His songs our tongues em-ploy!

CHORUS

Pre-cious name, O how sweet! Hope of earth and joy of heav'n;
Pre-cious name, O how sweet!

Pre-cious name, O how sweet! Hope of earth and joy of heav'n.
Pre-cious name, O how sweet, how sweet,

163 More Holiness Give Me

P. P. B.

P. P. Bliss

1. More ho - li-ness give me, More striv-ings with - in, More pa-tience in
2. More grat - i-tude give me, More trust in the Lord, More pride in His
3. More pu - ri - ty give me, More strength to o'er-come, More free-dom from

suf - f'ring More sor - row for sin, More faith in my Sav - ior,
glo - ry, More hope in His word, More tears for His sor - rows,
earth-stains, More long-ings for home; More fit for the king - dom,

More sense of His care, More joy in His serv - ice, More pur-pose in prayer.
More pain at His grief, More meekness in tri - al, More praise for re - lief.
More use - ful I'd be, More bless-ed and ho - ly, More, Sav-ior, like Thee.

164 Savior, Grant Me Rest and Peace

Grace Glenn

J. H. Fillmore

Slowly

1. Sav-ior, grant me rest and peace, Let my trou - bled dream-ings cease;
2. I would trust my all with Thee, All my cares and sor - rows flee,
3. I would seek Thy serv - ice, Lord, Lean-ing on Thy prom-ise - word;

With the chim - ing mid-night bell, Teach my heart that "All is well."
Till the break - ing light shall tell, Night is past, and "All is well."
Let my hour - ly la - bors tell, I am Thine, and "All is well."

165 Hide Me, O My Savior, Hide Me

F. J. Crosby

W. H. Doane

1. Hide me, O my Sav - ior, hide me In Thy ho - ly place;
2. Hide me, when the storm is rag - ing O'er life's trou - bled sea;
3. Hide me, when my heart is break - ing With its weight of woe;

Rest - ing there be-neath Thy glo - ry, O let me see Thy face.
Like a dove on o - cean's bil - lows, O let me fly to Thee.
When in tears I seek the com - fort Thou canst a - lone be - stow.

REFRAIN

Hide me, hide me, O bless - ed Sav - ior, hide me;
Hide me, hide me, safe - ly hide me,

O Sav - ior, keep me Safe - ly, O Lord, with Thee.
O my Sav - ior, keep Thou me,

166 We Have An Anchor

Priscilla J. Owens

Wm. J. Kirkpatrick

1. Will your an - chor hold in the storms of life, When the
2. It is safe - ly moored, 'twill the storm with - stand, For 'tis
3. It will firm - ly hold in the straits of fear, When the
4. When our eyes be - hold through the gath - 'ring night The

clouds un - fold their wings of strife? When the strong tides lift,
well se - cured by the Sav - ior's hand; And the ca - bles, passed
break-ers have told the reef is near; Tho' the tem - pest rage
cit - y of gold, our har - bor bright, We shall an - chor fast

and the ca - bles strain, Will your an - chor drift, or firm re - main?
from His heart to mine, Can de - fy the blast, through strength di - vine.
and the wild winds blow, Not an an - gry wave shall our bark o'er - flow.
by the heav'n-ly shore, With the storms all past for - ev - er - more.

REFRAIN

We have an an-chor that keeps the soul Steadfast and sure while the billows roll,

Fastened to the Rock which cannot move, Grounded firm and deep in the Sav-ior's love.

167   Again the Lord of Light and Life

Anna L. Barbauld

Thomas A. Arne

1. A - gain the Lord of light and life   A - wakes the kin - dling ray,
2. O   what a night was that which wrapt The hea - then world in gloom!
3. This day be grate - ful hom - age paid, And loud ho - san - nas sung;
4. Ten thou - sand dif - f'rent lips shall join To hail this wel - come morn,

Un - seals the eye - lids of   the morn, And pours in - creas - ing day.
O   what a Sun which rose this day Tri - um - phant from the tomb!
Let   glad - ness dwell in   ev - 'ry heart, And praise on ev - 'ry tongue.
Which scat - ters bless - ings from its wings To   na - tions yet un - born.

168   How Sweet, How Heavenly, Is the Sight

J. Swain

William B. Bradbury

1. How sweet, how heav'n - ly, is   the sight, When those that love the Lord
2. When each can feel his broth - er's sigh, And with him bear a   part;
3. When, free from en - vy, scorn, and pride, Our wish - es all a - bove,
4. Love is   the gold - en chain that binds The hap - py souls a - bove;

In   one an - oth - er's peace de - light, And   so   ful - fil   the word.
When sor - row flows from eye   to eye, And joy from heart to heart.
Each can his broth - er's fail - ings hide, And show a   broth - er's love.
And he's an heir of heav'n who finds His bos - om glow with love.

169   Peace! Be Still!

Mary A. Baker   H. R. Palmer

1. Mas-ter, the tem-pest is rag-ing! The bil-lows are toss-ing high!
2. Mas-ter, with an-guish of spir-it I bow in my grief to-day;
3. Mas-ter, the ter-ror is o-ver, The el-e-ments sweet-ly rest;

The sky is o'er-shadowed with black-ness, No shel-ter or help is nigh;
The depths of my sad heart are trou-bled; O wak-en and save, I pray!
Earth's sun in the calm lake is mir-rored, And heav-en's with-in my breast.

Car-est Thou not that we per-ish? How canst Thou lie a-sleep,
Tor-rents of sin and of an-guish Sweep o'er my sink-ing soul!
Lin-ger, O bless-ed Re-deem-er, Leave me a-lone no more;

When each mo-ment so mad-ly is threat-'ning A grave in the an-gry deep?
And I per-ish! I per-ish, dear Mas-ter; O has-ten, and take con-trol!
And with joy I shall make the blest har-bor, And rest on the bliss-ful shore.

Peace! Be Still! Concluded

Chorus

The winds and the waves shall o - bey Thy will, Peace,.... be still!......
Peace, be still! peace, be still!

Wheth-er the wrath of the storm-tossed sea, Or de-mons, or men, or what-

cre — — — — — — scen — — — — — —
ev - er it be, No wa - ter can swal-low the ship where lies The Mas-ter of

do *ff* *m*
o-cean and earth and skies; They all shall sweet-ly o - bey Thy will, Peace, be still!

p *m* *p* *pp*
Peace, be still! They all shall sweet-ly o - bey Thy will, Peace, peace, be still!

170 Above the Bright Blue

C. E. P.

Chas. Edw. Pollock

1. There's a beau - ti - ful place called heav - en, It is hid - den a-
2. This land of sweet rest a - waits us, Some day it will
3. We know not when He shall call us, Wheth-er soon, the glad

bove the bright blue, Where the good, who from earth-ties are riv - en,
break on our view, 'Tis prom-ised by Christ the Re-deem - er,
sum-mons shall be, But we know, when we pass o'er the riv - er,

CHORUS

Live and love an e - ter - ni - ty through.
To His fol - low-ers faith-ful and true. A - bove the bright blue, the
The glo - ry of Je - sus we'll see.

beau - ti - ful blue, Je - sus is wait-ing for me and for you;

Heav-en is there, not far from our sight, Beau-ti-ful cit - y of light.

171 Lead Me Gently Home, Father

W. L. T.

Will L. Thompson

1. Lead me gen-tly home, Fa-ther, Lead me gen-tly home, When life's toils are
2. Lead me gen-tly home, Fa-ther, Lead me gen-tly home, In life's dark-est
3. Lead me gen-tly home, Fa-ther, Lead me gen-tly home, In temp-ta-tion's

end - ed, and part - ing days have come; Sin no more shall tempt me,
hours, Fa-ther, when life's trou-bles come, Keep my feet from wan-d'ring,
hour, Fa-ther, when sore tri - als come; Be Thou near to keep me,

Ne'er from Thee I'll roam, If Thou'lt on-ly lead me, Fa-ther, Lead me gently home.
Lest from Thee I roam, Lest I fall up - on the way-side, Lead me gently home.
Take me as Thine own, For I can-not live without Thee, Lead me gently home.

CHORUS

Lead me gen - tly home, Fa - ther, lead me gen - tly
Lead me gen - tly home, Fa - ther, Lead me gen - tly home, Fa - ther,

Lest I fall up - on the way-side, Lead me gen - tly home.
gen - tly home.

172   I Am Thine, O Lord

Frances Jane Van Alstyne   W. H. Doane

1. I am Thine, O Lord; I have heard Thy voice, And it told Thy
2. Con - se - crate me now to Thy serv - ice, Lord, By the pow'r of
3. O the pure de - light of a sin - gle hour That be - fore Thy
4. There are depths of love that I can - not know Till I cross the

love to me, But I long to rise in the arms of faith,
grace di - vine; Let my soul look up with a stead-fast hope,
throne I spend, When I kneel in prayer, and with Thee, my God,
nar - row sea; There are heights of joy that I may not reach

REFRAIN

And be clos - er drawn to Thee.
And my will be lost in Thine.   Draw me near - - er,
I com-mune as friend with friend.
Till I rest in peace with Thee.   near - er, near - er,

near-er, bless-ed Lord, To the cross where Thou hast died, Draw me near - er,

near - er, near - er, bless-ed Lord, To Thy pre - cious bleed - ing side.

173 The Master's Touch

Mrs. Walla Calvert Smith   Tillet S. Teddlie

1. There's man-y a heart that's wea-ry, There's man-y a soul that's sad;
2. They scarce-ly will feel their weakness, In dark-ness they grope a - bout;
3. These wan-der-ing souls are ly - ing Per - haps at your ver - y door;

To them all the world seems drear-y; There's noth-ing to make them glad.
They strive in an emp - ty meek-ness To drive the dire hun - ger out.
Give heed to their heart - felt cry - ing And let them not hun - ger more.

These toil - worn souls are hun - gry; Their long-ing and pain are such
These toil - worn souls are help - less—It's pow'r that they need so much;
These toil - worn souls are struggling; Their path-way is hard and rough.

That naught can ap-pease their hun - ger, Ex - cept in the Mas-ter's touch.
There's on-ly one pow'r to save them—The pow'r of the Mas-ter's touch.
Go tell them Re-demp-tion's sto - ry And give them the Mas-ter's touch.

There's naught can ap-pease their hun - ger, There's naught but the Mas-ter's touch.
There's on-ly one pow'r to save them—The pow'r of the Mas-ter's touch.
Go tell them Re-demp-tion's sto - ry And give them the Mas-ter's touch.

174 Home Over There

D. W. C. Huntington

T. C. O'Kane

1. O think of the home o-ver there, By the side of the riv-er of
2. O think of the friends o-ver there, Who be-fore us the jour-ney have
3. I'll soon be at home o-ver there, For the end of my jour-ney I

light, Where the saints, all im-mor-tal and fair, Are
trod; Of the songs that they breathe on the air, In their
see; Man-y dear to my heart, o-ver there, Are

o - ver there,

CHORUS

robed in their gar-ments of white. O-ver there, o-ver
home in the pal-ace of God. O-ver there, o-ver
watch-ing and wait-ing for me. O-ver there, o-ver

o - ver there,

there, O think of a home o-ver there, O-ver
there, O think of the friends o-ver there, O-ver
there, I'll soon be at home o-ver there, O-ver

o - ver there,

o - ver there,

there, o-ver there, o-ver there, O think of a home o-ver there.
there, o-ver there, o-ver there, O think of the friends o-ver there.
there, o-ver there, o-ver there, I'll soon be at home o-ver there.

o - ver there,

175   The Hollow of God's Hand

E. D. Mund

E. S. Lorenz

1. I am safe, what - ev - er may be - tide me; I am safe, who-
2. What tho' fierce the storm - y blasts roar round me; What tho' sore life's
3. Ev - er - last - ing arms of love en - fold me; Words of peace the

ev - er may de - ride me; I am safe, as long as I con - fide me
tri - als oft con-found me; I am safe, for naught of ill can wound me
voice di-vine has told me; I am safe, while God Him-self doth hold me

CHORUS

In the hol - low of God's hand. In the hol - low, hol - low of His
In the hol - low of God's hand.
In the hol - low of His hand.   In the hol - low, in the

hand,   In the hol - low, hol - low of His hand;
hol - low of His hand,   In the hol - low, in the hol - low of His hand;

I am safe while God Him-self doth hold me In the hol - low of His hand.

176   I Am Coming to the Cross

Wm. McDonald   Wm. G. Fischer

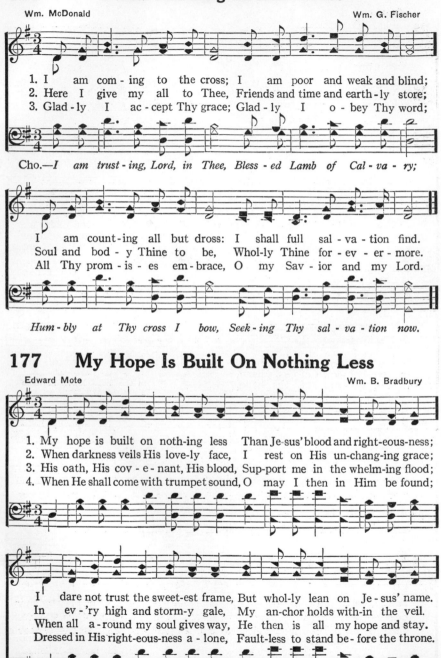

1. I am com-ing to the cross; I am poor and weak and blind;
2. Here I give my all to Thee, Friends and time and earth-ly store;
3. Glad-ly I ac-cept Thy grace; Glad-ly I o-bey Thy word;

Cho.—*I am trust-ing, Lord, in Thee, Bless-ed Lamb of Cal-va-ry;*

I am count-ing all but dross: I shall full sal-va-tion find.
Soul and bod-y Thine to be, Whol-ly Thine for-ev-er-more.
All Thy prom-is-es em-brace, O my Sav-ior and my Lord.

Hum-bly at Thy cross I bow, Seek-ing Thy sal-va-tion now.

177   My Hope Is Built On Nothing Less

Edward Mote   Wm. B. Bradbury

1. My hope is built on noth-ing less Than Je-sus' blood and right-eous-ness;
2. When darkness veils His love-ly face, I rest on His un-chang-ing grace;
3. His oath, His cov-e-nant, His blood, Sup-port me in the whelm-ing flood;
4. When He shall come with trumpet sound, O may I then in Him be found;

I dare not trust the sweet-est frame, But whol-ly lean on Je-sus' name.
In ev-'ry high and storm-y gale, My an-chor holds with-in the veil.
When all a-round my soul gives way, He then is all my hope and stay.
Dressed in His right-eous-ness a-lone, Fault-less to stand be-fore the throne.

My Hope Is Built, Concluded

CHORUS

On Christ, the Sol - id Rock, I stand; All oth - er ground is

sink - ing sand, All oth - er ground is sink - ing sand.

178 I Love Thy Kingdom, Lord

Timothy Dwight

A. B. Everett

1. I love Thy kingdom, Lord, The house of Thine a- bode; The church our blest Re-
2. For her my tears shall fall, For her my prayers as-cend; To her my cares and
3. Je - sus, Thou Friend divine, Our Sav-ior and our King! Thy hand from ev-'ry

deemer saved With His own precious blood. I love Thy church, O God! Her walls be-
toils be giv'n, Till toils and cares shall end. Be-yond my high-est joy I prize her
snare and foe Shall great deliv'rance bring. Sure as Thy truth shall last, To Zi - on

fore Thee stand, Dear as the ap - ple of Thine eye, And grav-en on Thy hand.
heav'n-ly ways, Her sweet communion, sol-emn vows, Her hymns of love and praise.
shall be giv'n The brightest glo-ries earth can yield, And brightest bliss of heav'n.

179 He Loves Me

Arranged Arranged

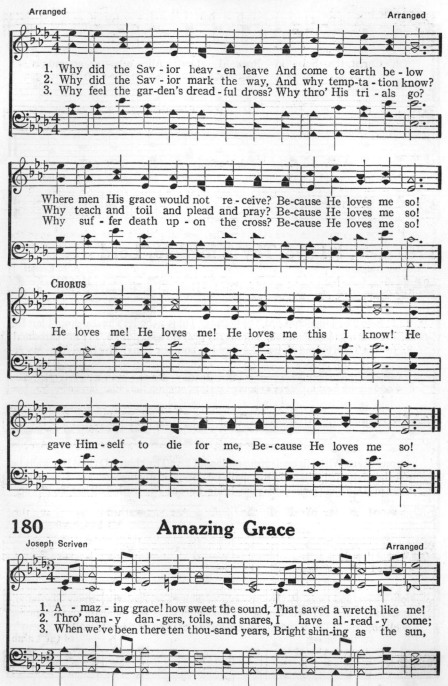

1. Why did the Sav-ior heav-en leave And come to earth be-low
2. Why did the Sav-ior mark the way, And why temp-ta-tion know?
3. Why feel the gar-den's dread-ful dross? Why thro' His tri-als go?

Where men His grace would not re-ceive? Be-cause He loves me so!
Why teach and toil and plead and pray? Be-cause He loves me so!
Why suf-fer death up-on the cross? Be-cause He loves me so!

Chorus

He loves me! He loves me! He loves me this I know! He

gave Him-self to die for me, Be-cause He loves me so!

180 Amazing Grace

Joseph Scriven   Arranged

1. A - maz - ing grace! how sweet the sound, That saved a wretch like me!
2. Thro' man-y dan-gers, toils, and snares, I have al-read-y come;
3. When we've been there ten thou-sand years, Bright shin-ing as the sun,

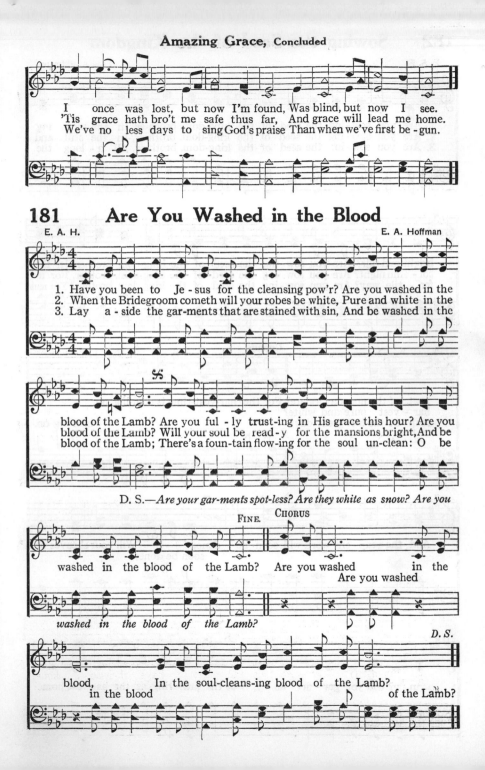

I once was lost, but now I'm found, Was blind, but now I see.
'Tis grace hath bro't me safe thus far, And grace will lead me home.
We've no less days to sing God's praise Than when we've first be-gun.

181   Are You Washed in the Blood

E. A. H.   E. A. Hoffman

1. Have you been to Je-sus for the cleansing pow'r? Are you washed in the
2. When the Bridegroom cometh will your robes be white, Pure and white in the
3. Lay a-side the gar-ments that are stained with sin, And be washed in the

blood of the Lamb? Are you ful-ly trust-ing in His grace this hour? Are you
blood of the Lamb? Will your soul be read-y for the mansions bright, And be
blood of the Lamb; There's a foun-tain flow-ing for the soul un-clean: O be

D. S.—*Are your gar-ments spot-less? Are they white as snow? Are you*

FINE.   CHORUS

washed in the blood of the Lamb?   Are you washed in the
Are you washed

washed in the blood of the Lamb?

D. S.

blood,   In the soul-cleans-ing blood of the Lamb?
in the blood   of the Lamb?

182 Sowing the Seed of the Kingdom

F. A. F.

Fred A. Fillmore

1. Are you sow-ing the seed of the king-dom, broth-er, In the morn-ing
2. Are you sow-ing the seed of the king-dom, broth-er, In the still and
3. Are you sow-ing the seed of the king-dom, broth-er, All a-long the

bright and fair? Are you sow-ing the seed of the king-dom, brother, In the
sol-emn night? Are you sow-ing the seed of the king-dom, brother, For a
fer-tile way? Are you sow-ing the seed of the king-dom, brother? You must

CHORUS

heat of the noonday's glare? For the har-vest-time is com-ing on,
har-vest pure and white?
reap at the last great day! com-ing on,

And the reap-ers' work will soon be done; Will your sheaves be
soon be done;

man-y? will you gar-ner an-y, For the gath-'ring at the har-vest home?

183 Where He Leads I'll Follow

W. A. O.

W. A. Ogden

1. Sweet are the prom-is-es, Kind is the word; Dear-er far than
2. Sweet is the ten-der love Je - sus hath shown, Sweet-er far than
3. List to His lov-ing words, "Come un - to me!" Wea-ry, heav-y-

an - y mes-sage man ev - er heard; Pure was the mind of Christ,
an - y love that mor-tals have known; Kind to the err-ing one,
la - den, there is sweet rest for thee; Trust in His prom-is - es,

Sin - less, I see; He the great ex-am-ple is, and pat-tern for me.
Faith-ful is He; He the great ex-am-ple is, and pat-tern for me.
Faith-ful and sure; Lean up-on the Sav-ior and Thy soul is se-cure.

CHORUS

Where . . . . . . He leads I'll fol - - - low,
Where He leads I'll fol-low, Where He leads I'll fol-low,

Fol - - low all the way; Fol-low Je-sus ev-'ry day.
Fol-low all the way, yes, follow all the way;

184 The Gate Ajar

Mrs. Lydia Baxter

Philip Phillips

1. There is a gate that stands a - jar, And through its por - tals gleam-ing,
2. That gate a - jar stands free for all Who seek through it sal - va - tion;
3. Press on - ward, then, tho' foes may frown, While mer - cy's gate is o - pen;

A ra-diance from the crown a - far, The Sav-ior's love re - veal - ing.
The rich and poor, the great and small, Of ev - 'ry tribe and na - tion.
Ac - cept the cross and win the crown, Love's ev - er - last - ing to - ken.

REFRAIN

Yes, in the blood of Christ I see The gate that stands a - jar for me,

For me,....... for me,....... That stands a - jar for me.
For me, for me,

185 Jesus Calls Us

Cecil F. Alexander

W. H. Jude

1. Je - sus calls us o'er the tu - mult Of our life's wild rest-less sea,
2. Je - sus calls us from the wor - ship Of the vain world's gold-en store;
3. In our joys and in our sor - rows, Days of toil, and hours of ease;

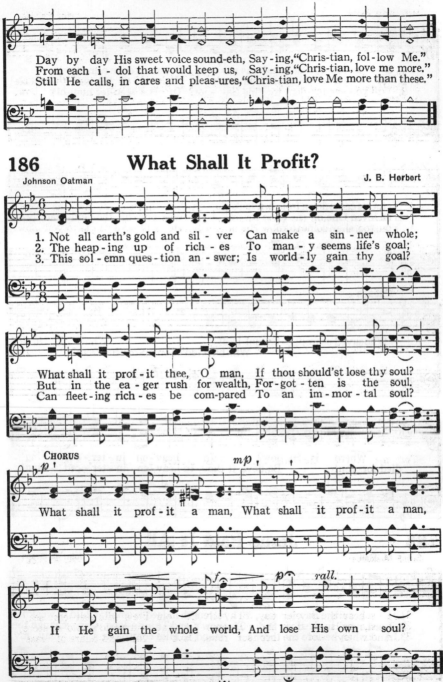

Day by day His sweet voice sound-eth, Say-ing, "Chris-tian, fol-low Me."
From each i - dol that would keep us, Say-ing, "Chris-tian, love me more."
Still He calls, in cares and pleas-ures, "Chris-tian, love Me more than these."

186   What Shall It Profit?

Johnson Oatman   J. B. Herbert

1. Not all earth's gold and sil - ver Can make a sin - ner whole;
2. The heap-ing up of rich - es To man - y seems life's goal;
3. This sol - emn ques-tion an - swer; Is world-ly gain thy goal?

What shall it prof-it thee, O man, If thou should'st lose thy soul?
But in the ea - ger rush for wealth, For-got - ten is the soul.
Can fleet-ing rich - es be com-pared To an im - mor - tal soul?

CHORUS

What shall it prof-it a man, What shall it prof-it a man,

If He gain the whole world, And lose His own soul?

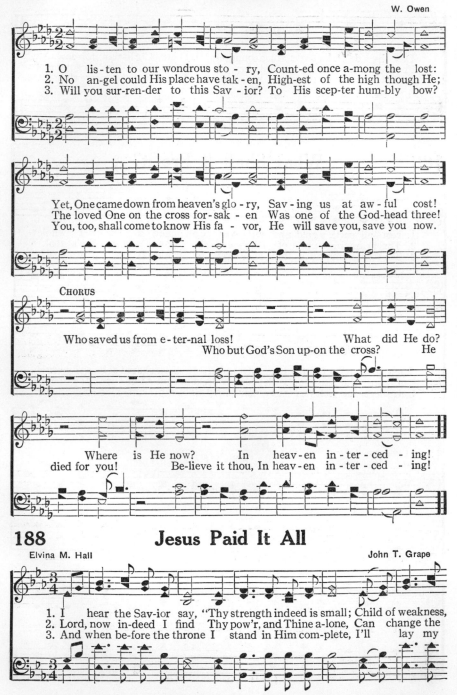

187   What Did He Do?

W. Owen

1. O lis-ten to our wondrous sto - ry, Count-ed once a-mong the lost:
2. No an-gel could His place have tak - en, High-est of the high though He;
3. Will you sur-ren-der to this Sav - ior? To His scep-ter hum-bly bow?

Yet, One came down from heaven's glo - ry, Sav-ing us at aw - ful cost!
The loved One on the cross for-sak - en Was one of the God-head three!
You, too, shall come to know His fa - vor, He will save you, save you now.

CHORUS

Who saved us from e-ter-nal loss!   What did He do?
Who but God's Son up-on the cross?   He

Where is He now? In heav-en in - ter - ced - ing!
died for you! Be-lieve it thou, In heav-en in - ter - ced - ing!

188   Jesus Paid It All

Elvina M. Hall   John T. Grape

1. I hear the Sav-ior say, "Thy strength indeed is small; Child of weakness,
2. Lord, now in-deed I find Thy pow'r, and Thine a-lone, Can change the
3. And when be-fore the throne I stand in Him com-plete, I'll lay my

Jesus Paid It All, Concluded

CHORUS

watch and pray, Find in me thine all in all.''
lep - er's spots, And melt the heart of stone. Je - sus paid it all,
tro - phies down, All down at Je - sus' feet.

All to Him I owe; Sin had left a crim-son stain, He washed it white as snow.

189   Far and Near

J. O. Thompson   J. B. O. Clemm

1. Far and near the fields are teem - ing With the waves of rip - ened grain;
2. Send them forth with morn's first beaming, Send them in the noontide's glare;
3. O thou, whom thy Lord is send - ing, Gath - er now the sheaves of gold;

FINE

Far and near their gold is gleam-ing O'er the sun - ny slope and plain.
When the sun's last rays are gleam-ing, Bid them gath - er ev - 'ry-where.
Heav'nward then at eve-ning wend - ing, Thou shalt come with joy un-told.

D. S.—*Send them now the sheaves to gath - er, Ere the har - vest time pass by.*

CHORUS   **D. S.**

Lord of har-vest, send forth reap-ers! Hear us, Lord, to Thee we cry;

190 Close to Thee

Fanny J. Crosby

S. J. Vail

1. Thou, my ev - er - last - ing por - tion, More than friend or life to me;
2. Not for ease or world - ly pleas - ure, Nor for fame my prayer shall be;
3. Lead me thro' the vale of shad - ows, Bear me o'er life's fit - ful sea;

FINE

D. S.–All a - long my pil - grim jour - ney, Sav - ior, let me walk with Thee.
D. S.–Glad - ly will I toil and suf - fer, On - ly let me walk with Thee.
D. S.–Then the gate of life e - ter - nal May I en - ter, Lord, with Thee.

REFRAIN

D. S.

Close to Thee, close to Thee, Close to Thee, close to Thee!

191 Purer Yet and Purer

J. W. Von Goethe

S. J. Vail

1. Pur - er yet and pur - er I would be in mind, Dear - er yet and
2. Calm - er yet and calm - er, Tri - al bear and pain; Sur - er yet and
3. High - er yet and high - er, Out of clouds and night; Near - er yet and

dear - er, Ev - 'ry du - ty find; Hop - ing still and trust - ing
sur - er, Peace at last to gain; Suf - f'ring still and do - ing,
near - er, Ris - ing to the light; Oft these ear - nest long - ings,

God with-out a fear, Pa-tient-ly be-liev-ing He will make all clear.
To His will re-signed, And to God sub-du-ing Heart and will and mind.
Swell with-in my breast; Yet their in-ner mean-ing Ne'er can be ex-pressed.

192   Something for Jesus

S. D. Phelps   Robert Lowry

1. Sav-ior, Thy dy-ing love Thou gav-est me, Nor should I aught with-hold,
2. Give me a faith-ful heart—Like-ness to Thee—That each de-part-ing day
3. All that I am and have—Thy gifts so free— In joy, in grief, thro' life,

Dear Lord, from Thee: In love my soul would bow, My heart ful-
Hence-forth may see Some work of love be-gun, Some deed of
Dear Lord, for Thee! And when Thy face I see, My ran-somed

fil its vow, Some of-f'ring bring Thee now, Some-thing for Thee.
kind-ness done, Some wan-d'rer sought and won, Some-thing for Thee.
soul shall be, Thro' all e-ter-ni-ty, Some-thing for Thee.

193 Come to Jesus

E. R. Latta

J. H. Tenney

1. Come to Je-sus! He will save you, Tho' your sins as crim-son glow;
2. Come to Je-sus! do not tar - ry, En - ter in at mer-cy's gate;
3. Come to Je-sus, dy-ing sin-ner! Oth-er Sav-ior there is none;

If you give your heart to Je - sus, He will make it white as snow.
Oh, de-lay not till the mor-row, Lest thy com-ing be too late.
He will share with you His glo - ry, When your pil-grim-age is done.

CHORUS

Come to Je - - - sus! Come to Je - - - sus! Come to Je - sus!
Come, come to-day! Come, come to-day! Come to Je - sus!

come to - day!   Come to Je - sus! come, come to - day!
come, yes, come, come to-day!

194 Only Waiting

Mrs. Frances L. Mace

Ira D. Sankey

1. On - ly wait-ing till the shad-ows Are a lit - tle lon-ger grown;
2. On - ly wait-ing till the reap-ers Have the last sheaf gathered home;
3. Wait-ing for a brighter dwell-ing Than I ev - er yet have seen,

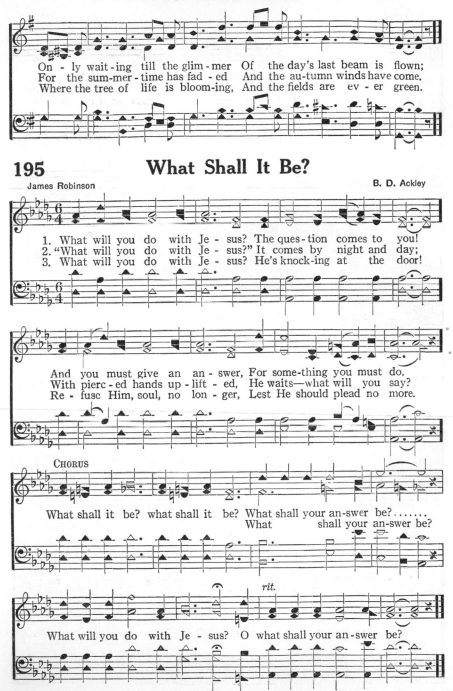

On - ly wait-ing till the glim-mer Of the day's last beam is flown;
For the sum-mer-time has fad - ed And the au-tumn winds have come.
Where the tree of life is bloom-ing, And the fields are ev - er green.

195 What Shall It Be?

James Robinson

B. D. Ackley

1. What will you do with Je - sus? The ques-tion comes to you!
2. "What will you do with Je - sus?" It comes by night and day;
3. What will you do with Je - sus? He's knock-ing at the door!

And you must give an an - swer, For some-thing you must do.
With pierc - ed hands up - lift - ed, He waits—what will you say?
Re - fuse Him, soul, no lon - ger, Lest He should plead no more.

CHORUS

What shall it be? what shall it be? What shall your an-swer be?.......
What shall your an-swer be?

rit.

What will you do with Je - sus? O what shall your an-swer be?

196   Savior, Like a Shepherd Lead Us

Dorothy A. Thrupp

William B. Bradbury

1. { Sav - ior, like a shep-herd lead us: Much we need Thy tend'rest care;
   { In Thy pleasant pastures feed us, For our use Thy folds pre - pare:

2. { We are Thine; do Thou be-friend us; Be the Guardian of our way;
   { Keep Thy flock, from sin de-fend us, Seek us when we go a - - stray:

3. { Ear - ly let us seek Thy fa - vor, Ear - ly let us do Thy will;
   { Bless-ed Lord and on - ly Sav - ior, With Thy love our bos-oms fill:

Bless-ed Je - sus, Bless-ed Je - sus, Thou hast bought us, Thine we are;
Bless-ed Je - sus, Bless-ed Je - sus, Hear, O hear us when we pray;
Bless-ed Je - sus, Bless-ed Je - sus, Thou hast loved us, love us still;

Bless-ed Je - sus, Bless-ed Je - sus, Thou hast bought us, Thine we are.
Bless-ed Je - sus, Bless-ed Je - sus, Hear, O hear us when we pray.
Bless-ed Je - sus, Bless-ed Je - sus, Thou hast loved us, love us still.

197   My Latest Sun Is Sinking Fast

Jefferson Hascall

Wm. B. Bradbury

1. { My lat - est sun is sink - ing fast, My race is near - ly run; }
   { My strong-est tri - als now are past, My tri - umph is be - gun. }

2. { I know I'm near the ho - ly ranks Of friends and kin - dred dear: }
   { I brush the dews on Jor-dan's banks: The cross - ing must be near. }

3. { I've al-most gained my heav'n-ly home, My spir - it loud - ly sings; }
   { Thy ho - ly ones, be-hold, they come! I hear the noise of wings. }

CHORUS

O come, an-gel band, Come, and a-round me stand; O bear me a-way on your

snow-y wings To my im-mor-tal home; To my im-mor-tal home.

198　　　I Gave My Life for Thee

Frances R. Havergal

P. P. Bliss

1. I gave My life for thee, My pre-cious blood I shed,
2. My Fa-ther's house of light, My glo-ry-cir-cled throne,
3. And I have brought to thee, Down from My home a-bove,

That thou might'st ran-somed be, And quick-ened from the dead;
I left for earth-ly night, For wan-d'rings sad and lone;
Sal-va-tion full and free, My par-don and My love;

REFRAIN

I gave, I gave My life for thee: What hast thou giv'n for Me?
I left, I left it all for thee: Hast thou left aught for Me?
I bring, I bring rich gifts to thee: What hast thou bro't to Me?

199 Have You Any Room for Jesus?

Vana R. Raye

L. O. Sanderson

1. Je - sus, born to bless the bur-dened, Found a kind-less Beth-le - hem—
2. Have you an - y room for Je - sus? You for oth - ers plan the room;
3. Have you an - y room for Je - sus? O - pen lest He go a - way,

His a - bode the low - ly man - ger, For there was no room for Him.
He's a guest of rar - est glo - ry— O - pen and with Him com-mune.
Leav-ing you a - lone to fal - ter Toward a cer-tain, bit - ter day.

CHORUS

Have you an - y room for Je - sus? Knock-ing at your heart is He!

Hear Him, o - pen, bid Him en - ter! He has much in store for thee.

200 I'm Not Ashamed to Own My Lord

Isaac Watts

Carl Glaser

1. I'm not a-shamed to own my Lord, Nor to de - fend His cause;
2. Firm as His throne His prom-ise stands, And He can well se - cure
3. Then will He own my worth-less name Be - fore His Fa-ther's face,

Main-tain the hon - ors of His word, The glo - ry of His cross.
What I've com - mit - ted to His hands, Till the de - ci - sive hour.
And in the new Je - ru - sa - lem Ap - point for me a place.

201 Is Thy Heart Right with God?

E. A. H.

E. A. Hoffman

1. Have thine af - fec-tions been nailed to the cross? Is thy heart right with God?
2. Hast thou do-min - ion o'er self and o'er sin? Is thy heart right with God?
3. Are all thy pow'rs un-der Je-sus' con-trol? Is thy heart right with God?

Dost thou count all things for Je - sus but loss? Is thy heart right with God?
O - ver all e - vil with-out and with-in? Is thy heart right with God?
Does He each mo-ment a - bide in thy soul? Is thy heart right with God?

REFRAIN

Is thy heart right with God, Washed in the crim-son flood, Cleansed and made

ho - ly, hum - ble and low - ly, Right in the sight of God (of God)?

202 Send the Light

C. H. G.

Chas. H. Gabriel

1. There's a call comes ring-ing o'er the rest-less wave: Send the light!......
2. We have heard the Mac-e-do-nian call to-day: Send the light!......
3. Let us pray that grace may ev-'ry-where a-bound: Send the light!......
4. Let us not grow wea-ry in the work of love: Send the light!......

Send the light!

Send the light!...... There are souls to res-cue, there are souls to save:
Send the light!...... And a gold-en of-f'ring at the cross we lay:
Send the light!...... And a Christ-like spir-it ev-'ry-where be found:
Send the light!...... Let us gath-er jew-els for a crown a-bove:

Send the light!

REFRAIN

Send the light!...... Send the light!........ Send the light!...... the
Send the light! Send the light! Send the light!

bless-ed gos-pel light; Let it shine........ from shore to
the bless-ed gos-pel light; Let it shine

shore!................ for-ev-er-more.................
from shore to shore! for-ev-er-more.

203 God Is Calling the Prodigal

C. H. G.

Chas. H. Gabriel

1. God is call-ing the prod-i-gal: come with-out de-lay; Hear, O hear Him calling,
2. Pa - tient, lov-ing, and ten-der-ly still the Fa-ther pleads; Hear, O hear Him calling,
3. Come, there's bread in the house of thy Father, and to spare; Hear, O hear Him calling,

call-ing now for thee; Tho' you've wandered so far from His presence, come today;
call-ing now for thee; O re-turn while the Spir-it in mer-cy in - ter - cedes;
call-ing now for thee; Lo! the ta - ble is spread and the feast is waiting there;
for thee;

CHORUS

Hear His loving voice calling still...... Call - - ing now for thee,........
calling still. Calling now for thee, Calling now for thee,

O wea - ry prod-i-gal, come;.......... Call - - ing
Wea-ry prod-i-gal, come, wea-ry prodigal, come; Calling now for thee,

now for thee,........ O wea - - ry prod-i-gal, come..........
Calling now for thee, Weary prodigal, come, wea-ry prodigal, come.

204 I Will Sing the Wondrous Story

F. H. Rowley

Peter P. Bilhorn

1. I will sing the won-drous sto - ry Of the Christ who died for me,
2. I was lost, but Je - sus found me, Found the sheep that went a - stray,
3. He will keep me till the riv - er Rolls its wa - ters at my feet;

How He left His home in glo - ry For the cross of Cal - va - ry.
Threw His lov - ing arms a-round me, Drew me back un - to His way.
Then He'll bear me safe - ly o - ver, Where the loved ones I shall meet.

CHORUS

Yes, I'll sing...... the wondrous sto - - ry Of the Christ...... who
Yes, I'll sing the wondrous sto-ry Of the Christ

Sing it with...... the saints in glo - - ry, (Omit . . . . . .
Sing it with the saints in glo - ry,

died for me,............ Gath-ered by....... the crys-tal sea..........
who died for me, Gath-ered by the crys-tal sea.

205 By Christ Redeemed

Geo. Rawson. Arranged

From A. H. Troyte's Chant

1. By Christ re-deemed, in Christ re-stored, We keep the Sup-per of the Word,
2. His bod - y giv - en in our stead Is seen in this me-mo-rial bread,
3. And thus that dark be-tray - al night With the last ad-vent we u - nite,

By Christ Redeemed, Concluded

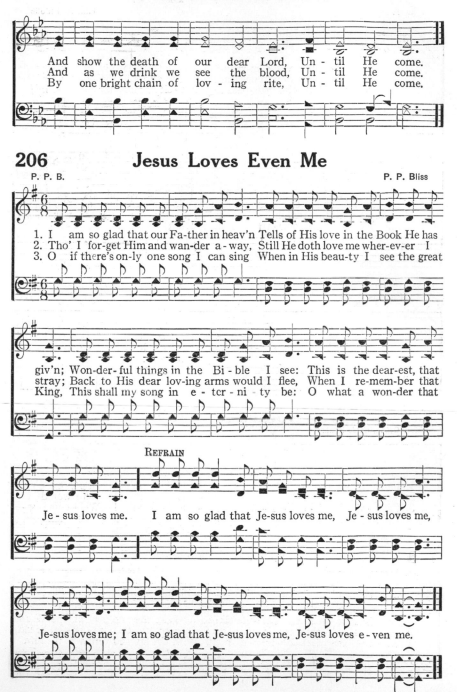

And show the death of our dear Lord, Un - til He come.
And as we drink we see the blood, Un - til He come.
By one bright chain of lov - ing rite, Un - til He come.

206   Jesus Loves Even Me

P. P. B.   P. P. Bliss

1. I am so glad that our Fa-ther in heav'n Tells of His love in the Book He has
2. Tho' I for-get Him and wan-der a - way, Still He doth love me wher-ev-er I
3. O if there's on-ly one song I can sing When in His beau-ty I see the great

giv'n; Won-der- ful things in the Bi - ble I see: This is the dear-est, that
stray; Back to His dear lov-ing arms would I flee, When I re-mem-ber that
King, This shall my song in e - ter - ni - ty be: O what a won-der that

REFRAIN

Je - sus loves me. I am so glad that Je-sus loves me, Je - sus loves me,

Je-sus loves me; I am so glad that Je-sus loves me, Je-sus loves e - ven me.

207 The Lord's Supper

T. S. T.

Tillit S. Teddlie

1. When we meet in sweet com-mun-ion Where the feast di-vine is spread;
2. "God so loved" what wondrous measure! Loved and gave the best of heav'n;
3. Feast di-vine, all else sur-pass-ing, Pre-cious blood for you and me,

rit. FINE

Hearts are brought in clos - er un - ion While par - tak - ing of the bread.
Bought us with that match-less treas-ure, Yea, for us His life was giv'n.
While we sup, Christ gen - tly whis-pers: "Do this in my mem - o - ry."

D. S.—*While we feast Christ gen - tly whis-pers: "Do this in my mem - o - ry."*

CHORUS D. S.

Pre-cious feast all else sur - pass-ing, Won-drous love for you and me,

208 Jesus Is Mine

Mrs. Catharine J. Bonar

T. E. Perkins

1. Fade, fade, each earth-ly joy, Je - sus is mine! Break ev - 'ry
2. Tempt not my soul a - way, Je - sus is mine! Here would I
3. Fare - well, mor - tal - i - ty, Je - sus is mine! Wel - come, e-

ten - der tie, Je - sus is mine! Dark is the wil - der-ness,
ev - er stay, Je - sus is mine! Per - ish - ing things of clay,
ter - ni - ty, Je - sus is mine! Wel - come, oh, loved and blest,

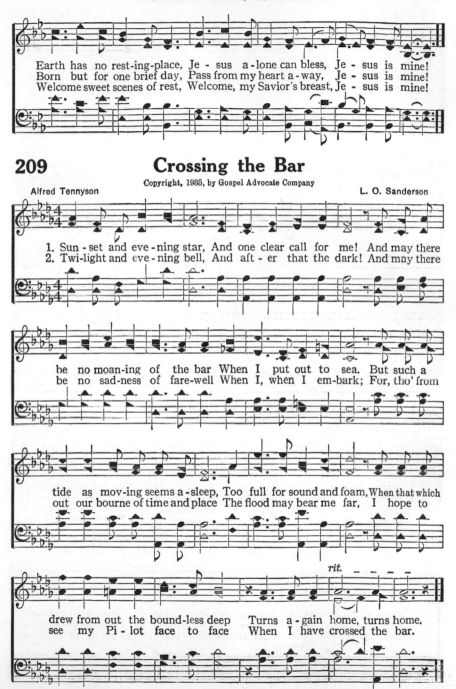

Earth has no rest-ing-place, Je - sus a-lone can bless, Je - sus is mine!
Born but for one brief day, Pass from my heart a-way, Je - sus is mine!
Welcome sweet scenes of rest, Welcome, my Savior's breast, Je - sus is mine!

209 Crossing the Bar

Copyright, 1935, by Gospel Advocate Company

Alfred Tennyson

L. O. Sanderson

1. Sun - set and eve - ning star, And one clear call for me! And may there
2. Twi-light and eve - ning bell, And aft - er that the dark! And may there

be no moan-ing of the bar When I put out to sea. But such a
be no sad-ness of fare-well When I, when I em-bark; For, tho' from

tide as mov-ing seems a-sleep, Too full for sound and foam, When that which
out our bourne of time and place The flood may bear me far, I hope to

rit.

drew from out the bound-less deep Turns a - gain home, turns home.
see my Pi - lot face to face When I have crossed the bar.

210 That's Enough for Me

E. A. H. Arr.   Elisha A. Hoffman

1. O love, sur-pass-ing knowl-edge! O grace so full and free!
2. O won-der-ful sal-va-tion, That I should ran-somed be!
3. We live in sweet com-mun-ion, In ho-ly har-mo-ny;

D. S.-I know that Je-sus loves me, And that's e-nough for me.
D. S.-The Gos-pel gives as-sur-ance, And that's e-nough for me.
D. S.-Thus would I en-ter glo-ry, And that's e-nough for me.

REFRAIN

And that's e-nough for me, And that's e-nough for me:

211 O 'Tis Wonderful

I. I. Leslie   F. A. Blackmer

1. When I was far a-way and lost, O 'tis won-der-ful!
2. I once was blind, but now I see; O 'tis won-der-ful!
3. Some day I'll see the Sav-ior's face, O 'tis won-der-ful!

That I was saved at such a cost! O 'tis won-der-ful!
Was bound by sin, but now am free; O 'tis won-der-ful!
And find with Him a rest-ing-place; O 'tis won-der-ful!

O 'Tis Wonderful, Concluded

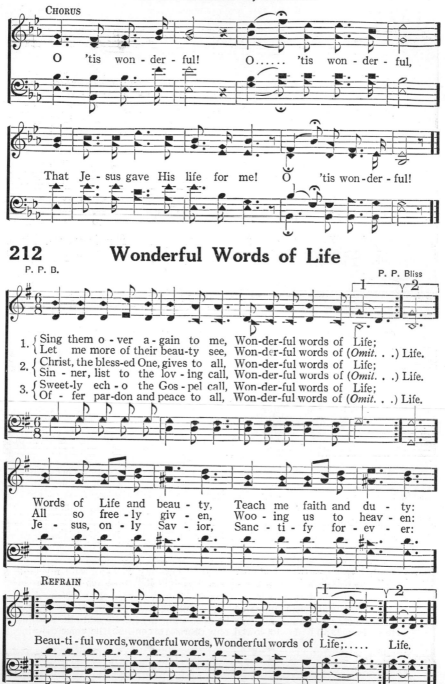

CHORUS

O 'tis won-der-ful! O...... 'tis won-der-ful,

That Je - sus gave His life for me! O 'tis won-der-ful!

212 Wonderful Words of Life

P. P. B.

P. P. Bliss

1. { Sing them o - ver a - gain to me, Won-der-ful words of Life;
   { Let me more of their beau-ty see, Won-der-ful words of (*Omit*. . .) Life.
2. { Christ, the bless-ed One, gives to all, Won-der-ful words of Life;
   { Sin - ner, list to the lov - ing call, Won-der-ful words of (*Omit*. . .) Life.
3. { Sweet-ly ech - o the Gos - pel call, Won-der-ful words of Life;
   { Of - fer par-don and peace to all, Won-der-ful words of (*Omit*. . .) Life.

Words of Life and beau - ty, Teach me faith and du - ty:
All so free - ly giv - en, Woo - ing us to heav - en:
Je - sus, on - ly Sav - ior, Sanc - ti - fy for - ev - er:

REFRAIN

Beau-ti-ful words, wonderful words, Wonderful words of Life;..... Life.

213 Nearer and Nearer

L. O. S.

L. O. Sanderson

1. Near - er and near - er, my Sav - ior, to Thee; Dear - er and
2. Near - er and near - er Thy like - ness to be; Clear - er and
3. Near - er and near - er to life's bound-a - ry; Care - ful and

dear - er Thy mer - cy to me; Hop - ing and striv - ing in
clear - er the pat - tern I see; Hav - ing Thy heart and Thy
prayer-ful, my Lord, I would be; Read - y and wait - ing the

liv - ing to be Near - er and dear - er, my Lord, to Thee.
Spir - it in me— Thou, Lord, with - in me, and I in Thee.
house made for me, For I would ev - er be near to Thee.

214 O Happy Day

Philip Doddridge

Edward F. Rimbault

1. { O hap - py day that fixed my choice On Thee, my Sav - ior and my God! }
   { Well may this glow-ing heart re - joice, And tell its rap-tures all a-broad! }

2. { O hap - py bond, that seals my vows To Him who mer - its all my love! }
   { Let cheer-ful an-thems fill His house, While to that sa - cred shrine I move. }

3. { 'Tis done, the great trans-ac-tion's done; I am my Lord's, and He is mine! }
   { He drew me, and I fol-lowed on, Charmed to con-fess the voice di - vine. }

O Happy Day, Concluded

Hap - py day, hap - py day, When Je - sus washed my sins a - way.

He taught me how to watch and pray, And live re - joic - ing ev - 'ry day;

215   Is It for Me?

Frances R. Havergal

T. C. O'Kane

1. Is it for me, dear Sav - ior, Thy glo - ry and Thy rest— For me, so
2. O Sav - ior, pre - cious Sav - ior, My heart is at Thy feet; I bless Thee,
3. I'll be with Thee for - ev - er, And nev - er grieve Thee more; Dear Sav - ior,

CHORUS

weak and sin - ful? O shall I be so blest?
and I love Thee, And Thee I long to meet.   O Sav - ior, my Re - deem - er,
I must praise Thee, And love Thee ev - er - more.

What can I but a - dore, And mag - ni - fy and praise Thee, And love Thee ev - er - more?

216 I Am Praying for You

S. O'Maley Cluff

Ira D. Sankey

1. I have a Sav-ior, He's plead-ing in glo-ry, A dear lov-ing Sav-ior, tho' earth-friends be few; And now He is watch-ing in ten-der-ness o'er me, But O that my Sav-ior were your Sav-ior too!

2. I have a Sav-ior, to me He has giv-en A hope for e-ter-ni-ty, bless-ed and true; And soon He will call me to meet Him in heav-en, But O that He'd let me bring you with me too!

3. I have a robe: 'tis re-splen-dent in white-ness, A-wait-ing in glo-ry my won-der-ing view; And when I re-ceive it all shin-ing in brightness, I pray I may see you re-ceiv-ing one too!

CHORUS

For you I am pray-ing, For you I am pray-ing,

For you I am pray-ing, I'm pray-ing for you.

217   We Shall See the King Some Day

L. E. J.

L. E. Jones

1. Tho' the way we jour-ney may be of-ten drear, We shall see the
2. Aft-er pain and an-guish, aft-er toil and care, We shall see the
3. Aft-er foes are con-quered, aft-er bat-tles won, We shall see the
4. There with all the loved ones who have gone be-fore, We shall see the

King some day (some day); On that bless-ed morn-ing clouds will dis-ap-pear:
King some day (some day); Thro' the end-less a - ges joy and bless-ing share:
King some day (some day); Aft-er strife is o - ver, aft-er set of sun,
King some day (some day); Sor-row past for-ev - er, on that peace-ful shore,

CHORUS

We shall see the King some day. We shall see the King some day,
some day,

We will shout and sing some day; some day; Gath-ered round the throne,

When He shall call His own, We shall see the King some day.

218 **Remember Me, O Mighty One**

Joanna Kinkel. Arr.

1. When storms a-round are sweep-ing, When lone my watch I'm keep-ing,
2. When walk-ing on life's o-cean, Con-trol its rag-ing mo-tion;
3. When weight of sin op-press-es, When dark de-spair dis-tress-es;

'Mid fires of e-vil fall-ing, 'Mid tempt-ers' voic-es call-ing,
When from its dan-gers shrink-ing, When in its dread deeps sink-ing,
All through the life that's mor-tal, And when I pass death's por-tal,

CHORUS

Re-mem-ber me, O might-y One! Re-mem-ber me, O might-y One!

219 **Yield Not to Temptation**

H. R. P.   H. R. Palmer

1. Yield not to temp-ta-tion, For yield-ing is sin; Each vic-t'ry will help you
2. Shun e-vil com-pan-ions, Bad language dis-dain, God's name hold in rev'rence,
3. To him that o'er-com-eth, God giv-eth a crown; Thro' faith we shall conquer,

Some oth-er to win; Fight man-ful-ly on-ward, Dark pas-sions sub-due,
Nor take it in vain; Be thoughtful and ear-nest, Kind-heart-ed and true,
Tho' of-ten cast down; He who is our Sav-ior Our strength will re-new;

Yield Not to Temptation, Concluded

CHORUS

Look ev-er to Je-sus: He'll car-ry you thro'. Ask the Sav-ior to help you,

Comfort, strengthen, and keep you; He is willing to aid you, He will carry you thro'.

---

220 One Step At A Time

T. J. Shelton

J. H. Rosecrans

1. One step at a time, dear Sav-ior, I can-not take an-y-more;
2. One step at a time, dear Sav-ior, I am not walk-ing by sight;
3. One step at a time, dear Sav-ior, Oh, guard my fal-ter-ing feet!

FINE.

The flesh is so weak and hope-less, I know not what is be-fore.
Keep step with my soul, dear Sav-ior, I walk by faith in Thy might.
Keep hold of my hand, dear Sav-ior, Till I my jour-ney com-plete.

D. S.—*step at a time, dear Sav-ior, Till hope grows strong-er in me.*

CHORUS

D. S.

One step at a time, dear Sav-ior, Till faith grows stronger in Thee; One
in Thee;

221 Safe in the Arms of Jesus

Fanny J. Crosby

W. H. Doane

1. Safe in the arms of Je - sus, Safe on His gen - tle breast,
2. Safe in the arms of Je - sus, Safe from cor - rod - ing care,
3. Je - sus, my heart's dear ref - uge, Je - sus has died for me;

Cho.—*Safe in the arms of Je - sus, Safe on His gen - tle breast,*

FINE

There by His love o'er - shad - ed, Sweet-ly my soul shall rest.
Safe from the world's temp-ta - tions, Sin can-not harm me there.
Firm on the Rock of A - ges, Ev - er my trust shall be.

There by His love o'er - shad - ed, Sweet-ly my soul shall rest.

Hark! 'tis the voice of an - gels, Borne in a song to me,
Free from the blight of sor - row, Free from my doubts and fears;
Here let me wait with pa - tience, Wait till the night is o'er;

D. C.

O - ver the fields of glo - ry, O - ver the jas - per sea:
On - ly a few more tri - als, On - ly a few more tears:
Wait till I see the morn - ing Break on the gold - en shore:

222   The Garden of Prayer

Eleanor Allen Schroll   J. H. Fillmore

1. There's a gar-den where Je-sus is wait-ing, There's a place that is
2. There's a gar-den where Je-sus is wait-ing, And I go with my
3. There's a gar-den where Je-sus is wait-ing— O can aught with His
4. There's a gar-den where Je-sus is wait-ing, And He bids you come

won-drous-ly fair; For it glows with the light of His pres-ence: 'Tis the
bur-den and care, Just to learn from His lips words of com-fort, In the
glo-ry com-pare? Just to walk and to talk with my Sav-ior, In the
meet with Him there, Just to bow and re-ceive a new bless-ing, In the

beau-ti-ful gar-den of prayer.

REFRAIN

O the beau-ti-ful gar-den, the
gar-den of prayer, O the beau-ti-ful gar-den of prayer; There my Sav-ior a-
waits, and He o-pens the gates To the beau-ti-ful gar-den of prayer.

223 The Rock That Is Higher Than I

E. Johnson

Wm. G. Fischer

1. O some-times the shad-ows are deep, And rough seems the path to the goal;
2. O some-times how long seems the day, And sometimes how wea-ry my feet;
3. O near to the Rock let me keep, Or bless-ings or sor-rows pre-vail,

And sorrows, sometimes how they sweep Like tempests down o - ver the soul.
But toil-ing in life's dust-y way, The Rock's blessed shadow, how sweet!
Or climb-ing the mountain way steep, Or walk-ing the shad-ow - y vale.

CHORUS

O then to the Rock let me fly,
let me fly,
To the
Rock that is high - er than I;
is high - er than I;
O then to the
Rock let me fly,
let me fly,
To the Rock that is high - er than I.

224 There Is a Sea

L. K. Z., v. 3; vs. 1, 2 (?)   Copyright, 1921, by E. L. Jorgenson   Lula Klingman Zahn

1. There is a sea which day by day Re-ceives the rip-pling rills, And streams that
2. There is a sea which day by day Re-ceives a full-er tide; But all its
3. Which shall it be for you and me, Who God's good gifts ob-tain? Shall we ac-

spring from wells of God, Or fall from ce-dared hills; But what it
store it keeps, nor gives To shore nor sea be-side; It's Jor-dan
cept for self a-lone, Or take to give a-gain? For He who

1. But what it thus re-ceives it gives With glad unsparing,
thus . . . . re-ceives it gives . . . With glad un-spar - - - ing
stream, . . . now turned to brine, . . Lies heavy as mol - - - ten
once . . . . was rich in-deed. . . . Laid all His glo - - - ry

1. un-spar-ing hand: A stream more wide, with deep-er tide,
hand: . . . . A stream more wide, . . . with deep-er tide, ...
lead; . . . . Its dread-ful name . . . doth e'er pro-claim . . . .
down; . . . . That by His grace, . . . our ransomed race . . . .

rit.

Flows on . . . . to low-er land. . . . . . .
That sea . . . . . . is waste and dead. . . . . . .
Should share . . . . . His wealth and crown.
1. Flows on, flows on to low-er land.

225 We Are Fellow Creatures

L. O. S.

Copyright.1948, by Gospel Advocate Company

L. O. Sanderson

1. We are fel-low crea-tures, Born in the king-dom of Christ,
2. We are fel-low trav-'lers, Pil-grims with-in a strange land,
3. We are fel-low pris-'ners, Suf-f'ring in fa-vor or shame,

Raised at the Mas-ter's bid-ding, Pledged to a right-eous life.
Seek-ing a bet-ter coun-try, Made by the Fa-ther's hand.
Bear-ing the cross of Je-sus, Prais-ing His ho-ly name.

We are fel-low serv-ants, Bought by a gra-cious love,
We are fel-low help-ers, Feel-ing for each a care,
We are fel-low sol-diers, Fight-ing the fight of faith,

Charged with a com-mon in-t'rest, Sav-ing for life a-bove.
Know-ing our strength is weak-ness, Striv-ing our all to share.
Fly-ing the blood-stained ban-ner, Loy-al and true till death.

226 Art Thou Weary?

Tr. J. M. Neale

H. W. Baker

1. Art thou wea-ry, art thou lan-guid, Art thou sore dis-tressed?
2. If I ask Him to re-ceive me, Will He say me nay!—
3. Find-ing Him, and fol-l'wing, keep-ing, Is He sure to bless?

"Come to Me," saith One, and com - ing, Be at rest.
"Not till earth and not till heav - en Pass a - way."
Saints, a - pos - tles, proph - ets, mar - tyrs, An - swer "Yes!"

227 Hold to God's Unchanging Hand

Jennie Wilson

F. L. Eiland

1. Time is filled with swift tran-si - tion—Naught of earth unmoved can stand—
2. Trust in Him who will not leave you, What - so - ev - er years may bring,
3. When your jour-ney is com-plet - ed, If to God you have been true,

rit.

Build your hopes on things e - ter - nal, Hold to God's un-chang-ing hand.
If by earth-ly friends for-sak - en, Still more close-ly to Him cling.
Fair and bright the home in glo - ry Your en-rap-tured soul will view.

p CHORUS *m*

Hold to God's unchanging hand! Hold to God's unchanging
Hold to His hand Hold to His hand

f *rit.*

hand! Build your hopes on things e-ter - nal, Hold to God's unchanging hand.

228 The Lord Has Been Mindful of Me

L. O. S.

L. O. Sanderson

1. Though I, thro' the val - ley of shad - ow, O'er moun-tain or trou-bled sea,
2. Much more than my grief and my sor - row, Much more than ad-ver - si - ty,
3. I'm rich! I am saved! I am hap - py! I've health and pros-per - i - ty!

And oft in the dark-ness, have trav-elled, The Lord has been mindful of me!
Much more than the all I have giv - en, The Lord has been mindful of me!
I've friends! I have doors ev - er o - pen! The Lord has been mindful of me!

CHORUS

The Lord has been mind-ful of me! He bless-es and bless-es a - gain!

My God is the God of the liv - ing! How ex - cel - lent is His name!

229 Asleep In Jesus

Margaret Mackay

Wm. B. Bradbury

1. A-sleep in Je - sus! bless-ed sleep, From which none ev - er wakes to weep!
2. A-sleep in Je - sus! O how sweet To be for such a slum-ber meet!
3. A-sleep in Je - sus! peace-ful rest, Whose wak-ing is su-preme-ly blest!

A calm and un-dis-turbed re-pose, Un-bro-ken by the last of foes.
With ho-ly con-fi-dence to sing, That death hath lost its ven-omed sting.
No fear, no woe, shall dim that hour That man-i-fests the Sav-ior's pow'r.

230 Sweeter Than All

Johnson Oatman, Jr.   J. Howard Entwisle

1. Christ will me His aid af-ford, Nev-er to fall, nev-er to fall;
2. Though a ves-sel I may be, Bro-ken and small, bro-ken and small,
3. When I reach the crys-tal sea, Voic-es will call, voic-es will call;

While I find my pre-cious Lord Sweet-er than all, sweet-er than all.
Yet His bless-ings fall on me, Sweet-er than all, sweet-er than all.
But my Sav-ior's voice will be Sweet-er than all, sweet-er than all.

Chorus

Je-sus is now, and ev-er will be, Sweet-er than all the world to me,

Since I heard His lov-ing call, Sweet-er than all, sweet-er than all.

231 The Old Rugged Cross

G. B.

Geo. Bennard

1. On a hill far a - way stood an old rug-ged cross, The em-blem of
2. Oh, that old rug-ged cross, so de-spised by the world, Has a won-drous at-
3. In the old rug-ged cross, stained with blood so di-vine, A won - drous
4. To the old rug-ged cross, I will ev - er be true, Its shame and re-

suf-f'ring and shame, And I love that old cross where the dear-est and best
trac-tion for me, For the dear Lamb of God left His glo - ry a - bove,
beau-ty I see; For 'twas on that old cross Je - sus suf-fered and died,
proach gladly bear; Then He'll call me some day to my home far a - way,

Chorus

For a world of lost sin-ners was slain. So I'll cher-ish the old rug-ged
To bear it to dark Cal - va - ry.
To par-don and sanc - ti - fy me.
Where His glo-ry for - ev - er I'll share. So I'll cher-ish the cross, the

cross,....... Till my tro-phies at last I lay down; I will cling to the
old rugged cross,

old rug-ged cross,.......... And ex-change it some day for a crown.
cross, the old rug-ged cross,

Give Me the Bible

Priscilla J. Owens

E. S. Lorenz

1. Give me the Bi - ble, star of glad-ness gleam-ing, To cheer the wan-d'rer
2. Give me the Bi - ble when my heart is bro - ken, When sin and grief have
3. Give me the Bi - ble, all my steps en-light - en, Teach me the dan - ger
4. Give me the Bi - ble, lamp of life im-mor - tal, Hold up that splen-dor

lone and tempest-tossed; No storm can hide that ra-diance peaceful beaming,
filled my soul with fear; Give me the pre-cious words by Je - sus spo - ken,
of these realms be-low; That lamp of safe - ty o'er the gloom shall brighten,
by the o - pen grave; Show me the light from heav-en's shin-ing por - tal,

CHORUS

Since Je - sus came to seek and save the lost.
Hold up faith's lamp to show my Sav-ior near. Give me the Bi - ble,
That light a - lone the path of peace can show.
Show me the glo - ry gild-ing Jor-dan's wave.

Ho-ly message shin-ing; Thy light shall guide me in the narrow way; Precept and

prom-ise, law and love com-bin-ing, Till night shall van-ish in e-ter-nal day.

233 O Come, All Ye Faithful

Tr. Fr. Oakeley. Alt.

Wade's Cantus Diversi

1. O come, all ye faith-ful, Joyful and triumphant, O come ye, O come ye, to
2. ♯ Sing, choirs of angels, Sing in ex-ul - ta-tion, Thro' heav-en's high arches be your
3. ♯ Yea, Lord, we bless Thee, Born for our salvation; O Je - sus, for-ev-er be Thy

p REFRAIN

Beth - le-hem; Come and a -dore Him, Born the King of an-gels;
praises poured; Now to our God be Glo-ry in the high-est; O come, let us a-
name a-dored; Word of the Fa - ther, Now in flesh ap-pear-ing;

f

dore Him, O come, let us a-dore Him, O come, let us a - dore Him, Christ, the Lord.

234 Revive Us Again

Wm. P. Mackay

J. J. Husband

1. We praise Thee, O God, For the Son of Thy love, For Je - sus who
2. We praise Thee, O God, For Thy Spir - it of light, Who has shown us our
3. All glo - ry and praise To the Lamb that was slain, Who has borne all our

CHORUS

died, and is now gone a - bove.
Sav - ior, and scat-tered our night. Hal - le - lu - jah! Thine the glo - ry:
sins, and has cleansed ev-'ry stain.

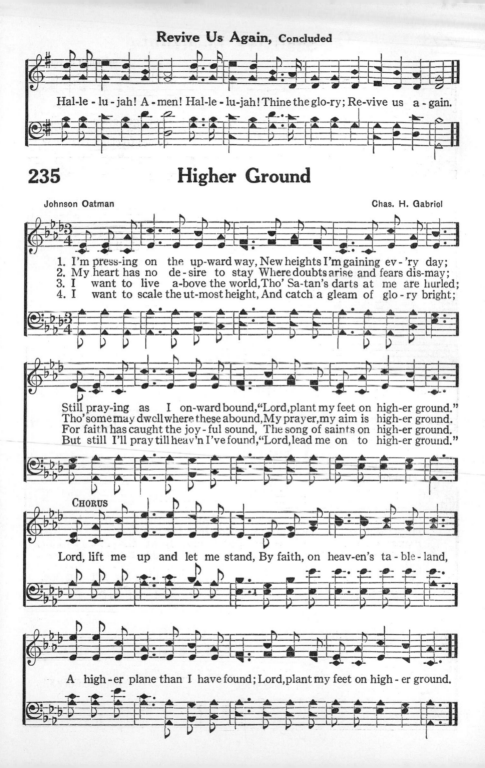

Revive Us Again, Concluded

Hal-le - lu - jah! A - men! Hal-le - lu-jah! Thine the glo-ry; Re-vive us a - gain.

235 Higher Ground

Johnson Oatman

Chas. H. Gabriel

1. I'm press-ing on the up-ward way, New heights I'm gaining ev-'ry day;
2. My heart has no de-sire to stay Where doubts arise and fears dis-may;
3. I want to live a-bove the world, Tho' Sa-tan's darts at me are hurled;
4. I want to scale the ut-most height, And catch a gleam of glo-ry bright;

Still pray-ing as I on-ward bound, "Lord, plant my feet on high-er ground."
Tho' some may dwell where these abound, My prayer, my aim is high-er ground.
For faith has caught the joy - ful sound, The song of saints on high-er ground.
But still I'll pray till heav'n I've found, "Lord, lead me on to high-er ground."

CHORUS

Lord, lift me up and let me stand, By faith, on heav-en's ta - ble - land,

A high-er plane than I have found; Lord, plant my feet on high - er ground.

236 Shall We Meet?

H. L. Hastings

Elihu S. Rice

1. Shall we meet be-yond the riv - er, Where the sur - ges cease to roll;
2. Shall we meet be-yond the riv - er, When our storm-y voyage is o'er?
3. Shall we meet with Christ our Sav-ior, When He comes to claim His own?

FINE.

Where in all the bright for - ev - er, Sor - row ne'er shall press the soul?
Shall we meet and cast the an - chor By the bright ce - les - tial shore?
Shall we know His bless - ed fa - vor, And sit down up - on His throne?

D. S.—Shall we meet be - yond the riv - er, Where the sur - ges cease to roll?

CHORUS

D. S.

Shall we meet, shall we meet Shall we meet be-yond the riv - er?

237 I Surrender All

J. W. Van De Venter

W. S. Weeden

DUET

1. { All to Je - sus I sur-ren - der, All to Him I free - ly give; }
   { I will ev - er love and trust Him, In His pres-ence dai - ly live. }
2. { All to Je - sus I sur-ren - der, Hum-bly at His feet I bow; }
   { World-ly pleas-ures all for-sak - en, Take me, Je - sus, take me now. }
3. { All to Je - sus I sur-ren - der, Lord, I give my - self to Thee; }
   { Fill me with Thy love and pow - er, Let Thy bless-ing fall on me. }

CHORUS

I sur-ren-der all, I sur-ren-der all;
I sur-ren-der all, I sur-ren-der all;

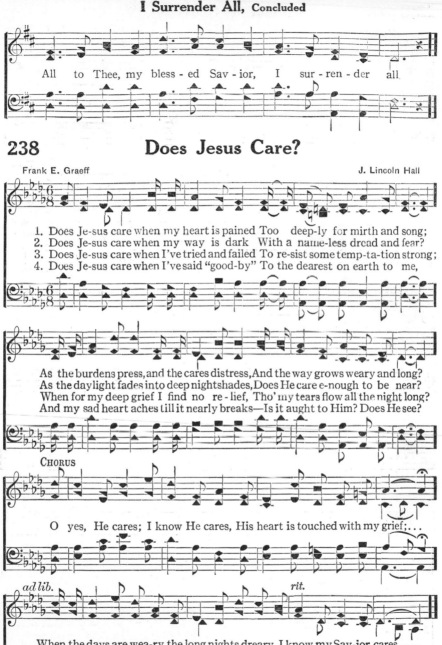

All to Thee, my bless - ed Sav - ior, I sur - ren - der all.

238 **Does Jesus Care?**

Frank E. Graeff   J. Lincoln Hall

1. Does Je-sus care when my heart is pained Too deep-ly for mirth and song;
2. Does Je-sus care when my way is dark With a name-less dread and fear?
3. Does Je-sus care when I've tried and failed To re-sist some temp-ta-tion strong;
4. Does Je-sus care when I've said "good-by" To the dearest on earth to me,

As the burdens press, and the cares distress, And the way grows weary and long?
As the daylight fades into deep night shades, Does He care e-nough to be near?
When for my deep grief I find no re - lief, Tho' my tears flow all the night long?
And my sad heart aches till it nearly breaks—Is it aught to Him? Does He see?

CHORUS

O yes, He cares; I know He cares, His heart is touched with my grief;....

ad lib.   *rit.*

When the days are wea-ry, the long nights dreary, I know my Sav-ior cares.....
He cares.

239   From Every Stormy Wind

(WILDER)

H. Stowell

S. Wilder

OBLIGATO SOLO (Soprano or Tenor)

Accompanying Voices pp

1. From ev - 'ry storm - y wind that blows, From ev - 'ry
2. O let my hand for - get her skill, My tongue be

1. From ev - 'ry storm - y wind that blows, From ev - 'ry
2. O let my hand for - get her skill, My tongue be

swell - ing tide of woes, There is a calm, a
si - - lent, cold and still, This bound - ing heart for-

swell - ing tide of woes, There is a calm, a
si - - lent, cold and still, This bound - ing heart for-

sure re - treat; 'Tis found be - neath the mer - cy - seat.
get to beat, If I for - get the mer - cy - seat.

sure re - treat; 'Tis found be - neath the mer - cy - seat.
get to beat, If I for - get the mer - cy - seat.

240   From Every Stormy Wind

(RETREAT)

Hugh Stowell   Thomas Hastings

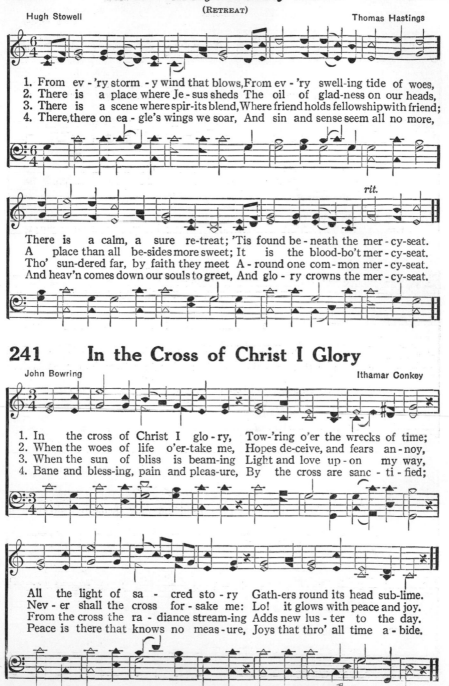

1. From ev-'ry storm-y wind that blows, From ev-'ry swell-ing tide of woes,
2. There is a place where Je-sus sheds The oil of glad-ness on our heads,
3. There is a scene where spir-its blend, Where friend holds fellowship with friend;
4. There, there on ea-gle's wings we soar, And sin and sense seem all no more,

rit.

There is a calm, a sure re-treat; 'Tis found be-neath the mer-cy-seat.
A place than all be-sides more sweet; It is the blood-bo't mer-cy-seat.
Tho' sun-dered far, by faith they meet A-round one com-mon mer-cy-seat.
And heav'n comes down our souls to greet, And glo-ry crowns the mer-cy-seat.

241   In the Cross of Christ I Glory

John Bowring   Ithamar Conkey

1. In the cross of Christ I glo-ry, Tow-'ring o'er the wrecks of time;
2. When the woes of life o'er-take me, Hopes de-ceive, and fears an-noy,
3. When the sun of bliss is beam-ing Light and love up-on my way,
4. Bane and bless-ing, pain and pleas-ure, By the cross are sanc-ti-fied;

All the light of sa-cred sto-ry Gath-ers round its head sub-lime.
Nev-er shall the cross for-sake me: Lo! it glows with peace and joy.
From the cross the ra-diance stream-ing Adds new lus-ter to the day.
Peace is there that knows no meas-ure, Joys that thro' all time a-bide.

242 I Love to Tell the Story

Catherine Hankey

William G. Fischer

1. I love to tell the sto - ry Of un-seen things a-bove, Of Je - sus
2. I love to tell the sto - ry: 'Tis pleas-ant to re-peat What seems, each
3. I love to tell the sto - ry, For those who know it best Seem hun-ger-

and His glo - ry, Of Je - sus and His love; I love to tell the sto - ry
time I tell it, More won-der-ful - ly sweet; I love to tell the sto-ry,
ing and thirst-ing To hear it like the rest; And when, in scenes of glo-ry,

Be-cause I know 'tis true; It sat - is-fies my longings As noth-ing else can do.
For some have never heard The message of sal-va-tion From God's own holy word.
I sing the new, new song, 'Twill be the old, old sto-ry That I have loved so long.

CHORUS

I love to tell the sto - ry! 'Twill be my theme in glo - ry

To tell the old, old sto - ry Of Je - sus and His love.

243   Only in Thee

T. O. Chisholm

Chas. H. Gabriel

1. On-ly in Thee, O Sav-ior mine, Dwell-eth my soul in peace di-vine,
2. On-ly in Thee a ra-diance bright, Shines like a bea-con in the night,
3. On-ly in Thee, when days are drear, When nei-ther sun nor stars ap-pear,
4. On-ly in Thee, dear Sav-ior, slain, Los-ing Thy life my own to gain,

Peace that the world, tho' all com-bine, Nev-er can take from me......
Guid-ing my pil-grim bark a-right, O-ver life's track-less sea......
Still I can trust and feel no fear, Sing when I can-not see......
Trust-ing, I'm cleansed from ev-'ry stain; Thou art my on-ly plea.....

Pleas-ures of earth, so seem-ing-ly sweet, Fail at the last my long-ings to
On-ly in Thee, when trou-bles mo-lest, When with temp-ta-tion I am op-
On-ly in Thee, what-ev-er be-tide, All of my need is free-ly sup-
On-ly in Thee my heart will de-light, Till in that land where com-eth no

meet; On-ly in Thee my bliss is com-plete, On-ly, dear Lord, in Thee!
pressed, There is a sweet pa-vil-ion of rest, On-ly, dear Lord, in Thee!
plied; There is no hope nor helper be-side, On-ly, dear Lord, in Thee!
night Faith will be lost in heav-en-ly sight, On-ly, dear Lord, in Thee!

244 Alone At Eve

Thos. R. Sweatmon

Will W. Slater

Slowly

1. Walk-ing a-lone at eve and view-ing the skies a-far, Bid-ding the
2. Sit-ting a-lone at eve and dream-ing the hours a-way, Watching the
3. Clos-ing my eyes at eve and think-ing of heav-en's grace, Long-ing to

dark-ness come to wel-come each sil-ver star; I have a great de-light
shad-ows fall-ing now at the close of day; God in His mer-cy comes
see my Lord, yes, meet-ing Him face to face; Trust-ing Him as my all

D. S.—Rest for a wea-ry soul

in the won-der-ful scenes a-bove, God in His pow'r and might is
with His word He is draw-ing near, Spread-ing His love and truth a-
where-so-ev-er my foot-steps roam, Plead-ing with Him to guide me

once re-deemed by the Sav-ior's love, Where I'll be pure and whole and

rit. FINE. REFRAIN

show-ing His truth and love.
round me and ev-'ry-where. O! for a home with God, a place in His
on to the spir-it's home!

live with my God a-bove!

D. S.

courts to rest, Sure in a safe a-bode with Je-sus and the blest;

245 There Stands a Rock on Shores of Time

S. S. Journal

T. C. O'Kane

1. There stands a Rock on shores of time, That rears to heav'n its head sub-lime;
2. That Rock's a cross, its arms outspread, Ce - les - tial glo - ry bathes its head;
3. That Rock's a tow'r, whose loft-y height, Il-lumed with heav'n's unclouded light,

That Rock is cleft, and they are blest Who find with-in this cleft a rest:
To its firm base my all I bring, And to the cross of A - ges cling.
Opes wide its gates be-neath the dome, Where saints find rest with Christ at home.

CHORUS

Some build their hopes on the ev - er - drift - ing sand, Some on their

fame or their treas-ure or their land; Mine's on the Rock that for-

ev - er shall stand, Je - sus, the "Rock of A - ges."

246   Jesus, the Loving Shepherd

W. A. O.

W. A. Ogden

1. Je - sus, the lov - ing Shep-herd, Call-eth thee now to come In - to the
2. Je - sus, the lov - ing Shep-herd, Gave His dear life for thee; Ten-der - ly
3. Lin-ger - ing is but fol - ly, Wolves are a-broad to - day, Seek-ing the

fold of safe - ty, Where there is rest and room; Come in the strength of manhood,
now He's call-ing, "Wan-der - er, come to Me;" Haste! for with-out is dan - ger,
sheep who're straying, Seek-ing the lambs to slay; Je - sus, the lov - ing Shep-herd,

Come in the morn of youth, En-ter the fold of safe-ty, En-ter the way of truth.
"Come," cries the Shepherd blest; En-ter the fold of safe-ty, En-ter the place of rest.
Call - eth thee now to come; En-ter the fold of safe-ty, Where there is rest and room.

CHORUS

Lov-ing-ly, ten-der - ly, call-ing is He, "Wan-der-er, wan-der-er, come un-to Me."

rit.

Pa-tient-ly wait-ing, there standing I see Je - sus, my Shep-herd di - vine.

247 We Saw Thee Not

Anne Richter

Knowles Shaw

1. We saw Thee not when Thou didst come To this poor world of sin and death;
2. We saw Thee not when lift - ed high, A - mid that wild and sav-age crew;
3. We gazed not in the o - pen tomb, Where once Thy mangled bod-y lay;
4. We walked not with the cho-sen few, Who saw Thee from the earth as-cend;

Nor yet be - held Thy cot-tage home, In that de - spis - ed Naz - a - reth;
Nor heard we that im - plor-ing cry, "For-give, they know not what they do!"
Nor saw Thee in that "up-per room," Nor met Thee on the o - pen way;
Who raised to heav'n their wond'ring view, Then low to earth all pros-trate bend;

REFRAIN

But we be - lieve Thy foot-steps trod Its streets and plains, Thou Son of God:
But we be - lieve the deed was done, That shook the earth and veiled the sun;
But we be - lieve that an - gels said, "Why seek the liv - ing with the dead?"
But we be - lieve that hu-man eyes Be - held that jour - ney to the skies;

But we be-lieve Thy foot-steps trod Its streets and plains, Thou Son of God.
But we be-lieve the deed was done, That shook the earth and veiled the sun.
But we be-lieve that an - gels said, "Why seek the liv - ing with the dead?"
But we be-lieve that hu-man eyes Be - held that jour - ney to the skies.

248   Follow On

W. O. Cushing   Robert Lowry

1. Down in the val-ley with my Sav-ior I would go, Where the flow'rs are
2. Down in the val-ley with my Sav-ior I would go, Where the storms are
3. Down in the val-ley, or up-on the mountain steep, Close be-side my

bloom-ing and the sweet wa-ters flow; Ev-'ry-where He leads me I would
sweep-ing and the dark wa-ters flow; With His hand to lead me I will
Sav-ior would my soul ev-er keep; He will keep me safe-ly in the

fol-low, fol-low on, Walk-ing in His foot-steps till the crown be won.
nev-er, nev-er fear, Dan-ger can-not fright me if my Lord is near.
path that He has trod, Up to where they gath-er on the hills of God.

REFRAIN

Fol-low! fol-low! I would follow Je-sus! Anywhere, ev'rywhere, I would follow on!

Fol-low! fol-low! I would follow Jesus! Ev'rywhere He leads me I would follow on!

249 The Way of the Cross Leads Home

Jessie Brown Pounds

Chas. H. Gabriel

1. I must needs go home by the way of the cross: There's no oth-er
2. I must needs go on in the blood-sprinkled way, The path that the
3. Then I bid fare-well to the way of the world, To walk in it

way but this; I shall ne'er get sight of the Gates of Light
Sav-ior trod, If I ev-er climb to the heights sub-lime,
nev-er-more; For my Lord says, "Come," and I seek my home,

If the way of the cross I miss.
Where the soul is at home with God.
Where He waits at the o-pen door.

CHORUS

The way of the cross leads home, The way of the cross leads home;
It is sweet to know, as I on-ward go, The way of the cross leads home.

250 There Is a Place of Refuge

T. O. Chisholm

Geo. C. Stebbins

1. There is a place of ref - uge For ev - 'ry trou - bled soul
2. There, heav - y loads are lift - ed; There, mys - t'ries dark grow plain;
3. There, One is al - ways with us, The Friend all friends a - bove,

Where tem - pests beat no lon - ger, Where bil - lows cease to roll;
There, pain and care for - get - ting, Sad fac - es smile a - gain;
The Christ who died to save us, Whom, though not seen, we love;

A calm and qui - et ha - ven, A har - bor safe and blest,
There bro - ken lives find heal - ing; There, sor - row's tears are dried;
O pre - cious, pre - cious Ref - uge! How dark this world would be

Where storm-tossed barques may an - chor, Where wea - ry hearts may rest.
There, all the soul's deep long - ings Are ful - ly sat - is - fied.
If, when its woes o'er - take us, We could not hide in Thee.

REFRAIN

Rock of A - ges, cleft for me, Let me hide my - self in Thee.

251 Rock in the Desert

F. M. D.

Frank M. Davis

1. O Rock in the des-ert, I fly un-to Thee, When tem-pest and
2. O Rock in the des-ert, my ref-uge and all, I hide in my
3. O Rock in the des-ert that gives per-fect peace, That bring-eth a

storms sweep the sky, I hide in the cleft that was riv-en for me,
weak-ness in Thee; Thy love is a shield and I find sweet re-pose,
joy to my soul; I rest in Thy shad-ow, I hide in Thy cleft,

CHORUS

For safe-ty on Thee I re-ly.
Where grace is a-bun-dant and free. O Rock in the des-ert, I'm
Thy love doth my spir-it con-trol.

hid-ing in Thee, Till the storms of life's jour-ney are past; Thou Rock of my

ref-uge, my soul safe-ly keep, O re-ceive it in heav-en at last.

252 More Like Jesus

J. M. S.

J. M. Stillman

1. I want to be more like Je - sus, And fol - low Him day by day;
2. I want to be kind and gen - tle To those who are in dis - tress;
3. I want to be meek and low - ly, Like Je - sus, our Friend and King;

I want to be true and faith - ful, And ev - 'ry com-mand o - bey.
To com-fort the bro - ken - heart - ed With sweet words of ten-der - ness.
I want to be strong and ear - nest, And souls to the Sav - ior bring.

REFRAIN

More and more like Je - sus, I would ev - er be; ....
ev - er be;

More and more like Je - sus, My Sav - ior who died for me.

253 O for a Faith!

W. H. Bathurst

L. O. Sanderson

1. O for a faith that will not shrink, Tho' pressed by ev - 'ry foe;
2. That will not mur - mur or com-plain Be-neath the chas-t'ning rod,
3. Lord, give us such a faith as this; And, then, what-e'er may come,

O for a Faith, Concluded

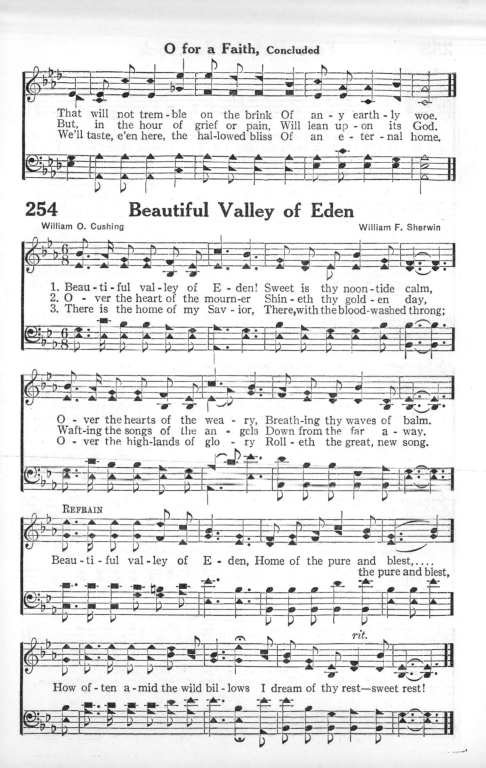

That will not trem-ble on the brink Of an-y earth-ly woe.
But, in the hour of grief or pain, Will lean up-on its God.
We'll taste, e'en here, the hal-lowed bliss Of an e-ter-nal home.

254 Beautiful Valley of Eden

William O. Cushing

William F. Sherwin

1. Beau-ti-ful val-ley of E-den! Sweet is thy noon-tide calm,
2. O-ver the heart of the mourn-er Shin-eth thy gold-en day,
3. There is the home of my Sav-ior, There, with the blood-washed throng;

O-ver the hearts of the wea-ry, Breath-ing thy waves of balm.
Waft-ing the songs of the an-gels Down from the far a-way.
O-ver the high-lands of glo-ry Roll-eth the great, new song.

REFRAIN

Beau-ti-ful val-ley of E-den, Home of the pure and blest,....
the pure and blest,

How of-ten a-mid the wild bil-lows I dream of thy rest—sweet rest!

255 Fear Not, Little Flock

Mrs. M. A. Kidder

J. G. Dailey

1. Fear not, lit - tle flock, says the Sav - ior di - vine; The Fa - ther has
2. Far whit - er than snow, and as fair as the day, For Christ is the
3. Ride o - ver temp - ta - tion and cease your a - larms: Your Shep - herd is

willed that the king - dom be thine; O soil not your gar-ments with
foun - tain to wash guilt a - way; O give Him, poor sin - ner, that
Je - sus, your ref - uge His arms; He'll nev - er for - sake you, a

sin here be - low: My sheep and my lambs must be whit - er than snow.
bur - den of thine, And en - ter the fold with the nine - ty - and-nine.
Broth-er and Friend, But love you and save you in worlds with-out end.

CHORUS

Whit - - - er than snow,   Whit - - - er than
Whiter than the snow,   I long to be, dear Savior, Whiter than the snow,

snow,   Whit - - - er than snow.
I long to be,   Whit-er than the snow, yes,   Whit-er than the snow.

256 Where the Gates Swing Outward Never

C. H. G.   Chas. H. Gabriel

1. Just a few more days to be filled with praise, And to tell the
2. Just a few more years with their toil and tears, And the jour-ney
3. Tho' the hills be steep and the val-leys deep, With no flow'rs my
4. What a joy 'twill be when I wake to see Him for whom my

old, old sto-ry; Then, when twi-light falls, and my Sav-ior calls,
will be end-ed; Then I'll be with Him, where the tide of time
way a-dorn-ing; Tho' the night be lone and my rest a stone,
heart is burn-ing! Nev-er-more to sigh, nev-er-more to die—

I shall go to Him in glo-ry.
With e-ter-ni-ty is blend-ed.
Joy a-waits me in the morn-ing.
For that day my heart is yearn-ing.

CHORUS

I'll ex-change my cross for a
star-ry crown, Where the gates swing out-ward nev-er; At His feet I'll
lay ev-'ry bur-den down, And with Je-sus reign for-ev-er.

257 Beulah Land

Edgar Page

Jno. R. Sweney

1. I've reached the land of corn and wine, And all its rich - es free - ly mine;
2. My Sav - ior comes and walks with me, And sweet com-mun-ion here have we;
3. A sweet per-fume up - on the breeze Is borne from ev - er - ver-nal trees,

Here shines undimmed one bliss-ful day, For all my night has passed a-way.
He gen - tly leads me by His hand, For this is heav-en's bor-der-land.
And flow'rs that, nev - er - fad - ing, grow Where streams of life for - ev - er flow.

CHORUS

O Beu - lah Land, sweet Beu-lah Land, As on thy high-est mount I stand,

I look a - way a - cross the sea, Where man-sions are pre-pared for me,

And view the shin - ing glo - ry-shore, My heav'n, my home for - ev - er-more!

258   I Want to Be a Worker

I. B.

I. Baltzell

1. I want to be a work-er for the Lord; I want to love and trust His
2. I want to be a work-er ev-'ry day; I want to lead the err-ing
3. I want to be a work-er strong and brave; I want to trust in Je-sus'

ho-ly word; I want to sing and pray, and be bus-y ev-'ry day,
in the way That leads to heav'n a-bove, where all is peace and love,
pow'r to save; All who will tru-ly come shall find a hap-py home,

Chorus

In the vine-yard of the Lord.   I will work,   I will pray,
In the king-dom of the Lord.
In the king-dom of the Lord.   I will work and pray, I will work and pray,

In the vine-yard, in the vine-yard of the Lord;   I will work,
of the Lord;

I will pray, I will la-bor ev-'ry day, In the vine-yard of the Lord.

259 There Will Be Light

Jennie Wilson

A. J. Showalter

1. Aft - er the life-paths we're tread-ing End up - on time's sol - emn shore,
2. There will be light for the wea - ry Who thro' sore tri - als have passed—
3. There will be light for the faith - ful, What-e'er the way they have trod—

There will be light at the riv - er While the re-deemed ones pass o'er.
Ra - di - ant light as they en - ter, Peace that for - ev - er shall last.
Glo - ri - ous light sent to guide them Safe to the cit - y of God.

REFRAIN

There............ will be light at the riv - er, There............
There will be light, bless - ed light at the riv - er, There will be light,

will be light at the riv - er, There............ will be
bless - ed light at the riv - er, There will be light, bless - ed

light at the riv - er, While the re-deemed ones pass o'er.........
pass o'er.

260 Savior Divine, Dwell in My Heart

G. C. T.

Grant Colfax Tullar

1. Lord, in Thy mer - cy, lend ear to my plea, Turn not a-
2. Test me and try me, O Sav - ior di - vine! Let me be
3. Dwell in me, Sav - ior, nor ev - er de - part! Ful - ly Thine

way, nor de - ny; May Thy word ev - er dwell rich - ly in me,
filled with Thy love; Then from my heart shall Thy glo - ry - light shine,
own I would be; Naught but Thy wis-dom shall rule in my heart,

CHORUS

Hear Thou and an - swer my cry.
Light - ing the path - way a - bove. Lord, I would keep soul and
Till Thy dear face I shall see.

bod - y for Thee, No room for self or for sin shall there be; Fit for Thy

dwell - ing, for Thee set a - part— Sav - ior di - vine, dwell in my heart.

261 Sweeter As the Years Go By

Copyright, 1940, by Mrs. W. R. Lunk. Renewal
Nazarene Publishing House, owner

Mrs. C. H. M.

Mrs. C. H. Morris

DUET

1. Of Je - sus' love that sought me, When I was lost in sin; Of won-drous
2. He trod in old Ju - de - a Life's path-way long a - go; The peo - ple
3. 'Twas wondrous love which led Him For us to suf - fer loss— To bear with-

grace that brought me Back to His fold a - gain; Of heights and depths of
thronged a-bout Him, His sav - ing grace to know; He healed the bro - ken-
out a mur - mur The an - guish of the cross; With saints re-deemed in

mer - cy, Far deep - er than the sea, And high - er than the heav-ens,
heart-ed, And caused the blind to see; And still His great heart yearn-eth
glo - ry, Let us our voic-es raise, Till heav'n and earth re - ech - o

CHORUS

My theme shall ev - er be. Sweet-er as the years go by,........
In love for e - ven me.
With our Re-deem-er's praise. Sweet - er as the years go by, 'Tis

Sweet-er as the years go by; Rich - er, full - er, deep - er,
Sweet - er as the years go by;

rit.

Je - sus' love is sweet - er, Sweet - er as the years go by.

262 Soul, a Savior Thou Art Needing

Jessie Brown Pounds

J. H. Fillmore

1. Soul, a Sav - ior thou art need ing! Soul, a Sav - ior waits for thee!
2. He has died for thy trans-gres-sion, If thou wilt, thou canst be free;
3. Do not lin - ger till the mor - row, Let thy lov - ing an - swer be,

Hear His words of ten - der plead-ing, Hear His gra - cious "Come to Me."
Soul, He waits for thy con - fes - sion, "Sav - ior, I will go to Thee."
"Sav - ior, in my joy or sor - row, I will ev - er go to Thee."

CHORUS

He is call - ing, soft-ly call - ing, On thine ear.... His voice is fall - ing;
He is call-ing, soft-ly call-ing, On thine ear His voice is fall - ing;

He is call - ing, soft-ly call - ing, "Come to Me..... and be at rest."
He is call-ing, soft-ly call-ing, "Come to Me and be at rest."

263 The Cross Is Not Greater

B. B.

Ballington Booth

1. The cross that He gave may be heav-y, But it ne'er out-weighs His grace;
2. The thorns in my path are not sharp-er Than composed His crown for me,
3. His will I have joy in ful - fill - ing; I am walk-ing in the light;

The storm that I feared may surround me, But it ne'er ex-cludes His face.
The cup that I drink not more bit - ter Than He drank in Geth-sem-a - ne.
My all to the Lord I am bring-ing, He a - lone can keep me right.

CHORUS

The cross is not great - er than His grace, The storm can-not

hide His bless - ed face; I am sat - is - fied to know

That with Je - sus here be - low, I can con-quer ev - 'ry foe.

264   # Gathering Home

Miss M. B. Slade   R. M. McIntosh

1. Up to the boun-ti-ful Giv-er of life, Gath-er-ing home! Gath-er-ing home!
2. Up to the cit-y where fall-eth no night, Gath-er-ing home! Gath-er-ing home!
3. Up to the beau-ti-ful man-sions a-bove, Gath-er-ing home! Gath-er-ing home!

Up to the dwell-ing where cometh no strife, The dear ones are gath-er-ing home.
Up where the Sav-ior's own face is the light, The dear ones are gath-er-ing home.
Safe in the arms of His in-fi-nite love, The dear ones are gath-er-ing home.

CHORUS

Gath-er-ing home!.......... Gath-er-ing home!............ Nev-er to
Gath-er-ing home!   Gath-er-ing home!

sor-row more, nev-er to roam; Gath-er-ing home!.................
Gath-er-ing home!

Gath-er-ing home!............. God's chil-dren are gath-er-ing home.
Gath-er-ing home!

265 Face to Face

Mrs. Frank A. Breck

Grant Colfax Tullar

1. Face to face with Christ my Sav - ior, Face to face—what will it be,
2. On - ly faint - ly now I see Him, With the dark-ling veil be-tween;
3. What re - joic - ing in His pres - ence, When are ban-ished grief and pain,
4. Face to face! O bliss-ful mo - ment! Face to face—to see and know;

When with rap-ture I be-hold Him, Je - sus Christ who died for me?
But a bless-ed day is com - ing, When His glo - ry shall be seen.
When the crook-ed ways are straightened, And the dark things shall be plain!
Face to face with my Re-deem - er, Je - sus Christ, who loves me so.

CHORUS

Face to face shall I be-hold Him, Far be-yond the star-ry sky;....

Face to face, in all His glo - ry, I shall see Him by and by.

266 When My Love to Christ Grows Weak

J. R. Wreford

Mrs. Jos. F. Knapp

1. When my love to Christ grows weak, When for deep - er faith I seek,
2. When my love for man grows weak, When for strong - er faith I seek,
3. Then to life I turn a - gain, Learn-ing all the worth of pain;

When My Love, Concluded

Then in thought I go to Thee, Gar-den of Geth-sem-a-ne!
Hill of Cal-va-ry! I go To thy scenes of fear and woe.
Learn-ing all the might that lies In a full self-sac-ri-fice.

267 The Haven of Rest

H. L. Gilmour

George D. Moore

1. My soul in sad ex-ile was out on life's sea, So bur-dened with
2. I yield-ed my-self to His ten-der em-brace, And faith tak-ing
3. The song of my soul, since the Lord made me whole, Has been the old

sin and dis-trest: I heard a sweet voice say-ing,"Make me your choice;"
hold of the word, My fet-ters fell off, and I an-chored my soul:
sto-ry so blest, Of Je-sus who'll save who-so-ev-er will have

D. S.—*The tem-pest may sweep o'er the wild storm-y deep:*

CHORUS

I en-tered the Ha-ven of Rest.
The Ha-ven of Rest is my Lord.
A home in the Ha-ven of Rest.

I've an-chored my

In Je-sus I'm safe ev-er-more.

soul in the Ha-ven of Rest; I'll sail the wide seas no more;

D. S.

268　O What Will You Do with Jesus?

Nathaniel Norton

Geo. C. Stebbins

1. O　what will you do　with Je - sus? The　call comes low and　sweet;
2. O　what will you do　with Je - sus? The　call comes loud and　clear;
3. O　think of the King　of　Glo - ry　From heav'n to　earth come down,

As　ten - der - ly　He bids you　Your bur - dens lay at His　feet;
The　sol - emn words are sound - ing　In　ev - 'ry lis - t'ning ear;
His　life　so　pure and ho - ly,　His death, His　cross, His　crown;

O　soul so sad　and wea - ry,　That　sweet voice speaks to　thee;
Im - mor - tal life's in the ques - tion, And joy thro' e - ter - ni - ty;
Of　His　di - vine com - pas - sion, His　sac - ri - fice for　thee;

FINE.

Then what will you do with Je - sus? O what shall the an - swer be?

D. S.—*What will you do with Je - sus? O what shall the an - swer be?*

REFRAIN

D. S.

What shall the an - swer be?　　What shall the an - swer be?

269 Leading Me

Myrtle Jordan

Geo. C. Stebbins

1. I do not ask that I may know The way that Christ would have me go;
2. I do not ask the way be bright, I on-ly ask Him for the light;
3. I do not ask where I am led, I on-ly ask for grace in-stead;

Each step I take, He's by my side, A lov-ing, help-ing, ten-der guide;
All shad-ows flee when He is near, And safe I walk with-out a fear;
His ten-der touch, His guid-ing hand, Will lead me to the prom-ised land;

He leads the way, I can-not stray, For He is with me night and day.
Se-cure am I from all a-larm, With Christ I'm safe from ev-'ry harm.
Where I may rest in peace at last, With all my pain and sor-row past.

CHORUS

Lead-ing me, lead-ing me, Christ is lead-ing me;

Dark or light, day or night, He is lead-ing me.

270 Nailed to the Cross

Mrs. Frank A. Breck

Grant Colfax Tullar

DUET *ad lib.*

1. There was One who was will-ing to die in my stead, That a soul so un-
2. He is ten-der and lov-ing and pa-tient with me, While He cleans-es my
3. I will cling to my Sav-ior and nev-er de-part, I will joy-ful-ly

wor-thy might live; And the path to the cross He was will-ing to tread,
heart of its dross, But "there's no con-dem-na-tion"—I know I am free,
jour-ney each day, With a song on my lips and a song in my heart,

All the sins of my life to for-give.
For my sins are all nailed to the cross.
That my sins have been tak-en a-way.

CHORUS

They are nailed to the cross! They are
nailed to the cross! O how much He was will-ing to bear! With what an-guish and

rit.

loss, Je-sus went to the cross! But He car-ried my sins with Him there.

271   I Am Resolved

Palmer Hartsough

J. H. Fillmore

1. I am re-solved no lon - ger to lin - ger, Charmed by the
2. I am re-solved to go to the Sav - ior, Leav - ing my
3. I am re-solved to fol - low the Sav - ior, Faith - ful and
4. I am re-solved to en - ter the king - dom, Leav - ing the

world's de - light; Things that are high - er, things that are no - bler,
sin and strife; He is the true One, He is the just One,
true each day, Heed what He say - eth, do what He will - eth,
paths of sin; Friends may op - pose me, foes may be - set me,

Chorus

These have al - lured my sight.
He hath the words of life.   I will has - ten to Him
He is the liv - ing way.
Still will I en - ter in.   I will has - ten, has - ten to Him,

Has - ten so glad and free,
Has - ten glad and free,

Je - sus, sus, great - est, high - est, I will come to Thee.
Je - sus, Je - sus,

272 In the Morning of Joy

Mrs. R. A. Evilsizer

A. J. Showalter

1. When the trumpet shall sound, And the dead shall a - rise, And the splendors im-
2. When the King shall ap-pear, In His beau-ty on high, And shall summon His
3. O   the bliss of that morn When our loved ones we meet, With the songs of the

mor - tal Shall en - vel - ope the skies, When the an - gel of death Shall no
chil - dren To the courts of the sky, Shall the cause of the Lord Have been
ran-somed We each oth - er shall greet, Sing - ing praise to the Lamb, Thro' e-

lon - ger de-stroy, And the dead shall a - wak-en In the morn-ing of joy.
all your em-ploy, That your soul may be spot-less In the morn-ing of joy?
ter - ni-ty's years, With the past all for-got-ten With its sor-rows and tears.

REFRAIN

In the morn-ing of joy, In the morn-ing of joy, We'll be gath-ered to

1.
glo - ry In the morn-ing of joy;

2.
In the morn-ing of joy.

273 O to Be Like Thee!

T. O. Chisholm

Wm. J. Kirkpatrick

1. O to be like Thee! blessed Redeemer: This is my constant
2. O to be like Thee! full of compassion, Loving, forgiving,
3. O to be like Thee! lowly in spirit, Holy and harmless,
4. O to be like Thee! Lord, I am coming, Now to receive th'a-

longing and prayer; Gladly I'll forfeit all of earth's treasures,
tender and kind, Helping the helpless, cheering the fainting,
patient and brave; Meekly enduring cruel reproaches,
nointing divine; All that I am and have I am bringing;

Jesus, Thy perfect likeness to wear.
Seeking the wandering sinner to find.
Willing to suffer, others to save.
Lord, from this moment all shall be Thine.

CHORUS

O to be like Thee!

O to be like Thee! Blessed Redeemer, pure as Thou art; Come in Thy

rit.

sweetness, come in Thy fulness; Stamp Thine own image deep on my heart.

274 Shall We Gather At the River?

R. L.
Robert Lowry

1. Shall we gath-er at the riv - er, Where bright an - gel feet have trod,
2. Ere we reach the shin-ing riv - er, Lay we ev - 'ry bur-den down;
3. Soon we'll reach the sil - ver riv - er, Soon our pil-grim-age will cease;

With its crys - tal tide for - ev - er Flow-ing by the throne of God?
Grace our spir - its will de - liv - er, And pro-vide a robe and crown.
Soon our hap - py hearts will quiv-er With the mel - o - dy of peace.

Chorus

Yes, we'll gath-er at the riv - er, The beau-ti - ful, the beau-ti - ful riv - er,

Gath-er with the saints at the riv - er, That flows by the throne of God.

275 Blessed Be the Name

W. H. Clark
Arranged

1. All praise to Him who reigns a-bove, In maj - es - ty su-preme; Who gave His
2. His name a - bove all names shall stand, Ex-alt - ed more and more, At God the
3. Re - deem-er, Sav - ior, Friend of man Once ru-ined by the fall; Thou hast de-

Blessed Be the Name, Concluded

Son for man to die, That He might man re-deem.
Father's own right hand Where an-gel hosts a - dore. ||: Bless-ed be the name,
vised sal-va-tion's plan, For Thou hast died for all.

bless-ed be the name, Bless-ed be the name of the Lord; :|| of the Lord.

276 Thou Thinkest, Lord, of Me

E. S. L.

E. S. Lorenz

1. A - mid the tri - als which I meet, A - mid the thorns which pierce my feet,
2. The cares of life come throng-ing fast, Up - on my soul their shad-ow cast;
3. Let shad-ows come, let shad-ows go, Let life be bright or dark with woe,

FINE

One thought re-mains su - preme-ly sweet, Thou think-est, Lord, of me!
Their gloom re-minds my heart at last, Thou think-est, Lord, of me!
I am con-tent, for this I know, Thou think-est, Lord, of me!

D.S.—*What need I fear when Thou art near And think-est, Lord, of me?*

CHORUS

D. S.

Thou think-est, Lord, of me (of me), Thou think-est, Lord, of me (of me);

277 Hiding In Thee

William O. Cushing

Ira D. Sankey

1. O safe to the Rock that is high-er than I, My soul in its
2. In calm of the noon-tide, in sor-row's lone hour, In times when temp-
3. How oft in the con-flict, when pressed by the foe, I've fled to my

con-flicts and sor-rows would fly; So sin-ful, so wea-ry, Thine,
ta-tion casts o'er me its pow'r, In tem-pests of life, on its
Ref-uge and breathed out my woe; How of-ten, when tri-als like

Thine would I be; Thou blest Rock of A-ges, I'm hid-ing in Thee.
wide, heav-ing sea, Thou blest Rock of A-ges, I'm hid-ing in Thee.
sea-bil-lows roll, I've hid-den in Thee, O Thou Rock of my soul.

CHORUS

Hid-ing in Thee, Hid-ing in Thee; Thou blest Rock of A-ges, I'm hid-ing in Thee.

278 Work for Jesus

J. H. Martin

R. M. McIntosh

1. Hear the voice of Je-sus say, Loud-ly cry-ing un-to all,
2. Why, He asks, thro' all the day, Stand ye i-dle, noth-ing do?
3. Thro' the long and toil-some day, 'Neath a blaz-ing, burn-ing sun,

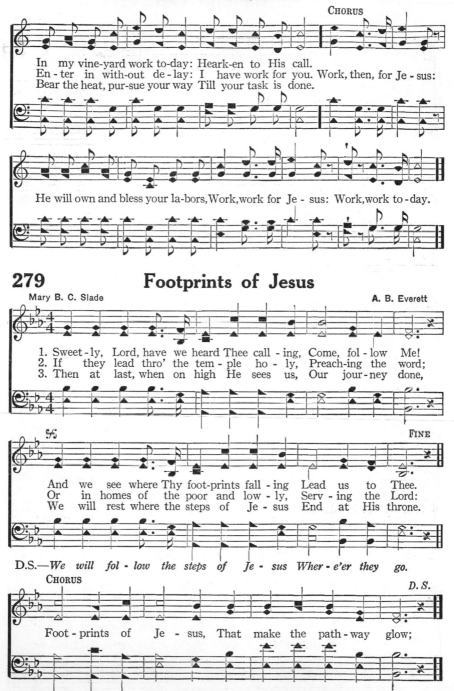

Work for Jesus, Concluded

CHORUS

In my vine-yard work to-day: Heark-en to His call.
En - ter in with-out de - lay: I have work for you. Work, then, for Je - sus:
Bear the heat, pur-sue your way Till your task is done.

He will own and bless your la-bors, Work, work for Je - sus: Work, work to - day.

279 Footprints of Jesus

Mary B. C. Slade

A. B. Everett

1. Sweet - ly, Lord, have we heard Thee call - ing, Come, fol - low Me!
2. If they lead thro' the tem - ple ho - ly, Preach-ing the word;
3. Then at last, when on high He sees us, Our jour-ney done,

FINE

And we see where Thy foot-prints fall - ing Lead us to Thee.
Or in homes of the poor and low - ly, Serv - ing the Lord:
We will rest where the steps of Je - sus End at His throne.

D.S.—*We will fol - low the steps of Je - sus Wher - e'er they go.*

CHORUS

D. S.

Foot - prints of Je - sus, That make the path - way glow;

280 Tell Me the Old, Old Story

Kate Hankey

W. H. Doane

1. Tell me the old, old Sto - ry, Of un-seen things a - bove, Of Je - sus
2. Tell me the sto - ry slow - ly, That I may take it in— That won-der-
3. Tell me the sto - ry soft - ly, With ear-nest tones and grave; Re - mem - ber

and His glo - ry, Of Je - sus and His love; Tell me the sto - ry
ful re - demp - tion, God's rem-e - dy for sin; Tell me the sto - ry
I'm the sin - ner Whom Je - sus came to save; Tell me the sto - ry

sim - ply, As to a lit - tle child, For I am weak and wea - ry, And
of - ten, For I for - get so soon: The "ear-ly dew" of morn-ing Has
al - ways, If you would real-ly be, In an - y time of trou - ble, A

m Chorus *f*

help - less and de - filed.
passed a - way at noon. Tell me the old, old Sto - ry, Tell me the old, old
com - fort-er to me.

ff

Sto - ry, Tell me the old, old Sto - ry Of Je - sus and His love.

281   How Happy Are They

Charles Wesley   Arr. Lowell Mason

1. How hap-py are they who their Sav-ior o-bey, And have laid up their
2. 'Tis a heav-en be-low my Re-deem-er to know; And the an-gels can
3. Now my rem-nant of days will I spend to His praise, Who has died, me from

treas-ures a-bove! Tongue can-not ex-press the sweet com-fort and peace
do noth-ing more Than to fall at His feet, and the sto-ry re-peat,
sin to re-deem; Whether man-y or few, all my years are His due—

Of a soul in its ear-li-est love, Of a soul in its ear-li-est love.
And the Lov-er of sin-ners a-dore, And the Lov-er of sin-ners a-dore.
They shall all be de-vot-ed to Him, They shall all be de-vot-ed to Him.

282   Thou Art the Way

G. W. Doane   Arr. by L. O. S.   James Walch

1. Thou art the Way, to Thee a-lone, From sin and death we flee;
2. Thou art the Truth: Thy word a-lone True wis-dom can im-part;
3. Thou art the Way, the Truth, the Life: Grant us that way to know,

And he who would the Fa-ther seek, Must seek Him, Lord, by Thee.
Thou on-ly canst in-struct the mind, And pu-ri-fy the heart.
That truth to keep, that life to win, Whose joys e-ter-nal flow.

283 Saved to the Uttermost

W. J. K.

W. J. Kirkpatrick

1. Saved to the ut-ter-most: I am the Lord's; Je - sus, my Sav - ior, re - demp - tion af - fords; He, with my spir - it, a wit - ness with - in, Whis - pers of par - don, sal - va - tion from sin.

2. Saved to the ut-ter-most: Je - sus is near; Keep-ing me safe - ly, He cast - eth out fear; Trust-ing His prom - is - es, now I am blest; Lean - ing up - on Him, how sweet is my rest.

3. Saved to the ut-ter-most; cheer-ful-ly sing Glo - ry and hon - or to Je - sus, my King; Ran-somed and par-doned, re-deemed by the Lord; Cleansed from un-right-eous-ness; led by the word.

REFRAIN

Saved, saved, saved to the ut-ter-most, Saved, saved by pow-er di-vine;

Saved, saved, saved to the ut-ter-most: Je-sus, the Sav-ior is mine!

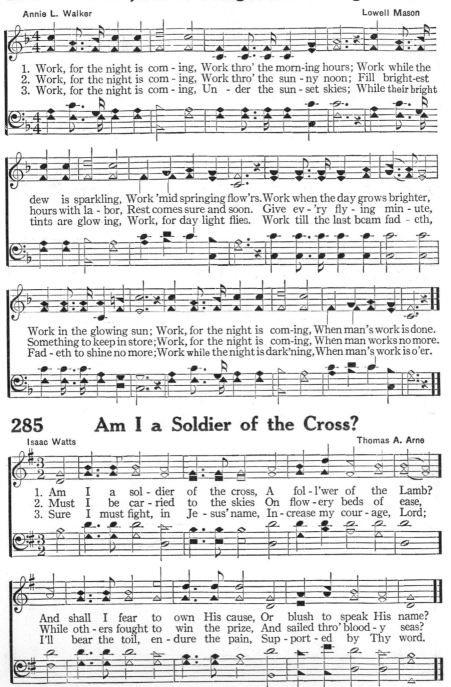

284 Work, for the Night Is Coming

Annie L. Walker

Lowell Mason

1. Work, for the night is com - ing, Work thro' the morn-ing hours; Work while the
2. Work, for the night is com - ing, Work thro' the sun - ny noon; Fill bright-est
3. Work, for the night is com - ing, Un - der the sun - set skies; While their bright

dew is sparkling, Work 'mid springing flow'rs. Work when the day grows brighter,
hours with la - bor, Rest comes sure and soon. Give ev - 'ry fly - ing min - ute,
tints are glow-ing, Work, for day light flies. Work till the last beam fad - eth,

Work in the glowing sun; Work, for the night is com-ing, When man's work is done.
Something to keep in store; Work, for the night is com-ing, When man works no more.
Fad - eth to shine no more; Work while the night is dark'ning, When man's work is o'er.

285 Am I a Soldier of the Cross?

Isaac Watts

Thomas A. Arne

1. Am I a sol - dier of the cross, A fol-l'wer of the Lamb?
2. Must I be car - ried to the skies On flow-ery beds of ease,
3. Sure I must fight, in Je - sus' name, In - crease my cour - age, Lord;

And shall I fear to own His cause, Or blush to speak His name?
While oth - ers fought to win the prize, And sailed thro' blood - y seas?
I'll bear the toil, en - dure the pain, Sup - port - ed by Thy word.

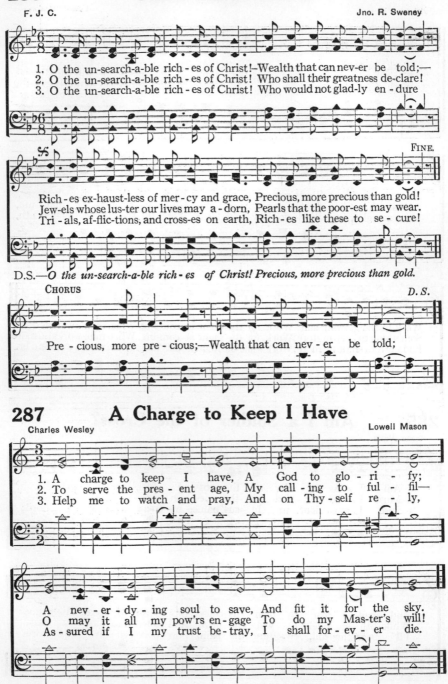

286 Unsearchable Riches

F. J. C.

Jno. R. Sweney

1. O the un-search-a-ble rich-es of Christ!—Wealth that can nev-er be told;—
2. O the un-search-a-ble rich-es of Christ! Who shall their greatness de-clare!
3. O the un-search-a-ble rich-es of Christ! Who would not glad-ly en-dure

Rich-es ex-haust-less of mer-cy and grace, Precious, more precious than gold!
Jew-els whose lus-ter our lives may a-dorn, Pearls that the poor-est may wear.
Tri-als, af-flic-tions, and cross-es on earth, Rich-es like these to se-cure!

FINE.

D.S.—*O the un-search-a-ble rich-es of Christ! Precious, more precious than gold.*

CHORUS

D. S.

Pre-cious, more pre-cious;—Wealth that can nev-er be told;

287 A Charge to Keep I Have

Charles Wesley

Lowell Mason

1. A charge to keep I have, A God to glo-ri-fy;
2. To serve the pres-ent age, My call-ing to ful-fil—
3. Help me to watch and pray, And on Thy-self re-ly,

A nev-er-dy-ing soul to save, And fit it for the sky.
O may it all my pow'rs en-gage To do my Mas-ter's will!
As-sured if I my trust be-tray, I shall for-ev-er die.

Never Grow Old

J. C. M.

Jas. C. Moore

1. I have heard of a land on the far a-way strand, 'Tis a beau-ti-ful
2. In that beau-ti-ful home where we'll nev-er-more roam, We shall be in the
3. When our work here is done and the life-crown is won, And our trou-bles and

home of the soul; Built by Je-sus on high, where we nev-er shall die,
sweet by and by; Hap-py praise to the King tho' e-ter-ni-ty sing,
tri-als are o'er; All our sor-row will end, and our voic-es will blend,

'Tis a land where we nev-er grow old. Nev-er grow old,
'Tis a land where we nev-er shall die.
With the loved ones who've gone on be-fore.

Where'll we'll

REFRAIN

Nev-er grow old, In a land where we'll nev-er grow old; Nev-er grow

old, nev-er grow old, In a land where we'll nev-er grow old.

where we'll

289 Pray All the Time

Vana R. Raye

L. O. Sanderson

1. The world has lost the right of prayer, And saints have failed to pray;
2. The Fa-ther speak-eth in His word—He talks no oth-er way!
3. There is no tri-al, grief, or pain, No mo-ment of the day,

What loss sus-tained be-yond re-pair! How blind of heart are they!
And to con-verse with Him, our Lord, We must take time to pray!
But that we may in Je-sus' name In-cline our souls and pray!

CHORUS

{ Pray in the Morn-ing,
{ Pray when you're hap-py,

Pray at the Noon-time,
Pray when in sor-row,

Regular parts

{ Pray in the Morn - - ing,
{ Pray when you're hap - - py,

Pray at the Noon - - time,
Pray when in sor - - row,

Special Bass Lead

Pray in the Eve-ning, Pray an-y-time;
Pray when you're tempted, (*Omit . . . .*) Pray all the time.

Pray in the Eve - - ning, Pray an-y-time;
Pray when you're tempt - ed, (*Omit . . . . .*) Pray all the time.

290 Wonderful Peace

W. D. Cornell. Alt.

W. G. Cooper

1. Far a-way in the depths of my spir-it to-night Rolls a
2. What a treas-ure I have in this won-der-ful peace, Bur-ied
3. And I think when I rise to that Cit-y of peace, Where the

mel-o-dy sweet-er than psalm; In ce-les-tial-like strains it un-
deep in the heart of my soul; So se-cure that no pow-er can
Au-thor of peace I shall see, That one strain of the song which the

ceas-ing-ly falls O'er my soul like an in-fi-nite calm.
mine it a-way, While the years of e-ter-ni-ty roll!
ran-somed will sing In that heav-en-ly king-dom will be:

CHORUS

Peace! peace! won-der-ful peace, Coming down from the Fa-ther a-bove; Sweep

o-ver my spir-it for-ev-er, I pray, In fath-om-less bil-lows of love.

291 I'm Going Home

Wm. Hunter

Wm. Miller

1. { My heav'n-ly home is bright and fair; Nor pain nor death can en-ter there; }
{ Its glit-t'ring tow'rs the sun out-shine; That heav'nly man-sion shall be mine. }

2. { My Fa-ther's house is built on high, Far, far a-bove the star-ry sky; }
{ When from this earth-ly pris-on free, That heav'nly man-sion mine shall be. }

3. { Let oth-ers seek a home be-low, Which flames devour, or waves o'erflow; }
{ Be mine the hap-pier lot to own A heav'n-ly man-sion near the throne. }

CHORUS

{ I'm go-ing home, I'm go-ing home, I'm go-ing home to die no more; }
{ To die no more, to die no more, I'm go-ing home to die no more. }

292 'Tis So Sweet to Trust in Jesus

Louisa M. R. Stead

Wm. J. Kirkpatrick

1. 'Tis so sweet to trust in Je-sus, Just to take Him at His word,
2. O how sweet to trust in Je-sus, Just to trust His cleans-ing blood,
3. Yes, 'tis sweet to trust in Je-sus, Just from sin and self to cease,
4. I'm so glad I learned to trust Thee, Pre-cious Je-sus, Sav-ior, Friend;

Just to rest up-on His prom-ise, Just to know, "Thus saith the Lord."
Just in sim-ple faith to plunge me 'Neath the heal-ing, cleans-ing flood.
Just from Je-sus sim-ply tak-ing Life and rest, and joy and peace.
And I know that Thou art with me, Wilt be with me to the end.

CHORUS

Je-sus, Je-sus, how I trust Him! How I've proved Him o'er and o'er!

Je - sus, Je - sus, pre - cious Je - sus! O for grace to trust Him more!

293 Though Your Sins Be As Scarlet

Fanny J. Crosby

William H. Doane

1. "Tho' your sins be as scar-let, They shall be as white as snow; as snow;
2. Hear the voice that en-treats you: Oh, re - turn ye un - to God! to God!
3. He'll for-give your transgressions, And re-mem-ber them no more; no more;

Tho' they be red............... like crim - son, They shall be as wool;"
He is of great............... com-pas - sion, And of won-drous love;
"Look un - to Me............... ye peo - ple," Saith the Lord your God;

Tho' they be red,

"Tho' your sins be as scar - let, Tho' your sins be as scar - let,
Hear the voice that en-treats you, Hear the voice that en-treats you,
He'll for - give your trans-gres-sions, He'll for - give your trans-gres-sions,

They shall be as white as snow, They shall be as white as snow."
Oh, re - turn ye un - to God! Oh, re - turn ye un - to God!
And re - mem - ber them no more, And re - mem - ber them no more.

294 True-Hearted, Whole-Hearted

Frances R. Havergal

Geo. C. Stebbins

1. True-heart-ed, whole-heart-ed, faith-ful and loy-al, King of our lives, by Thy
2. True-heart-ed, whole-heart-ed, full-est al-le-giance Yielding henceforth to our
3. True-heart-ed, whole-heart-ed, Sav-ior all-glo-rious! Take Thy great pow-er and

grace we will be; Un-der the stand-ard ex-alt-ed and roy-al, Strong in Thy
glo-ri-ous King; Val-iant en-deav-or and lov-ing o-be-dience, Free-ly and
reign there a-lone, O-ver our wills and af-fec-tions vic-to-rious, Free-ly sur-

Chorus

strength we will bat-tle for Thee. Peal out the watch-word! si-lence it nev-er!
joy-ous-ly now would we bring.
ren-dered and wholly Thine own. Peal out the watch-word! si-lence it nev-er!

Song of our spir-its, re-joic-ing and free; Peal out the watch-word!
Song of our spir-its, re-joic-ing and free; Peal out the watch-word!

loy-al for-ev-er, King of our lives, by Thy grace we will be.
loy-al for-ev-er, King of our lives, by Thy grace we will be.

295 · A Blessing in Prayer

E. E. Hewitt

Wm. J. Kirkpatrick

1. There is rest, sweet rest, at the Mas-ter's feet, There is fa-vor now at the
2. There is grace to help in our time of need, For our Friend a-bove is a
3. When our songs are glad with the joy of life, When our hearts are sad with its
4. There is per-fect peace tho' the wild waves roll, There are gifts of love for the

mer-cy seat, For a-ton-ing blood has been sprin-kled there: There is
friend in-deed; We may cast on Him ev-'ry grief and care; There is
ills and strife, When the pow'rs of sin would the soul en-snare, There is
seek-ing soul, Till we praise the Lord in His home so fair: There is

CHORUS

al-ways a bless-ing, a bless-ing in prayer. There's a bless-ing in prayer, in be-

liev-ing prayer, When our Savior's name to the throne we bear; Then a Fa-ther's

love will re-ceive us there: There is al-ways a bless-ing, a bless-ing in prayer.

296 He Will Hide Me

M. E. Servoss

James McGranahan

1. When the storms of life are rag - ing, Tem-pests wild on sea and land,
2. Tho' He may send some af - flic - tion,'Twill but make me long for home;
3. En - e - mies may strive to in - jure, Sa - tan all his arts em - ploy:

I will seek a place of ref - uge In the shad - ow of God's hand.
For in love, and not in an - ger, All His chas - ten - ings will come.
He will turn what seems to harm me In - to ev - er - last - ing joy.

CHORUS

{ He will hide me, He will hide me, Where no harm can e'er betide me,
{ He will hide me, safe-ly hide me, In the shad - ow of (*Omit. . .*) His hand.

297 Break Thou the Bread of Life

Mary A. Lathbury

William F. Sherwin

1. Break Thou the bread of life, Dear Lord, to me, As Thou didst
2. Bless Thou the truth, dear Lord, To me— to me, As Thou didst
3. Thou art the bread of life, O Lord, to me, Thy ho - ly

break the loaves Be - side the sea; Be - yond the sa - cred page
bless the bread By Gal - i - lee; Then shall all bond-age cease,
word the truth That sav - eth me; Give me to eat and live

I seek Thee, Lord, My spir-it pants for Thee, O liv-ing Word.
All fet-ters fall; And I shall find my peace, My All in all.
With Thee a-bove; Teach me to love Thy truth, For Thou art love.

298   **Jesus Saves**

Priscilla J. Owens   Wm. J. Kirkpatrick

1. We have heard the joy-ful sound: Je-sus saves! Je-sus saves!
2. Waft it on the roll-ing tide: Je-sus saves! Je-sus saves!
3. Sing a-bove the bat-tle strife: Je-sus saves! Je-sus saves!

Spread the ti-dings all a-round: Je-sus saves! Je-sus saves!
Tell to sin-ners far and wide: Je-sus saves! Je-sus saves!
By His death and end-less life, Je-sus saves! Je-sus saves!

Bear the news to ev-'ry land, Climb the steeps and cross the waves;
Sing, ye is-lands of the sea; Ech-o back, ye o-cean caves;
Sing it soft-ly thro' the gloom, When the heart for mer-cy craves;

On-ward! 'tis our Lord's com-mand: Je-sus saves! Je-sus saves!
Earth shall keep her ju-bi-lee: Je-sus saves! Je-sus saves!
Sing in tri-umph o'er the tomb: Je-sus saves! Je-sus saves!

299 Lead, Kindly Light

J. H. Newman

J. B. Dykes

1. Lead, kindly Light, a-mid th' en-circling gloom, Lead Thou me on; The night is
2. I was not ev - er thus, nor prayed that Thou Shouldst lead me on; I loved to
3. So long Thy pow'r has blest me, sure it still Will lead me on O'er moor and

dark, and I am far from home; Lead Thou me on. Keep Thou my feet; I
choose and see my path; but now Lead Thou me on. I loved the gar - ish
fen, o'er crag and tor-rent, till The night is gone. And with the morn those

do not ask to see The dis - tant scene—one step e - nough for me.
day, and spite of fears, Pride ruled my will: Re-mem-ber not past years.
an - gel - fac - es smile, Which I have loved long since, and lost a - while.

300 Hold Thou My Hand

Fanny J. Crosby

Hubert P. Main

1. Hold Thou my hand: so weak I am, and help - less, I dare not
2. Hold Thou my hand, and clos - er, clos - er draw me To Thy dear
3. Hold Thou my hand, that when I reach the mar - gin Of that lone

take one step with - out Thine aid; Hold Thou my hand, for then, O
self— my hope, my joy, my all; Hold Thou my hand, lest hap - ly
riv - er Thou didst cross for me, A heav'n - ly light may flash a-

lov - ing Sav - ior, No dread of ill shall make my soul a - fraid.
I should wan - der; And, miss - ing Thee, my trem-bling feet should fall.
long its wa - ters, And ev - 'ry wave like crys - tal bright shall be.

301 **Beyond the Sunset**

Josephine Pollard

Dr. W. O. Perkins

1. Be - yond the sun-set's ra-diant glow There is a brighter world, I know,
2. Be - yond the sun-set's pur-ple rim,— Be - yond the twilight, deep and dim,
3. Be - yond this des - ert, dark and drear, The gold - en cit - y will ap - pear;

Where gold - en glo - ries ev - er shine,—Be - yond the tho't of day's de - cline.
Where clouds and darkness nev-er come, My soul shall find its heav'n-ly home.
And morn-ing's love-ly beams a - rise Up - on my man-sion in the skies.

Chorus

Be - yond the sun-set's ra-diant glow, There is a brighter world, I
radiant glow,

know; Be - yond the sun-set I may spend De - light-ful days that nev-er end.

302 Sunlight, Sunlight

J. W. Van De Venter

W. S. Weeden

1. I wan-dered in the shades of night, Till Je-sus came to me, And
2. Tho' clouds may gath-er in the sky, And bil-lows 'round me roll, How-
3. Soon I shall see Him as He is, The Light that came to me; Be-

with the sun-light of His love Bid all my dark-ness flee.
ev - er dark the world may be, I've sun-light in my soul.
hold the brightness of His face, Thro'-out e - ter - ni - ty.

CHORUS

Sun-light, sun-light in my soul to-day, Sun-light, sun-light all a-long the way; Since the Sav-ior

found me, took a-way my sin, I have had the sun-light of His love with-in.

303 Jesus, Meek and Gentle

George R. Prynne

Clarence Hudson

1. Je - sus, meek and gen - tle, Son of God most high,..........
2. Par - don our of - fens - es, Loose our cap - tive chains,........
3. Lead us on our jour - ney: Be Thy-self the Way..........

Pity - ing, lov - ing Sav - ior, Hear Thy chil - dren's cry.
Break down ev - 'ry i - dol Which our soul de - tains.
Thro' ter - res - trial dark - ness To ce - les - tial day.

304

He Changes Not

T. O. Chisholm

Copyright, 1935, by Gospel Advocate Company

Bertha Mae Lillenas

1. A - mid the chang-ing scenes be-low, Where man-y come and man-y go,
2. The years pass on, a shift-ing train, Of things fa - mil - iar, few re-main,
3. As it has been, so will it be Till comes life's fi - nal hour for me,

My wist - ful soul will oft cry out For one who stays, who chang-es not.
How sweet, how com-fort-ing the tho't, That one re-mains who chang-es not.
Mine sure-ly is a fa-vored lot— I have a Friend who chang-es not.

CHORUS

He chang-es not, Christ chang-es not! Though I should be by all for-got,

rit.

He still re-mains and will re-main! My pre-cious Lord who chang-es not.

My

305 By and By

R. M. McIntosh

1. It may be far, it may be near, There is a hope, there is a fear,
2. Im-pa-tient soul, and murm'ring heart, Your murm'ring cease and bear your part
3. O ver-dant fields! O shin-ing shore! The Lamb of God spreads wide the door;

FINE

D. S.—But in the fu - ture wait-ing I Shall Je - sus see, yes, "by and by."
D. S.—Of pain and la - bor on life's road, For soon 'twill lead thee to thy God.
D. S.—Ah, gold-en cit - y, sure-ly I Shall see thy glo - ries "by and by."

CHORUS   **D. S.**

By and by, yes, by and by, By and by, yes, by and by;

306 Christ, the Lord, Is Risen Today

Charles Wesley   Lyra Davidica

1. Christ, the Lord, is ris'n to - day, Hal - - le - lu - jah!
2. Vain the stone, the watch, the seal, Hal - - le - lu - jah!
3. Lives a - gain our glo - rious King, Hal - - le - lu - jah!

Sons of men and an - gels say, Hal - - le - lu - jah!
Christ hath burst the gates of hell, Hal - - le - lu - jah!
Where, O death, is now thy sting? Hal - - le - lu - jah!

Raise your joys and tri-umphs high, Hal - - le - lu - jah!
Death in vain for-bids His rise, Hal - - le - lu - jah!
Once He died our souls to save, Hal - - le - lu - jah!

Sing, ye heav'ns; thou earth, re - ply, Hal - - le - lu - jah!
Christ hath o - pened par - a - dise, Hal - - le - lu - jah!
Where's thy vic - t'ry, boast-ing grave? Hal - - le - lu - jah!

307 The Solemn Feast

Joseph Hart

Copyright, 1935, by Gospel Advocate Company

L. O. Sanderson

Obligato

1. That dread-ful night be - fore His death, The Lamb for sin - ners slain,
2. To keep the feast, Lord, we have met, And to re - mem-ber Thee,

Regular Voices

1. That dread ful night be - fore His death, The Lamb for sin - ners slain,
2. To keep the feast, Lord, we have met, And to re - mem-ber Thee,

Did, al - most with His dy - ing breath, This sol - emn feast or - dain.
Help each re-deemed one to re - peat: For me He died, for me.

Did, al - most with His dy - ing breath, This sol - emn feast or - dain.
Help each re-deemed one to re - peat: For me He died, for me.

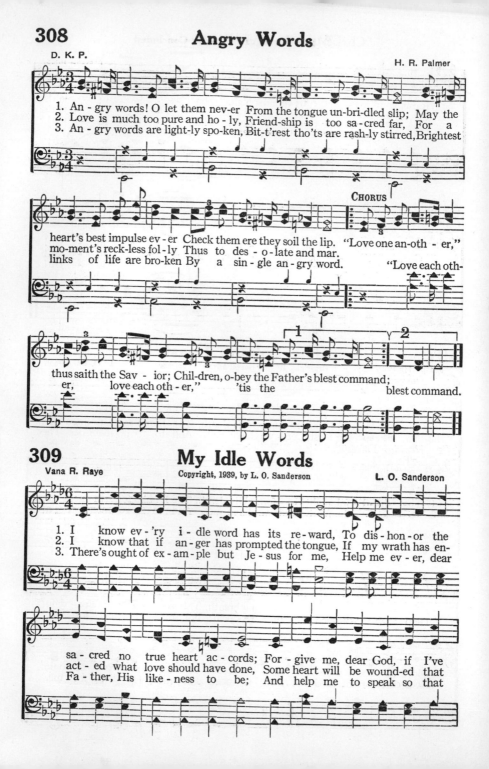

308   Angry Words

D. K. P.

H. R. Palmer

1. An - gry words! O let them nev-er From the tongue un-bri-dled slip; May the
2. Love is much too pure and ho - ly, Friend-ship is too sa-cred far, For a
3. An - gry words are light-ly spo-ken, Bit-t'rest tho'ts are rash-ly stirred, Brightest

CHORUS

heart's best impulse ev - er Check them ere they soil the lip. "Love one an-oth - er,"
mo-ment's reck-less fol-ly Thus to des - o-late and mar.
links of life are bro-ken By a sin - gle an-gry word.   "Love each oth-

thus saith the Sav - ior; Chil-dren, o-bey the Father's blest command;
er, love each oth - er," 'tis the   blest command.

309   My Idle Words

Vana R. Raye

Copyright, 1939, by L. O. Sanderson

L. O. Sanderson

1. I know ev - 'ry i - dle word has its re - ward, To dis - hon - or the
2. I know that if an - ger has prompted the tongue, If my wrath has en-
3. There's ought of ex - am - ple but Je - sus for me, Help me ev - er, dear

sa - cred no true heart ac - cords; For - give me, dear God, if I've
act - ed what love should have done, Some heart will be wound-ed that
Fa - ther, His like - ness to be; And help me to speak so that

ut - tered a word That would not have been said by my Lord.
I should have won, Lord, for - give if I've in - jured a one.
oth - ers may see, That the Sav - ior is liv - ing in me.

310   Precious Words

Mrs. Loula K. Rodgers

R. M. McIntosh

1. Pre - cious for - ev - er! O won - der - ful words, Teach me the
2. Free - ly He of - fers their prom - ise to all, "Come un - to
3. Wouldst thou re - fuse the sweet sol - ace He gives, In the mid-

path - way of du - ty; Lead me be - side the still wa - ters of life,
me who - so - ev - er," Sin - ners op-pressed with a bur-den of woe,
night of Thy sor - row? Wouldst thou go on in the dark-ness of sin,

FINE   REFRAIN

Flow-ing thro' val - leys of beau - ty.
Drink of the boun-ti - ful riv - er.   Pre-cious for-ev - er to you and to me,
Long-ing for no bright to-mor - row?

D.S.—*Heal-ing the hearts that are bro - ken!*

D. S.

Words that our Sav-ior has spo - ken, Bear-ing sal - va-tion far o - ver the sea,

311 Our Day of Praise Is Done

John Ellerton

A. Williams

1. Our day of praise is done, The eve - ning shad - ows fall;
2. A - round the throne on high, Where night can nev - er be,
3. 'Tis Thine each soul to calm, Each way - ward tho't re - claim,

But pass not from us with the sun, True light that light - est all.
The white-robed an - gels of the sky Bring cease - less hymns to Thee.
And make our life a dai - ly psalm Of glo - ry to Thy name.

312 In the Hour of Trial

James Montgomery

Spencer Lane

1. In the hour of tri - al, Je - sus, plead for me, Lest by base de-
2. With for - bid - den pleas-ures Would this vain world charm, Or its sor - did
3. Should Thy mer-cy send me Sor - row, toil and woe, Or should pain at-

ni - al I de - part from Thee; When Thou seest me wa - ver, With a
treas-ures Spread to work me harm; Bring to my re - mem-brance Sad Geth-
tend me On my path be - low, Grant that I may nev - er Fail Thy

look re - call, . . Nor for fear nor fa - vor Suf - fer me to fall.
sem - a - ne, . . . Or, in dark - er sem-blance, Cross-crowned Calvary.
hand to see; . . Grant that I may ev - er Cast my care on Thee.

313   Am I Nearer to Heaven Today?

Jessie Brown Pounds   Fred A. Fillmore

DUET (Soprano and Tenor)

1. O the yes-ter-day's mo-ments for pleas-ure or woe, Have been stealth-i-ly
2. I am near-er the time for the break-ing of ties, That are hold-ing my
3. I am near-er the close of my la-bor be-low, I am near-er the

car-ried a-way; I am near-er the val-ley of shad-ows, I know—
loved ones to me; I am near-er the time for my lat-est good-byes—
end of my way; I am near-er the edge of the val-ley, I know—

CHORUS

Am I near-er to heav-en to-day? Am I near-er........ Am I
Am I near-er, O Fa-ther to Thee?
Am I near-er to heav-en to-day?   to-day?

rit.

near-er........ Am I near-er to heav-en to-day?........ Am I
to-day?   near-er, near-er to-day?

near-er the gate where the blessed ones wait? Am I near-er to heav-en to-day?

314   We'll Never Say Good-by

Mrs. E. W. Chapman

J. H. Tenney

1. With friends on earth we meet in glad-ness, While swift the mo-ments fly,
2. How joy - ful is the hope that lin-gers, When loved ones cross death's sea,
3. No part - ing words shall e'er be spo-ken In yon - der home so fair,

Yea ev - er comes the thought of sad-ness, That we must say, "Good-by."
That we, when all earth's toils are end - ed, With Thee shall ev - er be.
But songs of joy, and peace, and glad-ness, We'll sing for - ev - er there.

CHORUS

We'll nev - er say good - by in heav'n, We'll nev - er say good - by,......
good-by,

For in that land of joy and song We'll nev - er say, good - by.

315   Room At the Cross

W. B. B.

Wm. B. Blake

DUET.

1. Room at the Cross for a trem-bling soul, Room at the Cross for you;
2. Room at the Cross for a break-ing heart, Room at the Cross for you;
3. Room at the Cross for the sad and worn, Room at the Cross for you;

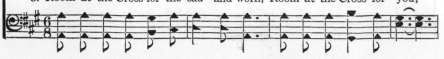

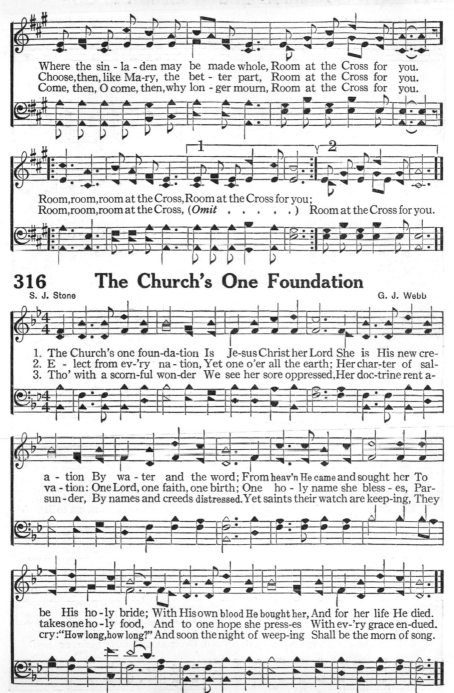

Where the sin - la - den may be made whole, Room at the Cross for you.
Choose, then, like Ma-ry, the bet - ter part, Room at the Cross for you.
Come, then, O come, then, why lon - ger mourn, Room at the Cross for you.

Room, room, room at the Cross, Room at the Cross for you;
Room, room, room at the Cross, (*Omit* . . . . . .) Room at the Cross for you.

316 **The Church's One Foundation**

S. J. Stone

G. J. Webb

1. The Church's one foun-da-tion Is   Je-sus Christ her Lord She is His new cre-
2. E - lect from ev-'ry na - tion, Yet one o'er all the earth; Her char-ter of sal-
3. Tho' with a scorn-ful won-der We see her sore oppressed, Her doc-trine rent a-

a - tion By wa - ter and the word; From heav'n He came and sought her To
va - tion: One Lord, one faith, one birth; One   ho - ly name she bless - es, Par-
sun - der, By names and creeds distressed. Yet saints their watch are keep-ing, They

be   His ho - ly bride; With His own blood He bought her, And for her life He died.
takes one ho - ly food, And to one hope she press-es With ev-'ry grace en-dued.
cry: "How long, how long?" And soon the night of weep-ing Shall be the morn of song.

317 I'll Go Where You Want Me to Go

Mary Brown

Carrie E. Rounsefell

1. It may not be on the mountain's height, Or o - ver the storm - y sea;
2. Per - haps to - day there are lov - ing words Which Je - sus would have me speak;
3. There's sure-ly somewhere a low - ly place, In earth's harvest fields so wide,

It may not be at the bat - tle's front My Lord will have need of me;
There may be now in the paths of sin Some wand'rer whom I should seek;
Where I may la - bor thro' life's short day For Je - sus, the Cru - ci - fied;

But if, I am need - ed an - y-where, In paths that I do not know,
O Sav - ior, if Thou wilt be my guide, Tho' dark and rug - ged the way,
So trust-ing my all to Thy ten-der care, And knowing Thou lov - est me,

FINE.

I'll an-swer, dear Lord, with my hand in Thine, I'll go where you want me to go.
My voice shall ech - o Thy mes-sage sweet, I'll say what you want me to say.
I'll do Thy will with a heart sin-cere, I'll be what you want me to be.

D.S.—*I'll say what you want me to say, dear Lord, I'll be what you want me to be.*

CHORUS

D. S.

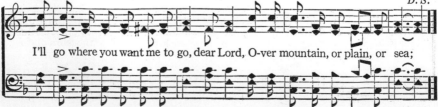

I'll go where you want me to go, dear Lord, O-ver mountain, or plain, or sea;

318 Somebody Loves You: 'Tis Jesus

Laurene Highfield

Samuel W. Beazley

1. Though you are help-less and lone-ly and poor, Some-bod-y
2. Though you are wea-ry and tri-als come fast, Some-bod-y
3. Though you have grieved Him and sad-dened His heart, Some-bod-y
4. Though you are friend-less and dark seems the way, Some-bod-y

loves you: 'tis Je-sus; Though bit-ter sor-rows you have to en-dure,
loves you: 'tis Je-sus; His strength will com-fort you un-to the last,
loves you: 'tis Je-sus; You in His ten-der-ness still have a part,
loves you: 'tis Je-sus; There is one Friend who for-ev-er will stay,

CHORUS

Some-bod-y loves you: 'tis Je-sus. Some-bod-y loves you wher-

ev-er you are; Tho' from life's bat-tles you've man-y a scar, Tho' in strange

by-ways you've wan-dered a-far, Some-bod-y loves you: 'tis Je-sus.

319 How Shall the Young Secure Their Hearts?

Isaac Watts. (Ps. 119)

Beethoven

1. How shall the young se - cure their hearts, And guard their lives from sin?
2. 'Tis like the sun, a heav'n-ly light, That guides us all the day;
3. Thy word is ev - er - last - ing truth; How pure is ev - 'ry page!

Thy word the choic-est rules im - parts To keep the con-science
And, thro' the dan - gers of the night, A lamp to lead our
That ho - ly book shall guide our youth, And well sup-port our

clean,....... To keep... the.... con - science clean.
way,........ A lamp... to..... lead our way.
age,......... And well.... sup - port our age.
keep the con-science clean, To keep the con-science clean!

keep the con-science clean, To keep the con - science clean!

320 Sometime, Somehow, Somewhere

C. H. G.

Chas. H. Gabriel

1. Sometime, somewhere my toil shall cease, And I from care shall find re - lease,
2. Sometime, somewhere, I'll fall a - sleep, And from a dreamless slumber deep—
3. Sometime, somewhere, some blessed place, Thro' wonders of a - maz-ing grace,

Sometime, Somehow, Somewhere, Concluded

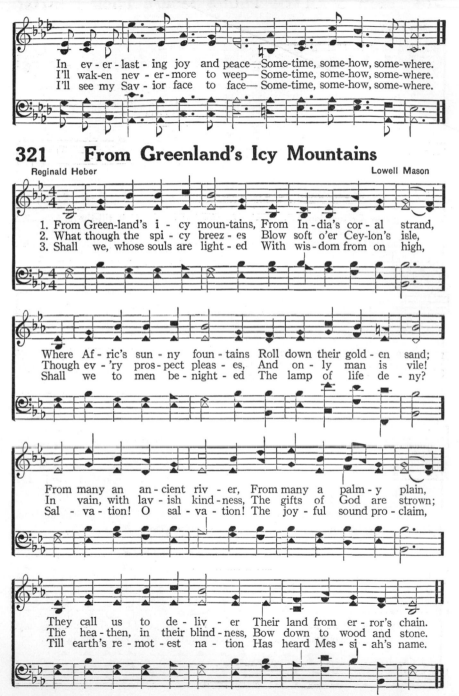

In ev - er - last - ing joy and peace—Some-time, some-how, some-where.
I'll wak-en nev - er - more to weep— Some-time, some-how, some-where.
I'll see my Sav - ior face to face— Some-time, some-how, some-where.

321 From Greenland's Icy Mountains

Reginald Heber

Lowell Mason

1. From Green-land's i - cy moun-tains, From In - dia's cor - al strand,
2. What though the spi - cy breez - es Blow soft o'er Cey-lon's isle,
3. Shall we, whose souls are light - ed With wis-dom from on high,

Where Af - ric's sun - ny foun - tains Roll down their gold - en sand;
Though ev - 'ry pros - pect pleas - es, And on - ly man is vile!
Shall we to men be - night - ed The lamp of life de - ny?

From many an an - cient riv - er, From many a palm - y plain,
In vain, with lav - ish kind - ness, The gifts of God are strown;
Sal - va - tion! O sal - va - tion! The joy - ful sound pro - claim,

They call us to de - liv - er Their land from er - ror's chain.
The hea - then, in their blind - ness, Bow down to wood and stone.
Till earth's re - mot - est na - tion Has heard Mes - si - ah's name.

322 Whispering Hope

Arr. Copyright, 1935, by Gospel Advocate Company

Alice Hawthorne

Arr. from A. H. by L. O. Sanderson

1. Soft   as the voice of an an - gel, Breathing a les-son un-heard, Hope with a
2. If   in the dusk of the twi-light, Dim be the re-gion a - far,   Will not the
3. Hope as an an-chor so steadfast, Rends the dark veil for the soul,   Whither the

gen - tle per-sua-sion, Whispers her comforting word.   Wait till the darkness is
deep-en-ing darkness Brighten the glimmering star?   Then when the night is up-
Mas-ter has en-tered, Robbing the grave of its goal.   Come then, O come glad fru-

o - ver, Wait till the tem-pest is   done, Hope for the sunshine to-mor-row,
on us Why should the heart sink a - way? When the dark midnight is o - ver,
i - tion, Come to my sad wea-ry   heart, Come, O Thou blest hope of glo-ry,

Aft - er the show-er is gone.
Watch for the breaking of day.
Nev - er, O nev-er de - part.

Chorus *(parts)*

Whis - - per-ing Hope......

Whis-per-ing Hope,   whispering Hope,

O how wel - - - come thy voice,........ Mak - - - ing my
welcome thy voice, O how welcome thy voice, Making my heart

Whispering Hope, Concluded

After last stanza

heart........ in its sor - - - row re - joice.   O bless-ed Hope!
Making my heart in   its sor-row, its sor-row

---

323   Give of Your Best to the Master

H. B. G.

Mrs. Charles Barnard

1. Give of your best to the Mas - ter; Give of the strength of your youth;
2. Give of your best to the Mas - ter; Give Him first place in   your heart;
3. Give of your best to the Mas - ter; Naught else is wor - thy His love;

Ref.—*Give of your best to the Mas - ter; Give of the strength of your youth;*

FINE

Throw your soul's fresh, glow-ing ar - dor In - to the bat - tle for truth.
Give Him first place in your serv - ice, Con - se - crate ev - 'ry part.
He   gave Him - self for your ran - som, Gave up His glo - ry a - bove;

Clad in sal - va - tion's full ar - mor, Join in the bat - tle for truth.

Je - sus has set the ex - am - ple; Daunt-less was He, young and brave;
Give, and to you shall be giv - en; God His be - lov - ed Son gave;
Laid down His life with-out mur-mur, You from sin's ru - in to save;

rall.   D. S.

Give Him your loy - al de - vo - tion, Give Him the best that you have.....
Grate-ful - ly seek-ing to serve Him, Give Him the best that you have.....
Give Him your heart's ad - o - ra - tion, Give Him the best that you have.....

324   O Sacred Word

George Tester   Copyright, 1948, by Gospel Advocate Company   Harry Dixon Loes

1. O sa-cred word, en-light-'ning page To thee we turn in ev-'ry age;
2. O let us glimpse the Fa-ther's love; These scales of darkness now re-move,
3. A com-pass may this vol-ume prove, A guide to lead our tho'ts a-bove;

Where else could mor-tals here be-low In-quire God's right-eous-ness to know?
And with the eye of faith be-hold Its won-drous truths more dear than gold.
A chart up-on life's trou-bled sea, Till, past the bar, we rest in Thee.

FINE.

D. S.—It's liv-ing mes-sage, sav-ing truth, Re-quired of men in age and youth.

CHORUS

'Tis here for com-fort we can turn! O, God, for-bid that we should spurn

D. S.

325   Jesus, Savior, Pilot Me

Edward Hopper   John E. Gould

1. Je - sus, Sav - ior, pi - lot me O - ver life's tem - pes-tuous sea;
2. As a moth - er stills her child, Thou canst hush the o - cean wild;
3. When at last I near the shore, And the fear - ful break-ers roar

Un-known waves be-fore me roll, Hid - ing rock and treach'rous shoal;
Bois-t'rous waves o - bey Thy will When Thou say'st to them, "Be still!"
'Twixt me and the peace-ful rest, Then, while lean - ing on Thy breast,

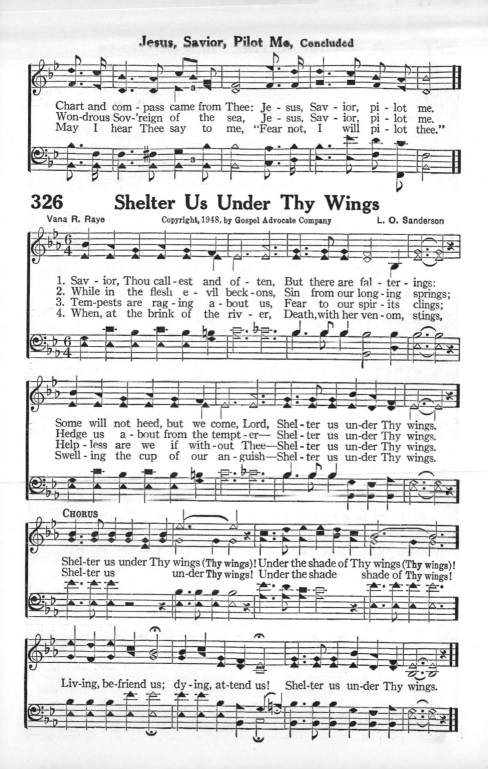

Chart and com - pass came from Thee: Je - sus, Sav - ior, pi - lot me.
Won-drous Sov-'reign of the sea, Je - sus, Sav - ior, pi - lot me.
May I hear Thee say to me, "Fear not, I will pi - lot thee."

326 Shelter Us Under Thy Wings

Vana R. Raye   Copyright, 1948, by Gospel Advocate Company   L. O. Sanderson

1. Sav - ior, Thou call - est and of - ten, But there are fal - ter - ings:
2. While in the flesh e - vil beck - ons, Sin from our long - ing springs;
3. Tem-pests are rag - ing a - bout us, Fear to our spir - its clings;
4. When, at the brink of the riv - er, Death, with her ven - om, stings,

Some will not heed, but we come, Lord, Shel - ter us un - der Thy wings.
Hedge us a - bout from the tempt - er— Shel - ter us un - der Thy wings.
Help - less are we if with - out Thee—Shel - ter us un - der Thy wings.
Swell - ing the cup of our an - guish—Shel - ter us un - der Thy wings.

CHORUS

Shel-ter us under Thy wings (Thy wings)! Under the shade of Thy wings (Thy wings)!
Shel-ter us   un-der Thy wings! Under the shade   shade of Thy wings!

Liv-ing, be-friend us; dy-ing, at-tend us! Shel-ter us un-der Thy wings.

327 A Shelter in the Time of Storm

Vernon J. Charlesworth
Arr. by Ira D. Sankey

Ira D. Sankey

1. The Lord's our Rock, in Him we hide, A shel-ter in the time of storm;
2. A shade by day, de-fense by night, A shel-ter in the time of storm;
3. The rag-ing storms may round us beat, A shel-ter in the time of storm;

Se - cure what-ev - er ill be - tide, A shel-ter in the time of storm.
No fears a - larm, no foes af - fright, A shel-ter in the time of storm.
We'll nev - er leave our safe re - treat, A shel-ter in the time of storm.

CHORUS

O, Je-sus is a Rock in a wea-ry land, A wea-ry land, a wea-ry land;

O, Je-sus is a Rock in a wea-ry land, A shel-ter in the time of storm.

328 O for a Soul

W. J. K.

Wm. J. Kirkpatrick

1. O for a soul a - glow with love, With love for God and man;
2. A soul so large that all man-kind Can be em-braced there-in.
3. A soul so great that God a - lone Can ac - tu - ate its will;

O for a Soul, Concluded

Re - joic - ing ev - 'ry pass - ing day To fol - low God's own plan!
The high, the low, the good, the bad, Be count - ed all a - kin.
That ev - 'ry pulse shall beat for Him, His pur - pose to ful - fil.

329   The Providence of God

W. E. Brightwell   L. O. Sanderson

1. The might - y God, Om - ni-scient One! His ways we can - not trace.
2. Lo! I can see Him in His word— I will not doubt or fear;
3. No tri - al can my spir - it break, For God will not for - sake;
4. The fu - ture beck - ons and I bow— My God re-moves the care!

He reck - ons ev - 'ry good be - gun And crowns it with His grace.
My steps are or - dered of the Lord, His guid - ing hand is near.
He will with each temp-ta - tion make A way for my es - cape.
Be - hold, He goes be - fore me now, And will my way pre - pare.

CHORUS

He's here, and there, and ev - 'ry-where In all the ways I've trod.

I've nev - er passed be - yond the sphere Of the prov - i - dence of God.

330 Everybody's Friend

Adaline H. Beery

J. D. Brunk

1. Je - sus, roy - al, heav'n - ly Friend, On thy kind - ness we de - pend;
2. None so poor or pressed with care, But their bur - dens He doth share;
3. But the kind - est deed of all, Was our ran - som from the fall;

Rich and poor and great and small, Thou hast gra - cious words for all.
Tho' our friends take oth - er ways, His dear pres - ence with us stays.
God - like friend - ship! free - ly He Died for na - tions, died for me.

D.S.—*Let my life Thy praise ex - tend, Je - sus, ev - 'ry - bod - y's Friend.*

REFRAIN

D. S.

Great of heart such Friend to be, Best of all a Friend to me!

331 O Come to the Savior

James Rowe

Samuel J. Spencer

Slowly

1. Soul bur-dened and stray-ing, Soul weak and un - true, Still Je - sus is
2. He lin - gers be - side you And, know-ing your plight, Is wait-ing to
3. His arms are out-stretch-ing To gath - er you in, His voice is be-

pray - ing, Still plead-ing for you!
guide you Safe out of the night.
seech - ing! O turn from your sin.

CHORUS

O come to the Sav - ior,

O Come to the Savior, Concluded

rit.

Seek com-fort a - bove; Come in - to the ref - uge, Come, rest in His love.

332 O Wonderful Love

Maxwell

J. W. McGarvey, Jr.

1. How shall I my Sav - ior set forth? How shall I His beau-ties de - clare?
2. Tho' once He was nailed to the cross, Vile reb - els like me to set free,
3. O sin - ners! be-lieve and a - dore This Sav - ior, so rich to re - deem;

Or how shall I speak of His worth, Or what His chief dig - ni - ties are?
His glo - ry sus-tain - ed no loss, E - ter - nal His king-dom shall be.
No crea-ture can ev - er ex - plore The treas-ure of good-ness in Him.

CHORUS

O won - - der-ful love!....... O won - - der-ful love!.......
O won-der-ful love! O won-der-ful love! won-der-ful love! O won-der-ful love!

O won - - - der-ful, won - der-ful love, My Sav - ior showed to me.
Won-der-ful, won-der-ful, won - der-ful love,

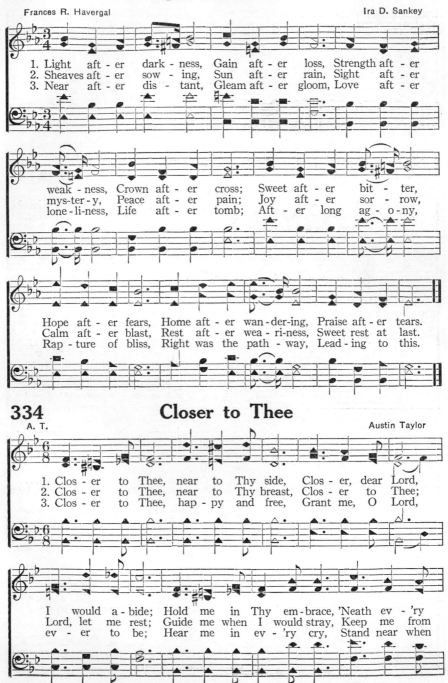

333 Light After Dark

Frances R. Havergal

Ira D. Sankey

1. Light aft - er dark - ness, Gain aft - er loss, Strength aft - er
2. Sheaves aft - er sow - ing, Sun aft - er rain, Sight aft - er
3. Near aft - er dis - tant, Gleam aft - er gloom, Love aft - er

weak - ness, Crown aft - er cross; Sweet aft - er bit - ter,
mys - ter - y, Peace aft - er pain; Joy aft - er sor - row,
lone - li - ness, Life aft - er tomb; Aft - er long ag - o - ny,

Hope aft - er fears, Home aft - er wan - der - ing, Praise aft - er tears.
Calm aft - er blast, Rest aft - er wea - ri - ness, Sweet rest at last.
Rap - ture of bliss, Right was the path - way, Lead - ing to this.

334 Closer to Thee

A. T.

Austin Taylor

1. Clos - er to Thee, near to Thy side, Clos - er, dear Lord,
2. Clos - er to Thee, near to Thy breast, Clos - er to Thee;
3. Clos - er to Thee, hap - py and free, Grant me, O Lord,

I would a - bide; Hold me in Thy em - brace, 'Neath ev - 'ry
Lord, let me rest; Guide me when I would stray, Keep me from
ev - er to be; Hear me in ev - 'ry cry, Stand near when

smile of grace, Grant me, Thy child, a place Clos - er to Thee.
sin each day, Draw me, dear Lord, I pray, Clos - er to Thee.
I must die, Then take me home on high, Clos - er to Thee.

335 Some Day We Shall Be Satisfied

F. M. D.

Frank M. Davis

1. Some day we shall be sat - is - fied, When in His like-ness we ap - pear,
2. Some day we shall be sat - is - fied, When we shall meet Him face to face,
3. Some day we shall be sat - is - fied, When all our bur-dens are laid down,

When we shall see Him as He is, When all that's dark shall be made clear.
And sing with an-gels round the throne, We're saved, we're saved from sin by grace.
When we shall stand be-fore the King, And there re-ceive the prom-ised crown.

CHORUS

Sat - is - fied, we shall be sat - is - fied, Some day we shall be sat - is -

fied; When in His like-ness we ap - pear We shall be sat - is - fied.

336

O Worship the King

Robert Grant

Haydn

1. O wor-ship the King, all - glo-rious a - bove, And grate-ful - ly
2. Thy boun - ti - ful care, what tongue can re - cite? It breathes in the
3. Frail chil-dren of dust, and fee - ble as frail, In Thee do we

sing His won - der - ful love; Our Shield and De - fend - er, the
air, it shines in the light; It streams from the hills, it de-
trust, nor find Thee to fail; Thy mer - cies, how ten - der! how

An - cient of Days, Pa - vil-ioned in splen-dor and gird - ed with praise.
scends to the plain, And sweet-ly dis-tills in the dew and the rain.
firm to the end! Our Mak - er, De-fend - er, Re - deem - er, and Friend!

337

One Sweetly Solemn Thought

Phoebe Cary

Philip Phillips

1. One sweet-ly sol - emn tho't Comes to me o'er and o'er; I'm near - er
2. Near - er the bound of life, Where bur-dens are laid down; Near - er to
3. Be near me when my feet Are slip-ping o'er the brink; For I am

CHORUS

home to-day, to-day, Than I have been be - fore.
leave the cross to-day, And near - er to the crown. Near-er my home,
near - er home to-day, Per - haps, than now I think.

Near-er my home, Near-er my home to-day, to-day, Than I have been be - fore.

338   Redeemed

Fanny J. Crosby   William J. Kirkpatrick

1. Redeemed–how I love to pro-claim it! Re-deemed by the blood of the Lamb;
2. Redeemed and so hap-py in Je - sus, No lan-guage my rapture can tell;
3. I know I shall see in His beau-ty The King in whose law I de - light;

Redeemed thro' His in - fi - nite mer - cy, His child, and for-ev - er, I am.
I know that the light of His pres-ence With me doth con-tin-ual-ly dwell.
Who lov - ing - ly guard-eth my foot-steps, And giv-eth me songs in the night.

CHORUS

Re - deemed,... re - deemed,... Re-deemed by the blood of the Lamb;
re-deemed,   re-deemed,

Re - deemed,... re - deemed,... His child, and for - ev - er, I am.
re-deemed,   re-deemed,

339 We Shall Be Like Him

W. A. S.

W. A. Spencer

1. When we shall reach the more ex-cel-lent glo-ry, And all our
2. We shall not wait till the glo-ri-ous dawn-ing Breaks on the
3. More and more like Him: re-peat the blest sto-ry O-ver and

tri-als are past, We shall be-hold Him, O won-der-ful sto-ry!
vi-sion so fair; Now we may wel-come the heav-en-ly morn-ing,
o-ver a-gain; Changed by His Spir-it from glo-ry to glo-ry,

Chorus

We shall be like Him at last.
Now we His im-age may bear.   We shall be like Him, We shall be
We shall be sat-is-fied then.

like Him, And in His beau-ty shall shine; We shall be like Him,

won-drous-ly like Him, Je-sus, our Sav-ior di-vine.

340   None of Self and All of Thee

Theo. Monod. Arr.   James McGranahan. Arr.

Not too fast

1. O, the bit - ter pain and sor - row That a time could ev - er be,
2. Yet He found me; I be - held Him Bleed-ing on th' ac-curs-ed tree,
3. Day by day His ten - der mer - cy Heal - ing, help - ing, full and free,
4. High - er than the high - est heav - ens, Deep - er than the deep-est sea,

When I proud - ly said to Je - sus "All of self, and none of Thee,"
And my wist - ful heart said faint - ly, "Some of self, and some of Thee,"
Bro't me low - er while I whis-pered "Less of self, and more of Thee,"
Lord, Thy love at last has con-quered "None of self, and *all* of Thee,"

All of self and none of Thee, All of self and none of Thee,
Some of self and some of Thee, Some of self and some of Thee,
Less of self and more of Thee, Less of self and more of Thee,
None of self and *all* of Thee, *None* of self and *all* of Thee,

When I proud - ly said to Je - sus "All of self and none of Thee."
And my wist - ful heart said faint - ly "Some of self and some of Thee."
Bro't me low - er while I whis-pered "Less of self and more of Thee."
Lord, Thy love at last has con-quered "*None* of self and *all* of Thee."

341   Every Cloud Has a Silver Lining

Vana R. Raye   L. O. Sanderson

1. Tho' the storm-clouds rise a - bout us; Tho' the arch a - bove is dark;
2. When the haze of ill sur-rounds us, When the heart is filled with fear,
3. There are nights of tears and sor - row, There are mo-ments bleak and dim;

'Round the cloud or aft - er tem-pests There is al - ways heav-en's mark:
And the art of sin con-founds us, There is help for souls sin - cere.
Thro' the dark-ness shines the mor - row, Time will have its sil - ver rim:

CHORUS

{ Ev - 'ry cloud has a sil - ver lin - ing! Ev - 'ry plight has a bright-er hue!
{ Ev - 'ry cloud has a sil - ver lin - ing! Ev - 'ry care has a bless-ing too!

1.
Aft - er night a love - ly morn - ing! Aft - er storm a calm a - new!

2.
If we look for the sil - ver lin - ing When the Lamp of God shines thro'!

342 The Kingdoms of Earth Pass Away

H. R. Trickett

J. H. Fillmore

1. The king-doms of earth pass a-way one by one, But the king-dom of
2. The tem-pest may rage and its an - ger ac-claim, Yea, the wind and the
3. The king-dom of God is now o - pen to all, E'en the vil - est may

heav-en re-mains; It is built on a rock and the Lord is its King,
tor - rents may roar, And the strong gates of hell may as - sail it in vain,
now en - ter in; There's a wel-come for all who will turn to the Lord,

CHORUS

And for - ev - er and ev - er He reigns. It shall stand, It shall stand,
Still the kingdom shall stand ev-er-more.
Full sal - va-tion and par-don for sin. It shall stand, It shall stand,

For - ev - er and ev - er and ev - er, It shall stand,
It shall stand, It shall stand,

It shall stand, For - ev - er and ev - er. A - men and A - men.
It shall stand,

343 The Heavens Declare the Glory of God

Psalms 19: 1–3

Arr. from H. R. Palmer. L. O. S.

The heav'ns de-clare the glo-ry of God, And the fir-ma-ment show-eth His hand-i-work. Day un-to day ut-ter-eth speech,

Day un-to day ut-ter-eth

Night unto night showeth knowledge;............. There is no speech nor speech, Night unto night showeth knowledge;

language where their voice, where their voice is not heard. Hal-le-lu-jah,

Hal-le-lu-jah,

Hal-le-lu-jah, A-men! Hal-le-lu-jah,

A-men! Hal-le-lu-jah,

Hal-le-lu-jah,

rit.

A-men, Hal-le-lu-jah, Amen, Hal-le-lu-jah, Amen, Hal-le-lu-jah, A-men!........

A-men, and A-men!

344 I Must Tell Jesus

E. A. H.

E. A. Hoffman

1. I must tell Je-sus all of my tri-als; I can-not bear these
2. I must tell Je-sus all of my trou-bles; He is a kind, com-
3. O how the world to e-vil al-lures me! O how my heart is

bur-dens a - lone; In my dis-tress He kind-ly will help me;
pas-sion-ate Friend; If I but ask Him, He will de-liv-er,
tempt-ed to sin! I must tell Je-sus, and He will help me

D. S.—*I must tell Je - sus, I must tell Je - sus!*

FINE   CHORUS

He ev-er loves and cares for His own.
Make of my trou-bles quick-ly an end.   I must tell Je-sus!
O-ver the world the vic-t'ry to win.

Je - sus can help me, Je - sus a - lone.

D. S.

I must tell Je-sus! I can-not bear my bur-dens a - lone;

345 Child of a King

Hattie E. Buell

John B. Sumner

1. My Fa - ther is rich in hous - es and lands, He hold - eth the
2. My Fa - ther's own Son, the Sav - ior of men, Once wan-dered o'er
3. A tent or a cot - tage, why should I care? They're build-ing a

wealth of the world in His hands! Of ru - bies and dia - monds, of
earth as the poor - est of them; But now He is reign - ing in
pal - ace for me o - ver there! Tho' here I'm a stran - ger yet

sil - ver and gold, His cof - fers are full,—He has rich - es un - told.
glo - ry on high, Pre - par - ing a place for the sweet by and by.
still I may sing: All glo - ry to God, I'm the child of a King!

CHORUS

I'm the child of a King, The child of a King!

ad lib.

With Je - sus, my Sav - ior, I'm the child of a King.

346 Back to the Bible for it All

Vana R. Raye

L. O. Sanderson

1. Vain - ly we seek aft - er men for guid-ing light, Or in dreams for a
2. If we the true and the liv-ing way would learn, And be safe when the
3. Whence cometh we? whith-er is our des - ti - ny? Where the faith and the

heav - en - ly call; Man, of him-self, can-not set his soul a-right;
night shad ows fall, We must the will of the Sav-ior tru - ly yearn,
hope for the pall? How may we see what a-waits for you and me?

CHORUS

So it's back to the Bi-ble for it all.
And it's back to the Bi-ble for it all. Back to the Bi-ble! The
It is back to the Bi-ble for it all.

God - giv-en Bi-ble! For grace and du-ty, great or small; Each one may

know what to do and where we go, But it's back to the Bi-ble for it all.

347 He Keeps Me Singing

L. B. B.

L. B. Bridgers

1. There's with-in my heart a mel - o - dy Je - sus whispers sweet and low,
2. Feast - ing on the rich - es of His grace, Resting 'neath His shelt'ring wing,
3. Soon He's com-ing back to wel-come me Far be-yond the star - ry sky;

Fear not, I am with thee, peace, be still, In all of life's ebb and flow.
Al - ways look-ing on His smil-ing face, That is why I shout and sing.
I shall wing my flight to worlds unknown, I shall live with Him on high.

CHORUS

Je - sus, Je - sus, Je - sus,— Sweet - est name I know,

Fills my ev - 'ry long - ing, Keeps me sing - ing as I go.

348 Savior, Teach Me

Jane E. Leeson

Carl von Weber

1. Sav - ior, teach me, day by day, Love's sweet les - son to o - bey:
2. With a child-like heart of love, At Thy bid-ding may I move,
3. Teach me all Thy steps to trace, Strong to fol - low in Thy grace,

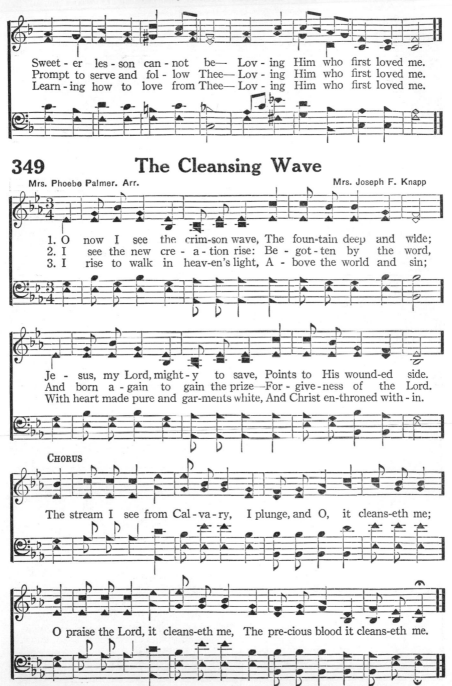

Sweet - er les - son can - not be— Lov - ing Him who first loved me.
Prompt to serve and fol - low Thee— Lov - ing Him who first loved me.
Learn - ing how to love from Thee— Lov - ing Him who first loved me.

349 The Cleansing Wave

Mrs. Phoebe Palmer. Arr.

Mrs. Joseph F. Knapp

1. O now I see the crim-son wave, The foun-tain deep and wide;
2. I see the new cre - a - tion rise: Be - got-ten by the word,
3. I rise to walk in heav-en's light, A - bove the world and sin;

Je - sus, my Lord, might-y to save, Points to His wound-ed side.
And born a - gain to gain the prize—For - give-ness of the Lord.
With heart made pure and gar-ments white, And Christ en-throned with - in.

CHORUS

The stream I see from Cal - va - ry, I plunge, and O, it cleans-eth me;

O praise the Lord, it cleans-eth me, The pre-cious blood it cleans-eth me.

350 Think On These Things

Copyright, 1948, by Gospel Advocate Company

Vana R. Raye

L. O. Sanderson

1. What - so - ev - er is hon - est, What - so - ev - er is true, What - so-
2. What - so - ev - er is love - ly— Good-ness brightens the way!— What is
3. Think of Christ and His king-dom; Think of grace, full and free; Think of

REFRAIN

ev - er is right-eous, And what-so - ev - er pure:
good-ly re - port - ed— That which is right al - way.   Think on these things!
debt and of du - ty, Death, and e - ter - ni - ty.

All of thy days! If there be vir - tue, If there be praise, Think on these things.

351 Crowned with Honor

Thomas Kelly

Oliver Holden

1. The head that once was crowned with thorns Is crowned with glo - ry now;
2. The high - est place that heav'n af - fords Is His by sov-'reign right;
3. The joy of all who dwell a - bove, The joy of all be - low,

A roy - al di - a - dem a - dorns The might - y Vic - tor's brow.
The King of kings, the Lord of lords, He reigns in glo - ry bright.
To whom He man - i - fests His love, And grants His name to know.

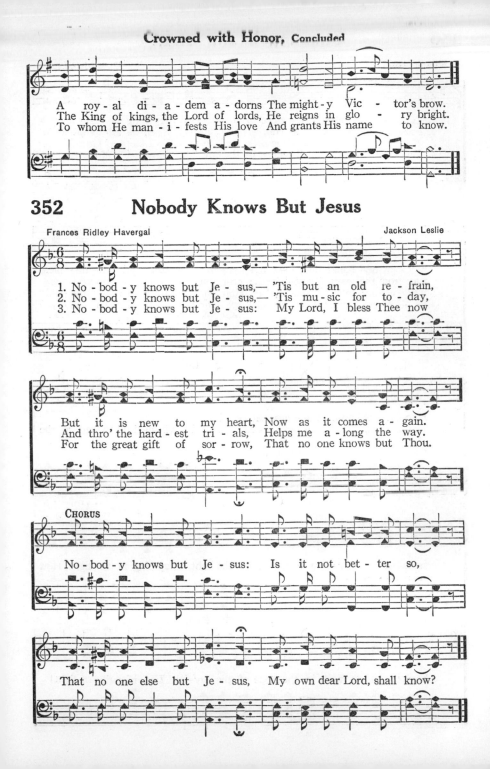

A roy-al di-a-dem a-dorns The might-y Vic - tor's brow.
The King of kings, the Lord of lords, He reigns in glo - ry bright.
To whom He man-i-fests His love And grants His name to know.

352 Nobody Knows But Jesus

Frances Ridley Havergal

Jackson Leslie

1. No-bod-y knows but Je-sus,— 'Tis but an old re-frain,
2. No-bod-y knows but Je-sus,— 'Tis mu-sic for to-day,
3. No-bod-y knows but Je-sus: My Lord, I bless Thee now

But it is new to my heart, Now as it comes a-gain.
And thro' the hard-est tri-als, Helps me a-long the way.
For the great gift of sor-row, That no one knows but Thou.

Chorus

No-bod-y knows but Je-sus: Is it not bet-ter so,

That no one else but Je-sus, My own dear Lord, shall know?

353 Stepping in the Light

Eliza E. Hewitt

William J. Kirkpatrick

1. Try - ing to walk in the steps of the Sav - ior, Try - ing to fol - low our
2. Press - ing more close-ly to Him who is lead-ing, When we are tempt-ed to
3. Walk-ing in foot-steps of gen - tle for-bear-ance, Foot-steps of faith-ful-ness,
4. Try - ing to walk in the steps of the Sav - ior, Up-ward, still up-ward we'll

Sav - ior and King; Shap - ing our lives by His bless - ed ex - am - ple,
turn from the way; Trust-ing the arm that is strong to de-fend us,
mer - cy and love; Look - ing to Him for the grace free - ly prom-ised,
fol - low our Guide; When we shall see Him, "the King in His beau - ty,"

CHORUS

Hap-py, how hap-py, the songs that we bring.
Hap-py, how hap-py, our prais - es each day. How beau-ti-ful to walk in the
Hap-py, how hap-py, our jour-ney a - bove!
Hap-py, how hap-py, our place at His side!

steps of the Sav - ior, Step-ping in the light, Step-ping in the light; How

beau-ti - ful to walk in the steps of the Sav - ior, Led in paths of light!

354 There Is Power in the Blood

L. E. J.

L. E. Jones

1. Would you be free from the bur-den of sin? There's pow'r in the blood,
2. Would you be free from your pas-sion and pride? There's pow'r in the blood,
3. Would you be whit-er, much whit-er than snow? There's pow'r in the blood,
4. Would you do serv-ice for Je-sus your King? There's pow'r in the blood,

pow'r in the blood; Would you o'er e-vil a vic-to-ry win?
pow'r in the blood; Come for a cleans-ing to Cal-va-ry's tide;
pow'r in the blood; Sin-stains are lost in its life-giv-ing flow;
pow'r in the blood; Would you live dai-ly His prais-es to sing?

CHORUS

There's won-der-ful pow'r in the blood. There is pow'r, pow'r,
there is pow'r,

Won-der-work-ing pow'r in the blood of the Lamb; There is
in the blood of the Lamb;

pow'r, pow'r, Won-der-work-ing pow'r In the pre-cious blood of the Lamb.
there is pow'r,

355 Christel for the World We Sing

Samuel Wolcott

Felice De Giardini

1. Christ for the world! we sing; The world to Christ we bring,
2. Christ for the world! we sing; The world to Christ we bring,
3. Christ for the world! we sing; The world to Christ we bring,

With lov - ing zeal; The poor and them that mourn, The faint and
With fer - vent prayer; The way - ward and the lost, By rest - less
With one ac - cord, With us the work to share, With us re-

o - ver-borne, Sin - sick and sor - row-worn, Whom Christ doth heal.
pas - sions tossed, Re - deemed at count - less cost From dark de - spair.
proach to dare, With us the cross to bear, For Christ our Lord.

356 Come, Ye Disconsolate

Thomas Moore, vs. 1, 2
Thomas Hastings, v. 3

Samuel Webbe

1. Come, ye dis - con - so - late, wher - e'er ye lan - guish; Come, at the
2. Joy of the des - o - late, light of the stray - ing, Hope of the
3. Here see the bread of life, see wa - ters flow - ing Forth from the

mer - cy - seat fer - vent - ly kneel; Here bring your wound - ed hearts.
pen - i - tent, fade - less and pure; Here speaks the Com - fort - er,
throne of God, pure from a - bove; Come to the feast of love;

Come, Ye Disconsolate, Concluded

here tell your an - guish; Earth has no sor - row that heav'n can - not heal.
ten - der - ly say - ing, "Earth has no sor - row that heav'n can - not cure."
come, ev - er know - ing Earth has no sor - row but heav'n can re - move.

357   There's a Fountain Free

Mrs. M. B. C. Slade   Dr. A. B. Everett

1. There's a foun-tain free, 'tis for you and me: Let us haste, O, haste to its brink;
2. There's a liv-ing stream, with a crystal gleam: From the throne of life now it flows;
3. There's a rock that's cleft and no soul is left, That may not its pure wa-ters share;

'Tis the fount of love from the Source a-bove, And He bids us all free-ly drink.
While the wa-ters roll let the wea-ry soul Hear the call that forth free-ly goes.
'Tis for you and me, and its stream I see: Let us has-ten joy-ful-ly there.

Chorus

Will you come   to the foun-tain free? Will you come?   'tis for you and me;
Will you come,   Will you come,

Thirst-y soul,   hear the wel-come call: 'Tis a foun-tain o-pened for all.
Thirst-y soul,

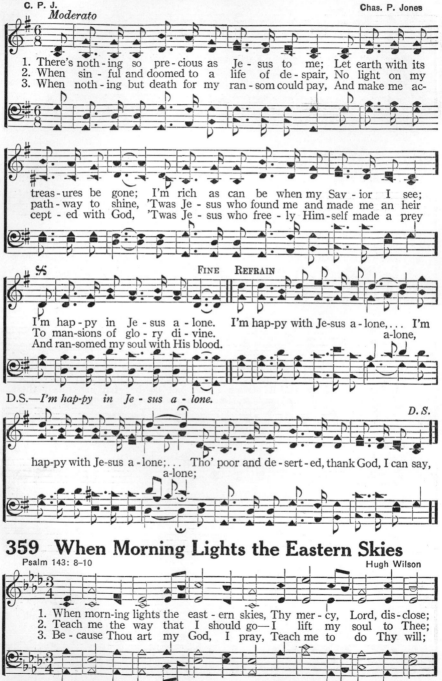

358 I'm Happy with Jesus Alone

C. P. J.
Moderato
Chas. P. Jones

1. There's noth-ing so pre-cious as Je - sus to me; Let earth with its
2. When sin - ful and doomed to a life of de - spair, No light on my
3. When noth - ing but death for my ran - som could pay, And make me ac-

treas-ures be gone; I'm rich as can be when my Sav - ior I see;
path-way to shine, 'Twas Je - sus who found me and made me an heir
cept - ed with God, 'Twas Je - sus who free - ly Him-self made a prey

FINE REFRAIN

I'm hap-py in Je - sus a - lone. I'm hap-py with Je-sus a-lone,... I'm
To man-sions of glo - ry di - vine. a-lone,
And ran-somed my soul with His blood.

D.S.—*I'm hap-py in Je - sus a - lone.*

D. S.

hap-py with Je-sus a-lone;... Tho' poor and de-sert-ed, thank God, I can say,
a-lone;

359 When Morning Lights the Eastern Skies

Psalm 143: 8-10
Hugh Wilson

1. When morn-ing lights the east - ern skies, Thy mer - cy, Lord, dis-close;
2. Teach me the way that I should go—I lift my soul to Thee;
3. Be - cause Thou art my God, I pray, Teach me to do Thy will;

And let Thy lov - ing kind-ness rise: On Thee my hopes re - pose.
Re - deem me from the rag - ing foe: To Thee, O Lord, I flee.
O lead me in the per - fect way By Thy good Spir - it still.

360 When God Forgives He Forgets

Copyright, 1934, by Nazarene Publishing House

Haldor Lillenas   Bertha Mae Lillenas

1. My heart is sing-ing a glad new song Since Christ redeemed me from sin and wrong,
2. The load of guilt that encumbered me, I lost while looking on Cal - va - ry,
3. And when I've end-ed life's wea-ry race, And look with rapture up - on His face,

To Him for - ev - er shall praise be-long: When God for-gives He for-gets.
My cap - tive soul there found lib - er - ty: When God for-gives He for-gets.
I'll sing this song of re-deem-ing grace: "When God for-gives He for-gets."

CHORUS

When God for-gives He for - gets,...... When God for-gives He for-gets,......
       He for-gets,   He for-gets,

My sins tho' as scar-let are made white as snow; When God forgives He for-gets.

361   When the Roll Is Called Up Yonder

J. M. B.

J. M. Black

1. When the trump-et of the Lord shall sound and time shall be no more, And the
2. On that bright and cloudless morning when the dead in Christ shall rise, And the
3. Let us la-bor for the Mas-ter from the dawn till set-ting sun, Let us

morning breaks e-ter-nal, bright and fair; When the saved of earth shall gath-er
glo-ry of His res-ur-rec-tion share; When His cho-sen ones shall gath-er
talk of all His wondrous love and care; Then when all of life is o-ver

o-ver on the oth-er shore, And the roll is called up yon-der, I'll be there.
to their home beyond the skies, And the roll is called up yon-der, I'll be there.
and our work on earth is done, And the roll is called up yon-der, I'll be there.

FINE

D. S.—*roll is called up yon-der, I'll be there.*

CHORUS

When the roll...... is called up yon - - der, When the roll...... is
When the roll is called up yonder I'll be there,   When the roll is

D. S.

called up yon - - der, When the roll...... is called up yon-der, When the
called up yonder I'll be there,   When the roll is called up yon-der,

362 It Pays to Serve Jesus

F. C. H.

Frank C. Huston

1. The serv - ice of Je - sus true pleas - ure af - fords, In Him there is
2. It pays to serve Je - sus what-e'er may be - tide, It pays to be
3. Tho' some-times the shad-ows may hang o'er the way, And sor-rows may

joy with - out an al - loy; 'Tis heav - en to trust Him and rest on His
true what-e'er you may do; 'Tis rich - es of mer - cy in Him to a -
come to beck - on us home, Our pre-cious Re-deem - er each toil will re -

Chorus

words; It pays to serve Je - sus each day.
bide; It pays to serve Je - sus each day.
pay; It pays to serve Je - sus each day.

It pays to serve Je - sus, it

pays ev-'ry day, It pays ev-'ry step of the way;........ Tho' the pathway to
ev-'ry step of the way;

glo - ry may sometimes be drear, You'll be hap-py each step of the way.

363   The End of the Way

* * *

Charlie D. Tillman

1. The sands have been washed in the footprints Of the Stranger on Gal-i-lee's shore,
2. There are so man-y hills to climb up-ward, And I of-ten am longing for rest;
3. When the last feeble step has been tak-en, And the gates of that city ap-pear,

D. C.—*And the toils of the road will seem nothing When I get to the end of the way;*

FINE.

And the voice that subdued the rough billows Is heard in Ju-de-a no more;
But the Lord who appoints me my pathway Knows just what is needful and best.
And the beau-ti-ful songs of the an-gels Float out on my lis-ten-ing ear;

And the toils of the road will seem nothing When I get to the end of the way.

D. C.

But the path of that lone Gal-i-le-an Will I joy-ful-ly fol-low to-day;
I know in His word He has promised That my strength it shall be as my day;
When all that now seems so mys-te-rious Will be bright and as clear as the day;

364   There's a Pardon Full and Sweet

E. E. Hewitt

E. O. Excell

1. There's a par-don full and sweet, 'Tis for you, 'tis for me; Bless-ed rest at
2. There's a help for ev-'ry day, 'Tis for you, 'tis for me; Joy and bless-ing
3. There's a robe of snow-y white, 'Tis for you; 'tis for me; There's a home of

There's a Pardon, Concluded

CHORUS

Je - sus' feet, 'Tis for you and me.
by the way, 'Tis for you and me. All for you, if you be-lieve, If sal-
glo - ry bright,'Tis for you and me.

va - tion you re-ceive; There's a welcome, warm and true, All for you, all for me.

365   Savior, to Thee We Humbly Bow

Vana R. Raye

Copyright, 1948, by Gospel Advocate Company

L. O. Sanderson

1. Sav - ior, to Thee we hum-bly bow, Thy will must be our own;
2. Help us the nar - row way to go; Help us the race to run;
3. Thou per - fect pat - tern of the free, Shield us from Sa - tan's darts;

By Thee are all our bless-ings now, By Thee we reach our home.
Help us in truth and grace to grow That we may hear "Well done."
Help us to live that men may see Thine im - age in our hearts.

D.S.—*Lord, we would live and serve and love, And leave the world be - hind.*

CHORUS

D. S.

With all the heart, with all the soul, With all our strength and mind,

366 When They Ring the Golden Bells

Dion De Marbelle

1. There's a land be-yond the riv-er, That we call the sweet for-ev-er, And we
2. We shall know no sin nor sor-row, In that ha-ven of to-mor-row, When our
3. When our days shall know their number, When in death we sweetly slumber, When the

on-ly reach that shore by faith's decree; One by one we'll gain the por-tals, There to
bark shall sail be-yond the sil-ver sea; We shall on-ly know the blessing Of our
King commands the spir-it to be free; Nev-er-more with anguish laden, We shall

dwell with the im-mor-tals, When they ring the gold-en bells for you and me.
Fa-ther's sweet ca-ress-ing, When they ring the gold-en bells for you and me.
reach that love-ly Ai-den, When they ring the gold-en bells for you and me.

CHORUS

Don't you hear the bells now ringing? Don't you hear the an-gels sing-ing? 'Tis the

glo-ry hal-le-lu-jah Ju-bi-lee (Ju-bi-lee), In that far-off sweet for-ev-er,

Just beyond the shining river, When they ring the golden bells for you and me.

you and me.

367 Good Morning in Glory

A. J. G.

A. J. Gordon

1. The night is fast passing, The day is at hand, Day is at hand;
2. The Lamb on Mount Zi-on With nail-pierc-ed hand, Nail-pierc-ed hand,
3. Then sing, wea-ry pil-grims, You're nearing the strand, Near-ing the strand,

We've sight-ed the moun-tains of Beu-lah land, Sweet Beu-lah land.
Has o-pened the por-tals of Beu-lah land, Sweet Beu-lah land.
Where loved ones a-wait you in Beu-lah land, Sweet Beu-lah land.

REFRAIN

We'll say good morn-ing in glo-ry, Good morn-ing in glo-ry; We'll

say good morn-ing in glo-ry, When the dark-ness has turned to day.

368 What Is Your Prospect?

L. O. S.

L. O. Sanderson

1. What is your pros - pect, what your de - sire? What ex - pec-
2. Heav - en - ly yearn - ing faith will pro - mote; Faith is the
3. O for a faith which noth - ing can mar; O for a

ta - tion for the last hour? What is your hope, your wit - ness, your
sub - stance for ev - 'ry hope; It is con - vic - tion of the un-
hope that reach - es a - far; O for a heart to trust and o-

faith?.... This is the need for com - fort in death.
seen,...... Bridg - ing the broad and time - end - ing stream.
bey,...... Bound - ed by love, the ex - cel - lent way.

369 On Zion's Glorious Summit

John Kent

Anon.

1. On Zi - on's glo - rious sum - mit stood A nu - m'rous host re - deemed by blood!
2. Here all who suf - fered sword or flame For truth, or Je - sus' love - ly name,
3. While ev - er - last - ing a - ges roll, E - ter - nal love shall feast their soul,

They hymned their King in strains di - vine; I heard the song, and
Shout vic - t'ry now and hail the Lamb, And bow be - fore the
And scenes of bliss, for - ev - er new, Rise in suc - ces - sion

strove to join, I heard the song, and strove to join.
great I AM, And bow be-fore the great I AM.
to their view, Rise in suc-ces-sion to their view.

370 Come Closer, Lord, Today

Copyright, 1948, by Gospel Advocate Company

G. C. T.   Grant Colfax Tullar

1. Come clos-er, Lord, to me to-day Than Thou hast been be-fore;
2. Come clos-er, Lord, and let me learn What joy Thou hast for me;
3. Come clos-er, Lord, with naught between, More like Thee I shall grow,

Yes, clos-er in the dai-ly walk, Nor let me leave Thee more.
What serv-ice Thou wilt have me do That I may help-ful be.
And when Thy like-ness I shall bear Thy per-fect love I'll show.

Chorus

Come clos-er, Lord, yes clos-er, And with me e'er a-bide. I would not

walk............ life's way a-lone, I'd walk, with Thee be-side.
I would not walk

371   Do You Know the Song?

A. P. Cobb

J. H. Fillmore

1. Do you know the song that the an-gels sang On that night in the
2. Do you know the song that the shep-herds heard As they watched o'er their
3. Do you know the story that the wise men heard As they journeyed from the

long a - go? When the heav'ns a - bove with their mu - sic rang, Till it
flocks by night? When the skies bent down, and their hearts were stirred By the
East a - far? O'er a path-way plain, for there night-ly burned In their

CHORUS

ech - oed in the earth be - low?
voic - es of the an - gels bright?   All glo - ry in the high-est, Peace on
sight a glo-rious guid-ing star?

earth, good-will to men; Glo - ry in the high-est, Peace, good-will to men;

Glo - ry in the highest, Glo - ry in the high-est, Peace on earth, good-will to men.

372 The Church of God

Vana R. Raye

L. O. Sanderson

1. God's fam - i - ly is His church di - vine—Be - gun, sus-tained, by His
2. Be - yond are those who have con-quered death; Be - low are they who a-
3. What glo - ry there! O what bless-ings here! One hope, one Lord, and His

wise de - sign; The ark of age and the shrine of youth! From her a-
bide in faith, The twain—yon host and the saints of earth—One house-hold
name to wear! One church, one creed, meet-ing ev - 'ry need—All na - tions

CHORUS

lone goes the word of truth. The church..... of Christ......
are by a ho - ly birth.
blest by His right-eous seed. The church of God is the bride of Christ!

Re-deemed by His blood—what a pur - chase price! The king-dom of

God and the saints' a - bode; The realm of life for the sons of God.

373 Only a Shadow Between

E. C. Baird   J. C. Blaker

1. I have a home in a fair sum-mer-land, Its beau-ties I
2. Je - sus has prom-ised a home to pre-pare, Thro' faith on this
3. When I have fin-ished my task here be-low, I pass thro' this

nev - er have seen (have seen), I have a place on an ev-er-green strand,
prom-ise I lean (I lean), I have a man-sion that's won-drous-ly fair,
shad-ow-y screen (the screen), Be with the ran-somed for - ev - er I know,

CHORUS

There's on - ly a shad-ow be - tween. On - ly a shad-ow, a

shad-ow be - tween, On - ly a shad-ow be - tween,..... One step to
be-tween,

go O the way's all a - glow, There's on - ly a shad-ow be - tween.

374 Scattering Precious Seed

W. A. Ogden

Geo. C. Hugg

1. Scat-ter-ing pre-cious seed by the way-side, Scat-ter-ing pre-cious seed
2. Scat-ter-ing pre-cious seed for the grow-ing, Scat-ter-ing pre-cious seed,
3. Scat-ter-ing pre-cious seed, doubting nev-er, Scat-ter-ing pre-cious seed,

by the hill-side; Scat-ter-ing pre-cious seed o'er the field, wide,
free-ly sow-ing; Scat-ter-ing pre-cious seed, trust-ing, know-ing,
trust-ing ev-er; Sow-ing the word with prayer and en-deav-or,

CHORUS

Scat-ter-ing pre-cious seed by the way. { Sow - - ing in the
Sure-ly the Lord will send it the rain. { Sow - - ing in the
Trusting the Lord for growth and for yield. Sow-ing the pre-cious seed,

morn - - - ing, Sow - - - ing at the
eve - - - ning, (*Omit* . . . .)
Sow-ing the pre-cious seed, Sow-ing the seed at noon-tide,

pp

noon - - tide; Sow-ing the pre-cious seed by the way. . . .
Sowing the precious seed; by the way.

375 With Thee

G. C. T.

Grant Colfax Tullar

1. With Thee I would jour-ney, Dear Sav-ior to-day, And leave to Thy
2. With Thee I would la-bor The whole of life's way, In cool of the
3. With Thee I would suf-fer If that be Thy will, With Thee in the

choos-ing The trend of my way; Tho' pleas-ant or thorn-y, Tho'
morn-ing, Or heat of the day. Thy grace all-suf-fi-cient For
gar-den, Or up Cal-v'ry's hill; With Thee in the val-ley Where

lev-el or steep, I'll sing with con-tent-ment, And cour-age I'll keep.
me shall pre-vail; Thy strength is my por-tion, Nor can I e'er fail.
deep shad-ows lie, Then with Thee, for-ev-er, I'll dwell by and by.

376 O Love That Wilt Not Let Me Go

George Matheson

Albert L. Peace

1. O Love that wilt not let me go, I rest my wea-ry
2. O Light that fol-low'st all my way, I yield my flick-'ring
3. O Cross that lift-est up my head, I dare not ask to

soul in Thee; I give Thee back the life I owe,
torch to Thee; My heart re-stores its bor-rowed ray,
hide from Thee; I lay in dust life's glo-ry dead,

O Love That Wilt Not Let Me Go, Concluded

That in Thine o - cean depths its flow May rich - er, full - er be.
That in Thy sun-shine's glow its day May bright-er, fair - er be.
And from the ground there blossoms red, Life that shall end - less be.

377 An Empty Mansion

Mrs. J. B. Karnes   Copyright, 1939, by Stamps-Baxter Music Company   C. A. Luttrell

1. Here I la - bor and toil as I look for a home, Just an hum - ble a-
2. Ev - er thank-ful am I that my Sav-ior and Lord Promised un - to the
3. When my la - bor and toil-ing have end-ed be - low And my hands shall lie

bode a - mong men, While in heav - en a man-sion is wait-ing for me
wea - ry sweet rest; Noth-ing more could I ask than a man-sion a - bove,
fold - ed in rest, I'll ex-change this old home for a man-sion up there

D. S.—*Man - y friends and dear loved ones will wel-come me there*

Chorus

And a gen - tle voice plead-ing "Come in."
There to live with the saved and the blest.   There's a man - sion now
And in - vite the arch an - gel as guest.

Near the door of that man-sion some day.

D. S.

emp - ty, just wait-ing for me At the end of life's trou - ble-some way,

378 Joy to the World

Isaac Watts

Handel

1. Joy to the world, the Lord is come! Let earth re-ceive her King; Let
2. Joy to the earth, the Sav-ior reigns! Let men their songs em-ploy, While
3. He rules the world with truth and grace, And makes the na-tions prove The

ev - 'ry heart pre-pare Him room, And heav'n and nature sing, And
fields, and floods, rocks, hills, and plains Re-peat the sound-ing joy, Re-
glo - ries of His right-eous-ness, And won-ders of His love, And

(1) And heav'n and na-ture

heav'n and na - ture sing, And heav'n, and heav'n and na - ture sing.
peat the sound-ing joy, Re - peat, re - peat the sound-ing joy.
won-ders of His love, And won - ders, won - ders of His love.

sing,...............

sing, And heav'n and na-ture sing,

379 Even Me

Elizabeth Codner

William B. Bradbury

1. {Lord, I hear of show'rs of bless-ing Thou art scat-t'ring full and free, }
   {Show'rs the thirst-y land re-fresh-ing: Let Thy mer - cy fall on me. }

2. {Faith - ful - ly, O gra-cious Sav - ior, I would live and cling to Thee; }
   {Grant to me Thy lov - ing fa - vor—Not my will but Thine to be. }

3. {Love of God, so pure and change-less, Blood of Christ so rich, so free, }
   {Grace of God, so strong and bound-less, Mag - ni - fy them all in me. }

Even Me, Concluded

E - ven me, E - ven me, Let Thy mer - cy fall on me.

380   Beautiful Zion, Built Above

George Gill   Thos. J. Cook

1. Beau-ti-ful Zi-on, built a-bove, Beau-ti-ful cit-y that I love;
2. Beau-ti-ful heav'n,where all is light, Beau-ti-ful an-gels, clothed in white;
3. Beau-ti-ful throne for Christ our King, Beau-ti-ful songs the an-gels sing;

Beau-ti-ful gates of pearl-y white, Beau-ti-ful tem-ple—God its light;
Beau-ti-ful strains that nev-er tire, Beau-ti-ful harps thro' all the choir;
Beau-ti-ful rest—all wand'rings cease, Beau-ti-ful home of per-fect peace;

He who was slain on Cal-va-ry O-pens those pearl-y gates to me.
There shall I join the cho-rus sweet, Wor-ship-ing at the Sav-ior's feet.
There shall my eyes the Sav-ior see: Haste to this heav'nly home with me.

Zi-on, Zi-on, love-ly Zi-on! Beau-ti-ful Zi-on, cit-y of our God!

381 After the Shadows

James Rowe

Samuel W. Beazley

1. Aft-er the mid-night, morning will greet us; Aft-er the sad-ness, joy will ap-
2. Aft-er the bat-tle, peace will be giv-en; Aft-er the weep-ing, song there will
3. Shadows and sunshine all thro' the sto-ry, Teardrops and pleasure, day aft-er

pear; Aft-er the tem-pest, sun-light will meet us; Aft-er the jeer-ing,
be; Aft-er the jour-ney there will be heav-en,—Burdens will fall and
day; But when we reach the king-dom of glo-ry, Tri-als of earth will

praise we shall hear. Aft-er the shad-ows, there will be sun - shine;
we shall be free.
van-ish a-way. Aft-er the shadows, there will be sunshine;

CHORUS

Aft-er the frown, the soul-cheering smile;.... Cling to the Sav-ior,
Aft-er the frown, soul-cheering smile; Cling to the Savior,

rit.

love Him for-ev - - er; All will be well in a lit-tle while.
love Him for-ev - er;

382 **God Be with You**

J. E. Rankin

W. G. Tomer

1. God be with you till we meet a-gain; By His counsels guide, up-hold you,
2. God be with you till we meet a-gain; 'Neath His wings protecting hide you,
3. God be with you till we meet a-gain; When life's perils thick confound you,
4. God be with you till we meet a-gain; Keep love's banner floating o'er you,

With His sheep se-cure-ly fold you; God be with you till we meet a-gain.
Dai-ly man-na still pro-vide you; God be with you till we meet a-gain.
Put His arms un-fail-ing 'round you; God be with you till we meet a-gain.
Smite death's threat'ning wave before you; God be with you till we meet a-gain.

CHORUS

Till we meet,.......... till we meet, Till we
Till we meet, till we meet, till we meet,

meet at Je-sus' feet; Till we meet,..........
till we meet; Till we meet,

till we meet, God be with you till we meet a-gain.
till we meet a-gain,

383 The Lord's Return

G. C. T.

Grant Colfax Tullar

1. He may come at morn-ing—just at break of day, As the
2. Wheth-er long de-part-ed, or we still re-main, We shall
3. E-ven so, Lord Je-sus, come at break of day,—Come at

sun-rise greets the sight; He may come at noon-time when the heart is gay,
meet Him in the air; Ev-er-more to be with Him and with Him reign,
mid-night, or at noon. Come to ban-ish dark-ness from the world a-way,

CHORUS

Or at eve-ning's az-ure light.
In an-oth-er world, so fair. May we all be read-y When the
And to heav'n our hearts at-tune.

trump shall sound, For His com-ing may be near, Be it at the

noon-tide, Or the dark of night, When to us He shall ap-pear.

384 He Knows

Mary G. Brainard

P. P. Bliss

1. I know not what a-waits me, God kind-ly veils mine eyes,
2. One step I see be-fore me, 'Tis all I need to see,
3. So on I go not know-ing, I would not if I might;

And o'er each step of my on-ward way He makes new scenes to rise;
The light of heav-en more bright-ly shines, When earth's il-lu-sions flee;
I'd rath-er walk in the dark with God Than go a-lone in light;

And ev-'ry joy He sends me, comes A sweet and glad sur-prise.
And sweet-ly thro' the si-lence, came His lov-ing "Fol-low Me."
I'd rath-er trav-el faith with Him Than go a-lone by sight.

CHORUS

Where He may lead I'll fol-low, My trust in Him re-pose; And ev-'ry

hour in per-fect peace I'll sing, He knows, He knows; sing, He knows, He knows.

385 Where Livest Thou?

Vana R. Raye

L. O. Sanderson

1. Where liv-est thou? In pleas-ures of the world? Or in that
2. Where liv-est thou? In mal-ice and in strife? Where dark-ness
3. Where liv-est thou? There is a place to stay— 'Tis in the

realm whence Sa-tan's darts are hurled? Choose now to fol-low with the
veils and mars the right-eous life? Choose now to make a liv-ing
Christ, the true and liv-ing way! With-in His king-dom la-bor

sons of God; Far bet-ter this than where the great have trod.
sac-ri-fice— 'Tis bet-ter thus; for we be-long to Christ.
while you may; Hear what He says, in loy-al trust o-bey.

386 Now the Day Is Over

Sabine Baring-Gould

Joseph Barnby

1. Now the day is o - ver, Night is draw-ing nigh;....
2. Je - sus, give the wea-ry Calm and sweet re-pose;....
3. When the morn-ing wak-ens, Then may I a-rise.....

Shad-ows of the eve-ning Steal a-cross the sky.
With Thy ten-d'rest bless-ing May our eye-lids close.
Pure, and fresh, and sin-less In Thy ho-ly eyes.

eve-ning Steal a-cross the sky.

387 Just Such a Friend Is He

G. C. T.

Grant Colfax Tullar

1. When I am lone-ly and need-ing a friend, Al-ways to
2. When in my pov-er-ty, sick-ness or pain, I must find
3. If in the dark-ness my path-way I lose, Light for my
4. When I, a-wea-ry, at last near the shore, Launch my frail

Je - sus I flee. He for my lone-li-ness com-fort will lend,
some-where re-lief, He is the One to re-store me a-gain,
way He will be. His friend-ly guid-ance I ev-er would choose,
bark on the sea, I know that Je-sus will bear me safe o'er—

CHORUS

Just such a Friend He will be.
Giv-ing me glad-ness for grief. Won-der-ful friend-ship with
Know-ing He car-eth for me.
Just such a Pi-lot is He.

Je-sus I claim, Dear-er than oth-ers He ev-er will be.

What-ev-er need for a friend be my aim—Just such a Friend is He.

388 The Silver Star

D. K. En

H. R. Palmer

1. On the brow of night there shines a sil - ver star, On the brow of
night there shines a sil - ver star, And the wise men gaze on its
heav'n - ly rays, Till they find the King, whose throne they sought a - far,
In the Babe of Beth - le - hem.

2. 'Tis the lamp of God high hang-ing in the air, 'Tis the lamp of
God high hang-ing in the air, And it guides our feet thro' the
roy - al street; There is sweet soul - rest for those who seek it there,
From the Babe of Beth - le - hem.

3. Bring your gifts of gold, of frank-in-cense and myrrh, Bring your gifts of
gold, of frank - in - cense and myrrh, For the King we own is on
Da - vid's throne; Let the priest and King your best af - fec - tions stir,
'Tis the Babe of Beth - le - hem.

Chorus

Sil - ver star, ho - ly night, shine a - far, o'er the night, Till the
Sil - ver star, ho - ly night, shine a - far, o'er the night,

rit.

world shall come from its sin-stained way, And en-ter the gates of a new-born day.

389   Whiter Than Snow

James Nicholson

Wm. G. Fischer

1. Lord Je-sus, I long to be per-fect-ly whole; I want Thee for-ev-er
2. Lord Je-sus, look down from Thy throne in the skies, And help me to make a
3. Lord Je-sus, Thou see-est I pa-tient-ly wait; Come now, and within me

to live in my soul; Break down ev-'ry i-dol, cast out ev-'ry foe:
com-plete sac-ri-fice; I give up my-self and what-ev-er I know:
a new heart cre-ate; To those who have sought Thee, Thou never saidst No:

CHORUS

Now wash me, and I shall be whit-er than snow. Whit-er than snow, yes,

whit-er than snow; Now wash me, and I shall be whit-er than snow.

390 Then Be Prepared

Arr. Copyright, 1948, by Gospel Advocate Company

Words arr. by Vana R. Raye

C. E. Leslie. Arr. by L. O. S.

1. There is a cit - y God hath made, Whose street is paved with gold; The
2. It is ap-point - ed men to die, There aft - er judg-ment day; And

glo - ry of that heav'n-ly place, By proph-ets has been told. Then be pre-pared
each ac-count to God must give—How sad to hear: "A - way!" to

.... to en - ter the pearl-y gates; The King of kings.......... in
meet thy God, The Judge of all in

jus-tice there a-waits. { Men of the world, why stand you i - dle all the day?
{ Then be prepared to meet thy God, and life par-take;

Look up to Christ, His will obey, Your sins He'll wash a-way.
The Living Bread is free to all, Who (*Omit.* . . . .) will their sins for-sake.

391 Welcome for Me

Fanny J. Crosby

Wm. J. Kirkpatrick

1. Like a bird on the deep, far a-way from its nest, I had
2. I am safe in the ark; I have fold-ed my wings On the
3. I am safe in the ark, and I dread not the storm, Tho' a-

wan-dered, my Sav-ior, from Thee; But Thy dear lov-ing voice called me
bos-om of mer-cy di-vine; I am filled with the light of Thy
round me the sur-ges may roll; I will look to the skies, where the

home to Thy breast, And I knew there was wel-come for me.
pres-ence so bright, And the joy that will ev-er be mine.
day nev-er dies, I will sing of the joy in my soul.

CHORUS

Wel-come for me, Sav-ior, from Thee; A smile and a wel-come for me;

Now, like a dove, I rest in Thy love, And find a sweet ref-uge in Thee....
in Thee.

392 What Will Christ Do with Me?

Vana R. Raye

H. R. Russell

1. When the de-par-ture for worlds un-known Is at hand for me;
2. When from the grave I shall hear the sound Of His voice to me;
3. When I am bro't to the bar of God And e-ter-ni-ty;

When the last breath of my life is gone—What will Christ do with me?
When the arch-an-gels the call re-sound—What will Christ do with me?
When I am judged by the paths I've trod—What will Christ do with me?

CHORUS

What will He do with me? What will He do with me? When the

Mas-ter shall say "En-ter in" or "A-way"—O what will He do with me.

393 Have Thine Own Way, Lord

Adelaide Pollard

Slowly

Geo. C. Stebbins

1. Have Thine own way, Lord! Have Thine own way! Thou art the
2. Have Thine own way, Lord! Have Thine own way! Search me and
3. Have Thine own way, Lord! Have Thine own way! Hold o'er my

Pot - ter; I am the clay. Mold me and make me
try me, Mas - ter, to - day! Whit - er than snow, Lord,
be - ing Ab - so - lute sway! Fill with Thy spir - it

Aft - er Thy will, While I am wait - ing, Yield - ed and still.
Wash me just now, As in Thy pres - ence Hum - bly I bow.
Till all shall see Christ on - ly, al - ways, Liv - ing in me!

394   Ready to Suffer

Arr.

Charlie D. Tillman

1. Read-y to suf - fer grief or pain, Read-y to stand the test;
2. Read-y to go, pre - pared to bear, Read-y to watch and pray;
3. Read-y to speak, a - lert to warn, Read-y His way to learn;

Read-y to stay at home and send Oth-ers, if He sees best.
Read-y to stand a - side and give, Till He shall clear the way.
Read-y in life, no fear of death Read-y for His re - turn.

{ Read-y to go, or read-y to stay, Read-y my place to fill;
{ Read-y for serv-ice, low-ly or great, Read-y to do (*Omit* . . . . . .) His will.

Onward, Christian Soldiers

Sabine Baring-Gould

Arthur Sullivan

1. On - ward, Chris-tian sol - diers! March-ing as to war, With the cross of
2. Crowns and thrones may per - ish, King-doms rise and wane, But the Church of
3. On - ward, then, ye peo - ple, Join our hap-py throng; Blend with ours your

Je - sus Go - ing on be - fore; Christ, the roy - al Mas - ter,
Je - sus Con - stant will re - main; Gates of hell can nev - er
voic - es In the tri - umph-song; Glo - ry, laud and hon - or

Leads a - gainst the foe; For-ward in - to bat - tle, See His ban-ners go!
'Gainst that Church pre-vail; We have Christ's own promise, And that cannot fail.
Un - to Christ the King, This thro' countless a - ges Men and an-gels sing.

REFRAIN

On - ward, Chris-tian sol - diers! March-ing as to war,

With the cross of Je - sus Go - ing on be - fore.

396 There's a Wideness in God's Mercy

Frederick W. Faber

Lizzie S. Tourjee

1. There's a wide-ness in God's mer-cy, Like the wide-ness of the sea;
2. There is wel-come for the sin-ner, And more grac-es for the good;
3. If our love were but more sim-ple, We should take Him at His word;

There's a kind-ness in His jus-tice, Which is more than lib-er-ty.
There is mer-cy with the Sav-ior; There is heal-ing in His blood.
And our lives would be all sun-shine In the sweet-ness of our Lord.

397 Jesus Now Is Calling

R. E. H.

R. E. Hudson

1. Come, ye wea-ry and op-pressed, Je-sus now is call-ing you;
2. Tho' your sins like moun-tains rise, Je-sus now is call-ing you;
3. Tho' your sins like scar-let be, Je-sus now is call-ing you;

REFRAIN

Come to Him, He'll give you rest—Je-sus bids you come. Je-sus now is call-ing,
He has made the sac-ri-fice— And He bids you come.
From your sins He'll set you free—And He bids you come. call-ing,

Call-ing, call-ing; Je-sus now is call-ing you—Call-ing you to come.
call-ing, call-ing;

398 In the Kingdom

Vana R. Raye

L. O. Sanderson

1. In the king-dom of the Lord There is grace for ev - 'ry heart; In the
2. In the king-dom, there a - lone, Are the saved, the good, the blest; Here the
3. In the king-dom of the Lord Christ a - bides—He is the King! It is

king - dom of the Lord Bless-ings come and sins de - part.
Sav - ior knows His own, Here is joy and peace and rest.
ours to love His word, To sub-mit in ev - 'ry - thing.

O glo - rious

King-dom! Bride of the Sav-ior! Liv-ing for - ev-er God's purpose to ful - fil.

399 Silent Night, Holy Night

Joseph Mohr

Franz Gruber

1. Si - lent night! Ho - ly night! Land and deep si - lent sleep!
2. Si - lent night! Ho - ly night! On the plain wakes the strain,
3. Si - lent night! Ho - ly night! Earth, a - wake! si - lence break!

Soft - ly glit - ters bright Beth - le-hem's star, Beck - 'ning Is - ra - el's
Sung by heav - en - ly har - bin-gers bright, Fraught with ti - dings of
High your an - thems of mel - o - dy raise! Heav'n and earth in full

eye from a-far, Where the Sav-ior is born, Where the Sav-ior is born.
boundless delight; Christ the Sav-ior has come, Christ the Sav-ior has come.
cho-rus of praise! Peace for-ev-er shall reign, Peace for-ev-er shall reign.

400   Glory for Me

N. H. Lines

Chas. Edw. Pollock

Vigoroso

1. When in His glo-ry the Sav-ior I see, And in His like-ness for-
2. When I shall see Him de-scend-ing the skies, See the dead mil-lions from
3. When I shall stand on the right of His throne, When I shall know as I

ev-er shall be; There from the tri-als of earth to be free,
slum-ber a-rise, Hear their glad shouts as the Sav-ior they see,
al-so am known, Meet with my loved ones I've longed so to see,

CHORUS

That will be glo-ry, be glo-ry for me. That will be glo-ry for me,........
be glo-ry for me,

D.S.—*That will be glo-ry, be glo-ry for me.*

That will be glo-ry for me,........ There at His side in His love to a-bide
be glo-ry for me,

401 Ye Must Be Born Again

W. T. Sleeper

George C. Stebbins

1. A rul - er once came to the Sav - ior by night To ask Him the
2. Ye chil - dren of men, now at - tend to the word So sol - emn - ly
3. O ye who would en - ter that glo - ri - ous rest, And sing with the

way of sal - va - tion and light; The Mas - ter made an - swer in words true and plain,
ut - tered by Je - sus the Lord; And let not this mes - sage to you be in vain,
ransomed the song of the blest; The life ev - er - last - ing if ye would ob - tain,

CHORUS

"Ye must be born a - gain."...... "Ye must be born a - gain.
a - gain.

gain,...... Ye must be born a - gain;...... I ver - i - ly,
a - gain, a - gain;

ver - i - ly say to thee, Ye must be born a - gain."......
a - gain.

402 Jesus Loves Me

Anna B. Warner

Wm. B. Bradbury

1. Je - sus loves me! this I know, For the Bi - ble tells me so;
2. Je - sus loves me! He who died, Heav-en's gate to o - pen wide;
3. Je - sus, take this heart of mine, Make it pure and whol-ly Thine;

Lit - tle ones to Him be - long; They are weak but He is strong.
He will wash a - way my sin, Let His lit - tle child come in.
Thou hast bled and died for me; I will hence-forth live for Thee.

CHORUS

Yes, Je-sus loves me; Yes, Je-sus loves me; Yes, Je-sus loves me; The Bible tells me so.

403 A Child's Evening Prayer

W. T. G.

W. T. Giffe

Andante

1. Je - sus, wilt Thou guard the slum-ber Of a lit - tle child like me?
2. Yes, I know that Thou wilt keep me, So I close my wea - ry eyes;
3. In Thine arms, O Je - sus, fold me Let me be Thy lit - tle lamb;

Wilt Thou watch in dark-ness o'er me, That pro - tect - ed I may be?
Trust-ing Thee to guard my slum-ber 'Neath Thy gra-cious, shel-t'ring skies.
Close un - to Thy bos - om hold me, Give me slum-ber deep and calm.

404   **Love Him, Love Him**

Arranged

1. Love Him, love Him, all ye little chil-dren: God is Love, God is Love; God is Love.
2. Praise Him, praise Him, all ye little chil-dren: God is Love, God is Love; God is Love.

405   **Jesus Bids Us Shine**

Anna B. Warner   E. O. Excell

1. Je - sus bids us shine, with a clear, pure light, Like a lit - tle
2. Je - sus bids us shine, first of all for Him: Well He sees and
3. Je - sus bids us shine, then, for all a - round Man - y kinds of

can - dle burn - ing in the night; In this world of dark - ness
knows it if our light is dim; He looks down from heav - en,
dark - ness in this world a - bound: Sin and want and sor - row—

we must shine, You in your small cor - ner, and I in mine.
sees us shine, You in your small cor - ner, and I in mine.
we must shine, You in your small cor - ner, and I in mine.

406   **Children, Obey Your Parents**

Eph. 6: 1–3. Arr.   L. O. Sanderson

Chil-dren, o-bey your par-ents in the Lord, for this is right;
That you may lon-ger live and well en-joy a (*Omit . . . .*) bet-ter life.

407 **Jesus, Friend of Children**

Vana R. Raye   Copyright, 1935, by Gospel Advocate Company   L. O. Sanderson

1. Je - sus, Friend of chil - dren, ev - er Be a Friend to me;
2. Friend of saint, and Friend of sin - ners, Pre - cious Friend di - vine!
3. I would grow in love and fa - vor Of this pre - cious Friend;

Hold my hand and al - ways keep me Close to Thee.
Friend to poor and Friend to need - y, Friend of mine!
He shall be my life's ex - am - ple To the end.

408 **The Lord Is Watching You**

L. O. S.   Copyright, 1948, by Gospel Advocate Company   L. O. Sanderson

1. Be ye kind, ev - er kind, to an - oth - er, Ten - der - heart - ed, for-
2. Keep your light shin-ing bright all a - round you! Let a smile bring your

D. S.—*There's an all - see - ing*

giv - ing, and true; Keep your heart set a - part un - to mer - cy,
glad - ness to view; Let your love with its ha - lo sur-round you,

eye watch-ing you! Guard your tho'ts and your words and your ac - tions,

FINE.   *D.S.*

For the Lord is always watching you! Watching you!.... Watching you!......
For the Lord is always watching you! Watching you! Watching you!

For the Lord is al-ways watching you!

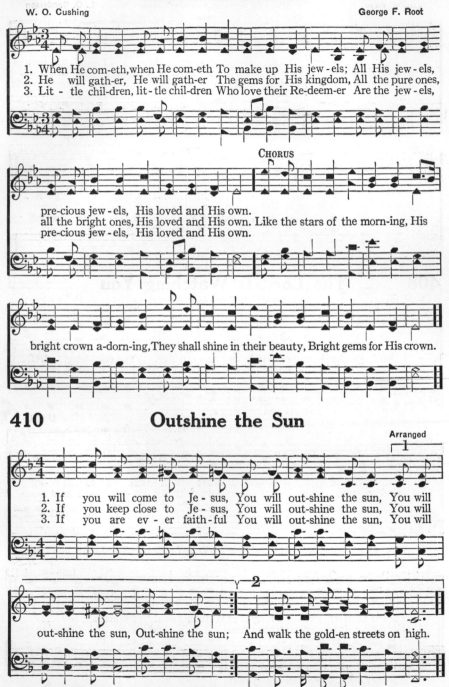

409 When He Cometh

W. O. Cushing

George F. Root

1. When He com-eth, when He com-eth To make up His jew-els; All His jew-els,
2. He will gath-er, He will gath-er The gems for His kingdom, All the pure ones,
3. Lit-tle chil-dren, lit-tle chil-dren Who love their Re-deem-er Are the jew-els,

pre-cious jew-els, His loved and His own.
all the bright ones, His loved and His own. Like the stars of the morn-ing, His
pre-cious jew-els, His loved and His own.

CHORUS

bright crown a-dorn-ing, They shall shine in their beauty, Bright gems for His crown.

410 Outshine the Sun

Arranged

1. If you will come to Je-sus, You will out-shine the sun, You will
2. If you keep close to Je-sus, You will out-shine the sun, You will
3. If you are ev-er faith-ful You will out-shine the sun, You will

out-shine the sun, Out-shine the sun; And walk the gold-en streets on high.

411 The Golden Rule

Vana R. Raye

L. O. Sanderson

1. Do you un-to oth-ers As if they were you, And you were re-
2. Be hon-est and faith-ful, Be truth-ful and kind; Have pit-y for

ceiv-er Of that which they do; Be free with your serv-ice, For
oth-ers, Their need bear in mind; Have mer-cy, be tho't-ful, For-

life is a school Where-in you should live by the gold-en rule.
get rid-i-cule, For this is the gold of the gold-en rule.

412 I Would Be Holy

Vana R. Raye

L. O. Sanderson

1. I would be ho-ly, ho-ly, ho-ly; I would be ho-ly and pure;
2. I would be hum-ble, hum-ble, hum-ble; I would be hum-ble and kind;
3. I would be loy-al, loy-al, loy-al; I would be loy-al and true;

Je-sus was ho-ly, pure and ho-ly, And I would His way pur-sue.
Je-sus was hum-ble, kind and hum-ble, And I would pos-sess His mind.
Je-sus was loy-al, true and loy-al, And I would be faith-ful too.

413 I Would Shine for Jesus

Copyright, 1935, by L. O. Sanderson

Vana R. Raye

L. O. Sanderson

1. I would be a ray of sun-shine, Bright-ly beam-ing ev - 'ry day,
2. I would make a sil - ver lin - ing 'Round the dark - est clouds of woe,
3. I would be a ray of sun-shine—Help me, Lord, that I may be!

Shed-ding ra - diance in the dark-ness, Driv-ing gloom - y clouds a - way.
I would shine and shine for Je - sus, Ev - 'ry - where I chance to go.
May the im - age of Thy Be - ing E'er re - flect it - self in me.

CHORUS

I would shine, shine for Jesus, Each moment of the day; And drive the gloom away.

414 Away in a Manger

Martin Luther

Arr. by L. O. S.

1. A - way in a man-ger, no crib for His bed, The lit - tle Lord
2. Be near me Lord Je - sus, I ask Thee to stay, Close by me for-

Je - sus laid down His sweet head; The stars in the sky looked
ev - er, and love me, I pray; Bless all the dear chil - dren in

down where He lay, The lit - tle Lord Je - sus, a - sleep in the hay.
Thy ten - der care, And take us to glo - ry, to live with Thee there.

415 All Things Bright and Beautiful

Copyright, 1935, by Gospel Advocate Company

C. F. Alexander

L. O. Sanderson

1. The lit - tle flow'r that o - pens, The lit - tle bird that sings
2. The cold wind in the win - ter, The pleas-ant sum - mer sun,
3. He gave us eyes to see them, And lips that we might tell

God made their glow-ing col - ors, He made their ti - ny wings.
The ripe fruits in the gar - den, He made them ev - 'ry one.
How great is God Al - might - y, Who has made all things well.

Chorus

All things bright and beau - ti - ful, Crea - tures great and small,

All things wise and won - der - ful, The Lord God made them all.

416   Faith Is the Victory

John H. Yates

Ira D. Sankey

1. En-camped a - long the hills of light, Ye Chris-tian sol - diers, rise, And
2. His ban - ner o - ver us is love, Our sword the Word of God; We
3. On ev - 'ry hand the foe we find Drawn up in dread ar - ray; Let

press the bat - tle ere the night Shall veil the glow-ing skies. A-gainst the foe in
tread the road the saints a-bove With shouts of triumph trod. By faith, they like a
tents of ease be left be-hind, And—on-ward to the fray. Sal-va-tion's hel-met

vales be - low Let all our strength be hurled; Faith is the vic - to - ry, we know,
whirlwind's breath, Swept on o'er ev - 'ry field; The faith by which they conquered Death
on each head, With truth all girt a - bout, The earth shall tremble 'neath our tread,

CHORUS

That o - ver-comes the world.   Faith is the vic - to - ry! Faith is the
Is still our shin - ing shield.
And ech - o with our shout.   Faith is the vic - to - ry! Faith is the

vic - to - ry! Oh, glo - ri - ous vic - to - ry, That o - ver-comes the world.

417 For Christ and the Church

E. E. Hewitt

Wm. J. Kirkpatrick

1. "For Christ and the church" let our voic-es ring, Let us hon-or the
2. "For Christ and the church" be our ear-nest prayer, Let us fol-low His
3. "For Christ and the church" will-ing of-f'rings make, Time and tal-ents and
4. "For Christ and the church" let us cast a-side, By His con-quer-ing

name of our own bless-ed King; Let us work with a will in the
ban-ner, the cross dai-ly bear; Let us yield, whol-ly yield, to the
gold for the dear Mas-ter's sake; We will ren-der the best we can
grace, chains of self, fear, and pride; May our lives be en-riched by an

strength of youth, And loy-al-ly stand for the king-dom of truth.
gos-pel's pow'r, And serve faith-ful-ly ev-'ry day, ev-'ry hour.
bring to Him, The heart's wealth of love, that will nev-er grow dim.
aim so grand; Then hap-py the call to the Sav-ior's right hand.

Chorus

For Christ,.... our dear Re-deem-er, For Christ,.... the cru-ci-fied;
For Christ, For Christ,

For the church...... His blood hath purchased; The church, His ho-ly bride.
For the church.

418   Beneath the Cross of Jesus

Elizabeth C. Clephane   Frederick C. Maker

1. Be-neath the cross of Je - sus I fain would take my stand, The shadow of a
2. Up - on that cross of Je - sus Mine eye at times can see The ver-y dy -ing
3. I take, O cross, thy shadow For my a - bid-ing place; I ask no oth-er

might-y Rock With-in a wea - ry land; A home with-in the wil-der-ness, A
form of One Who suffered there for me; And from my smitten heart with tears, Two
sun-shine than The sunshine of His face; Con-tent to let the world go by, To

rest up-on the way, From the burning of the noon-tide heat, And the burden of the day.
wonders I con-fess,—The wonders of His glorious love, And my own worthlessness.
know no gain nor loss, My sin-ful self my on-ly shame, My glo-ry all the cross!

419   Take Time to Be Holy

W. D. Longstaff   Geo. C. Stebbins

1. Take time to be ho - ly, Speak oft with thy Lord; A - bide in Him
2. Take time to be ho - ly, The world rush-es on; Spend much time in
3. Take time to be ho - ly, Let Him be thy Guide; And run not be-
4. Take time to be ho - ly, Be calm in thy soul; Each tho't and each

al - ways, And feed on His Word; Make friends of God's chil - dren;
se - cret, With Je - sus a - lone; By look - ing to Je - sus,
fore Him, What - ev - er be - tide; In joy or in sor - row,
mo - tive Be - neath His con - trol; Thus led by His Spir - it

Help those who are weak; For - get-ting in noth-ing His bless-ing to seek.
Like Him thou shalt be; Thy friends in thy con-duct His like-ness shall see.
Still fol-low thy Lord; And, look-ing to Je - sus, Still trust in His Word.
To foun-tains of love, Thou soon shalt be fit-ted For serv-ice a - bove.

420 My Gracious Redeemer I Love!

B. Francis

Lewis Edson
FINE.

1. { My gra-cious Re-deem-er I love! His prais-es a - loud I'll proclaim, }
{ And join with the ar - mies a-bove, To shout His a - dor - a - ble name. }

2. { Earth's pal - a - ces, scepters, and crowns, Their pride with dis-dain I sur-vey; }
{ Their pomps are but shadows and sounds, And pass in a mo-ment a - way. }

D.C.—And feel them in - ces-sant-ly shine, My bound-less, in - ef - fa - ble joy.
D.C.—My joy ev - er - last-ing-ly flows—My God, my Re-deem-er, is mine.

D. C.

To gaze on His glo - ries di - vine Shall be my e - ter - nal em-ploy,
The crown that my Sav-ior be-stows Yon per - ma-nent sun shall out-shine;

421 I Shall Know Him

Fanny J. Crosby

Jno. R. Sweney

1. When my life-work is end-ed, and I cross the swell-ing tide, When the bright and glorious morning I shall see; I shall know my Re-deem-er when I reach the oth-er side, And His smile will be the first to wel-come me.

2. Oh, the soul-thrill-ing rap-ture when I view His bless-ed face, And the lus-ter of His kind-ly beam-ing eye; How my full heart will praise Him for the mer-cy, love, and grace, That pre-pare for me a man-sion in the sky.

3. Thro' the gates to the cit-y in a robe of spot-less white, He will lead me where no tears will ev-er fall; In the glad song of a-ges I shall min-gle with de-light: But I long to meet my Sav-ior first of all.

CHORUS

I shall know ... Him, I shall know Him, And redeemed by His side I shall stand;
I shall know Him,

I shall know ... Him, I shall know Him By the print of the nails in His hand.
I shall know Him,

422 We Are Going Down the Valley

Jessie Brown Pounds   J. H. Fillmore

1. We are go-ing down the val-ley one by one, With our fa - ces tow'rd the
2. We are go-ing down the val-ley one by one, When the la - bors of the
3. We are go-ing down the val-ley one by one: Hu - man com-rade you or

set - ting of the sun; Down the val - ley where the mourn-ful cy-press grows,
wea - ry day are done; One by one, the cares of earth for ev - er past,
I will there have none; But a ten - der hand will guide us lest we fall:

CHORUS

Where the stream of death in si-lence on-ward flows.
We shall stand up-on the riv - er brink at last.   We are go-ing down the val-ley,
Christ is go-ing down the val-ley with us all.

Go-ing down the val-ley, Go-ing tow'rd the setting of the sun; We are go-ing

down the val-ley, Go-ing down the val-ley, Go-ing down the val-ley one by one.

423 **Nearer to Jesus**

Frank E. Roush   L. O. Sanderson

1. Near-er to Je-sus, the Cru-ci-fied One, Lord of great
2. Near-er to Je-sus, so why should I fear? He has be-
3. Near-er to Je-sus, what com-fort and rest! With lov-ing
4. Near-er to Je-sus, the Sav-ior of love, Near-er to

mer-cy, and God's on-ly Son. Near-er to Je-sus, who
quethed me His mes-sage of cheer. Near-er to Je-sus, the
kind-ness I sure-ly am blest; Near-er to Je-sus, who
heav-en, His king-dom a-bove; Near-er the robe and the

saves me from sin; I'm trust-ing my all in the Sav-ior of men.
strength of my life— And He is my lead-er, thro' dan-ger and strife.
giv-eth me peace And joy and sal-va-tion,which nev-er shall cease.
crown I shall wear, And near-er the rich-es of glo-ry up there!

424 **Let Us with a Gladsome Mind**

John Milton   Handel

1. Let us with a glad-some mind Praise the Lord, for He is kind;
2. He with all-com-mand-ing might Filled the new-made world with light;
3. All the liv-ing He doth feed, His full hand sup-plies the need;
4. Let us then, with glad-some mind, Praise the Lord, for He is kind;

For His mer-cies aye en-dure, Ev-er faith-ful, ev-er sure.

425 He Hideth My Soul

Fanny J. Crosby

Wm. J. Kirkpatrick

1. A won-der-ful Sav-ior is Je-sus my Lord, A won-der-ful
2. A won-der-ful Sav-ior is Je-sus my Lord, He tak-eth my
3. When clothed in His brightness, trans-port-ed I rise To meet Him in

Sav-ior to me, He hid-eth my soul in the cleft of the rock, Where
bur-den a-way, He hold-eth me up, and I shall not be moved, He
clouds of the sky, His per-fect sal-va-tion, His won-der-ful love, I'll

CHORUS

riv-ers of pleas-ure I see.
giv-eth me strength as my day. He hid-eth my soul in the cleft of the rock
shout with the mil-lions on high.

That shad-ows a dry, thirst-y land; He hid-eth my life in the depths of His love,

And cov-ers me there with His hand, And cov-ers me there with His hand.

426 Who Will Follow Jesus?

E. E. Hewitt

Wm. J. Kirkpatrick

1. Who will fol-low Je-sus, Standing for the right, Hold-ing up His ban-ner
2. Who will fol-low Je-sus In life's bus-y ways, Work-ing for the Mas-ter,
3. Who will fol-low Je-sus; When the tempter charms, Flee-ing, then, for safe-ty
4. Who will fol-low Je-sus In His work of love, Lead-ing oth-ers to Him,

In the thick-est fight? Lis-t'ning for His or-ders, Read-y to o-bey,
Giv-ing Him the praise; Ear-nest in His vine-yard, Hon-or-ing His laws,
To the Sav-ior's arms; Trust-ing in His mer-cy, Trust-ing in His pow'r,
Lift-ing prayers a-bove? Cour-age, faith-ful serv-ant! In His word we see,

CHORUS

Who will fol-low Je-sus, Serv-ing Him to-day?
Faith-ful to His coun-sel, Watch-ful for His cause? Who will fol-low Je-sus?
Seek-ing fresh re-new-als Of His grace each hour?
On our side for-ev-er Will this Sav-ior be.

Who will make re-ply, "I am on the Lord's side; Master, here am I"? Who will fol-low

Je-sus? Who will make reply, "I am on the Lord's side; Mas-ter, here am I"?

427 O Spread the Tidings 'Round

F. Bottome. Arr. L. O. S. Wm. J. Kirkpatrick

1. O spread the ti-dings 'round, wher-ev-er man is found, Wher-
2. Lo, the great King of kings, with heal-ing in His wings, To
3. O bound-less love di-vine! how shall this tongue of mine To

ev-er hu-man hearts and hu-man woes a-bound; Let ev-'ry Chris-tian
ev-'ry cap-tive soul a full de-liv-'rance brings; And thro' the va-cant
wond'ring mor-tals tell the match-less grace di-vine— That I, in earth's de-

D.S.—*name, the sweet-est heard; His will re-demp-tion brings; O spread the ti-dings*

tongue pro-claim the joy-ful sound: Our Lord is Lord of lords.
cells the song of tri-umph rings, Our Lord is King of kings.
cline should in His im-age shine! In Him, the Word of heav'n.

'round, wher-ev-er man is found—The Lord is King of kings.

CHORUS D. S.

Of lords, He is the Lord! Di-vine, the liv-ing Word! His

428   There Is Rest for the Weary

Jessie Brown Pounds   J. H. Fillmore

1. There is rest for the wea-ry, if rest they will seek, There is cheer for the
2. There is sight for the blind-ed and cure for the ill, There is balm for the
3. There is peace for the trou-bled and free-dom for slaves, There is hope for the

lone-ly and strength for the weak; There is par-don and bless-ing, and
wound-ed—be healed if you will; There is zest for your la-bors, and
hope-less, and light up-on graves; O hear the glad mes-sage and

end-less re-ward, There is per-fect sal-va-tion in Je-sus the Lord.
sweet-ness in rest, There is all that is pur-est and dear-est and best.
heed the sweet call: There is room and a wel-come with Je-sus for all.

CHORUS

Will you come, will you come to the Lord? Will you come? will you come? Will you,
    Will you come,   Will you come?

trust-ing His word, Give your all to the Lord, Will you come? will you come?
                                          Will you come?

429 There's a Royal Banner

El Nathan
V. 3 by L. O. S.

James McGranahan

1. There's a roy-al ban-ner giv-en for dis-play To the sol-diers
2. O-ver land and sea, wher-ev-er man may dwell, Make the glo-rious
3. When the Great Com-mand-er, from the vault-ed sky, Sounds the res-ur-

of the King; As an en-sign fair we lift it up to-day,
ti-dings known; Of the crim-son ban-ner now the sto-ry tell,
rec-tion day, Then be-fore our King the faint and foe shall die

CHORUS

While as ran-somed ones we sing. March-ing on!........ march-ing
While the Lord shall claim His own.
And the saints shall march a-way. March-ing on, and on! march-ing

on!........ For Christ count ev-'ry-thing but loss,.............. For the
on, and on! For Christ count ev-'ry-thing, ev-'ry-thing but loss, For the

King of kings toil and sing 'Neath the ban-ner of the cross.
King of kings, we'll toil and sing Be-neath the ban-ner of the cross.

430 The Lord's My Shepherd, I'll Not Want

From Scottish Psalter

John Campbell

1. The Lord's my Shep - herd, I'll not want: He makes me
2. My soul He doth re - store a - gain, And me to
3. Yea, though I walk in death's dark vale, Yet will I
4. My ta - ble Thou hast fur - nish - ed In pres - ence
5. Good - ness and mer - cy all my life Shall sure - ly

down to lie. In pas - tures green; He lead - eth me In
walk doth make With - in the paths of right - eous - ness, With -
fear none ill; For Thou art with me, and Thy rod, For
of my foes; My head Thou dost with oil a - noint, My
fol - low me; And in God's house for - ev - er - more, And

pas - tures green, He lead - eth me The qui - et wa - ters by.
in the paths of right - eous - ness, E'en for His own name's sake.
Thou art with me, and Thy rod, And staff me com - fort still.
head Thou dost with oil a - noint, And my cup o - ver - flows.
in God's house for - ev - er - more, My dwell - ing - place shall be.

431 Jesus, the Very Thought of Thee

Arranged

George F. Händel

1. Je - sus, the ver - y thought of Thee With sweet - ness
2. No voice can sing, no heart can frame, Nor can the
3. O hope of ev - 'ry con - trite heart! O joy of
4. O Lord, our on - ly way art Thou, Our im - mor -

fills my breast; But sweet-er far Thy face to see,
mem-'ry find A sweet-er sound than Thy blest name
all the meek! To those who fall, how kind Thou art!
tal-i-ty! O Lord, be Thou our glo-ry now

And in Thy pres-ence rest, And in Thy pres-ence rest.
O Sav-ior of man-kind! O Sav-ior of man-kind.
How good to those who seek! How good to those who seek!
And through e-ter-ni-ty And through e-ter-ni-ty.

432   Dear Lord and Father of Mankind

John G. Whittier   Frederick C. Maker

1. Dear Lord and Fa-ther of man-kind, For-give our fool-ish ways; Re-clothe us
2. In sim-ple trust like theirs who heard, Be-side the Syr-ian sea, The gra-cious
3. O Sab-bath rest by Gal-i-lee, O calm of hills a-bove, Where Je-sus
4. Drop Thy still dews of qui-et-ness, Till all our strivings cease; Take from our

in our right-ful mind, In pur-er lives Thy service find, In deep-er rev'rence, praise.
call-ing of the Lord, Let us, like them, without a word Rise up and fol-low Thee.
knelt to share with Thee The si-lence of e-ter-ni-ty, In-ter-pret-ed by love!
souls the strain and stress, And let our ordered lives confess The beauty of Thy peace.

433   A Mighty Fortress Is Our God

M. L.
Tr. F. H. Hedge

Martin Luther

1. A might-y for-tress is our God, A bul-wark nev-er fail - ing;
   Our help-er He, a-mid the flood Of mor-tal ills pre-vail - ing.
2. Did we in our own strength confide Our striv-ing would be los - ing;
   Were not the right One on our side The Man of God's own choos - ing.
2. And tho' this world, with e-vil filled, Should threaten to un-do us;
   We will not fear, for God hath willed His truth to tri-umph through us.

For still our an-cient foe Doth seek to work us woe; His craft and pow'r are
Dost ask who that may be? Christ Je-sus, it is He; Lord Sabaoth is His
Let goods and kin-dred go, This mor-tal life al-so; The bod-y they may

great, And, armed with cru-el hate, On earth is not his e - qual.
name, From age to age the same, And He must win the bat - tle.
kill: God's truth a-bid-eth still, His king-dom is for-ev - er.

434   For the Beauty of the Earth

Folliott S. Pierpoint

Arranged from Conrad Kocher

1. For the beau-ty of the earth, For the glo-ry of the skies,
2. For the joy of hu-man love, Broth-er, sis-ter, par-ent, child,
3. For Thy church that ev-er-more Lift-eth ho-ly hands a-bove,

For the Beauty of the Earth, Concluded

For the love which from our birth O - ver and a - round us lies,
Friends on earth, and friends a - bove, For all gen - tle tho'ts and mild,
Of - f'ring up on ev - 'ry shore Her pure sac - ri - fice of love,

REFRAIN

Lord of all, to Thee we raise This our hymn of grate - ful praise.

435 While We Pray, and While We Plead

El Nathan

C. C. Case

1. While we pray, and while we plead, While you see your soul's deep need,
2. You have wan-dered far a - way: Do not risk an - oth - er day;
3. In the world you've failed to find Aught of peace for trou-bled mind:
4. Come to Christ, con - fes - sion make; Come to Christ and par - don take;

While your Fa - ther calls you home, Will you not, my broth-er, come?
Do not turn from God your face, But to - day ac - cept His grace.
Come to Christ, on Him be - lieve, Peace and joy you shall re - ceive.
Trust in Him from day to day, He will keep you all the way.

CHORUS

Why not now? why not now? Why not come to Je-sus now?
Why not now? why not now?
Why not come to Je - - - - - sus now?

436 Till the Sun Goes Down

Arr. Vana Raye

Wm. J. Kirkpatrick. Arr. L. O. S.

1. There is work e-nough to do Ere the sun goes down; Time is swift-ly
2. We must love in word and deed Till the sun goes down; Err - ing ones must
3. We must go the nar-row way Till the sun goes down; God's commands we

pass-ing too–Soon the sun goes down. Ev-'ry i - dle whis-per still-ing, Ev - 'ry
hear and heed Ere the sun goes down; With the message swiftly speeding, For the
must o - bey Till the sun goes down; Ev-'ry day the Lord con-fess-ing, With true

pur-pose firm and willing, Ev-'ry Christian task ful-fill-ing, Till the sun goes down.
in-jured in - ter-ced-ing, To the light the lost ones leading, Ere the sun goes down.
hearts our wrongs redressing, If we would obtain the blessing When the sun goes down.

437 The Lord Is Our Salvation

L. O. Sanderson

Alexander Ewing. Arr. L. O. S.

1. The Lord is our sal - va - tion, What foe have we to fear? In dark-ness
2. On Christ we place re - li - ance, Our cap-tain will not fail; To er - ror
3. The Lord pre-pares a ha-ven—We need no oth - er rest; His word will

The Lord Is Our Salvation, Concluded

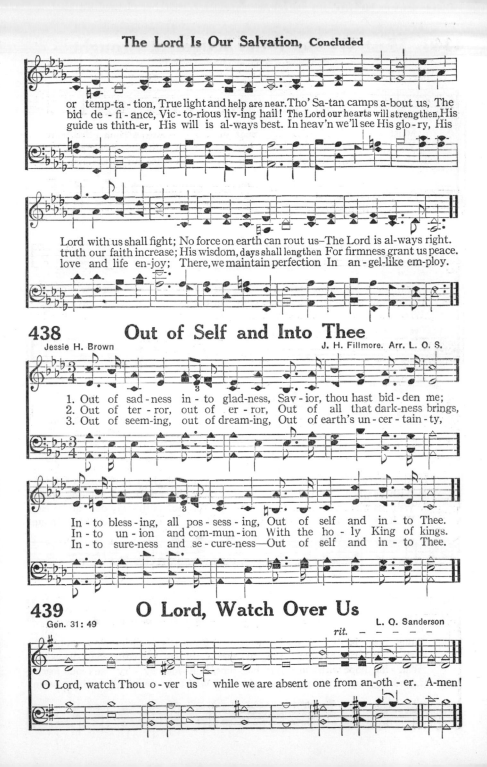

or temp-ta - tion, True light and help are near. Tho' Sa-tan camps a-bout us, The
bid de - fi - ance, Vic - to-rious liv-ing hail! The Lord our hearts will strengthen, His
guide us thith-er, His will is al-ways best. In heav'n we'll see His glo-ry, His

Lord with us shall fight; No force on earth can rout us–The Lord is al-ways right.
truth our faith increase; His wisdom, days shall lengthen For firmness grant us peace.
love and life en-joy; There, we maintain perfection In an - gel-like em-ploy.

438 Out of Self and Into Thee

Jessie H. Brown

J. H. Fillmore. Arr. L. O. S.

1. Out of sad - ness in - to glad-ness, Sav - ior, thou hast bid - den me;
2. Out of ter - ror, out of er - ror, Out of all that dark-ness brings,
3. Out of seem-ing, out of dream-ing, Out of earth's un - cer - tain - ty,

In - to bless - ing, all pos - sess - ing, Out of self and in - to Thee.
In - to un - ion and com-mun-ion With the ho - ly King of kings.
In - to sure-ness and se - cure-ness—Out of self and in - to Thee.

439 O Lord, Watch Over Us

Gen. 31: 49

L. O. Sanderson

rit.

O Lord, watch Thou o - ver us while we are absent one from an-oth - er. A-men!

440 Must We Be to the Judgment Brought

Charles Wesley. Arr. L. O. S.

Albert L. Peace

1. Must we be to the judg-ment bro't To an-swer in that day
2. Yes, ev-'ry se-cret of my heart Shall sure-ly be made known;
3. How care-ful, then, ought we to live, With what im-pres-sive fear,

For ev-'ry vain and i-dle tho't, And ev-'ry word we say?
God's word shall be the meas-uring chart For all that we have done.
Who such a strict ac-count must give For our be-hav-ior here!

441 Always with Us

E. S. C.

E. S. Carter

1. Al-ways with us, al-ways with us—Words of cheer and words of love;
2. With us when we toil in sad-ness, Sow-ing much and reap-ing none,
3. With us when the storm is sweep-ing O'er our path-way dark and drear,
4. With us in the lone-ly val-ley, When we cross the chill-ing stream—

Thus the ris-en Sav-ior whis-pers, From His dwell-ing-place a-bove:
Tell-ing us that in the fu-ture Gold-en har-vests shall be won;—
Wak-ing hope with-in our bos-oms, Still-ing ev-'ry anx-ious fear;—
Light-ing up the steps to glo-ry With sal-va-tion's ra-diant beam.

444 My God, My Father, Though I Stray

Charlotte Elliott   Arthur S. Sullivan

1. My God, my Fa-ther, tho' I stray Far from my home, on life's rough way,
2. Tho' dark my path, and sad my lot, Let me be still and mur-mur not,
3. Re-new my will from day to day; Blend it with thine, and take a-way
4. Then, when on earth I breathe no more The prayer oft mixed with tears be-fore,

O teach me from my heart to say, "Thy will be done!"
Or breathe the prayer di-vine-ly taught, "Thy will be done!"
All that now makes it hard to say, "Thy will be done!"
I'll sing up-on a hap-pier shore, "Thy will be done!" A-men.

445 My Lord, My Truth, My Way

Charles Wesley   George Kingsley

1. My Lord, my Truth, my Way, My sure, un-err-ing Light,
2. My Wis-dom and my Guide, My Coun-sel-or Thou art;
3. Teach me the hap-py art In all things to de-pend

On Thee my fee-ble steps I stay, Which Thou wilt guide a-right.
O nev-er let me leave Thy side, Or from Thy paths de-part!
On Thee: O nev-er, Lord, de-part, But love me to the end!

446 My Savior, as Thou Wilt!

Benjamin Schmolke
Tr. Jane Borthwick

Carl von Weber

1. My Sav-ior, as Thou wilt! O may Thy will be mine; In - to Thy
2. My Sav-ior, as Thou wilt! If need-y here and poor, Give me Thy
3. My Sav-ior, as Thou wilt! Tho' seen thro' man-y a tear, Let not my
4. My Sav-ior, as Thou wilt! All shall be well with me; Each changing

hand of love I would my all re - sign; Thro' sor-row and thro' joy,
people's bread, Their por-tion rich and sure; The man-na of Thy word,
star of hope Grow dim or dis-ap - pear; Since Thou on earth hast wept
fu - ture scene I glad-ly trust with Thee; Straight to my home a - bove

Con-duct me as Thine own, And help me still to say, "My Lord, Thy will be done."
Let my soul feed up-on, And, if all else should fail, "My Lord, Thy will be done."
And sor-rowed oft a-lone, If I must weep with Thee, "My Lord, Thy will be done."
I trav - el calm-ly on, And sing, in life or death, "My Lord, Thy will be done."

447 *O Lord, Our Lord

Arranged

L. O. Sanderson

1. O Lord, our Lord, how ex - cel - lent Thy name in all the earth!
2. O Lord, Thy name is won - der - ful—Its hon - or is our aim!

No name is giv'n, on earth, in heav'n, To match its glo - rious worth.
In it we pray, we're saved, we stay! How ex - cel - lent Thy name!

*This hymn may be followed by the chorus on following page.

448 O Lord, Our Lord

Ps. 8: 1

H. R. Palmer

Alto voice

O Lord, our Lord, how ex - cel-lent Thy name; How ex - cel-lent is Thy

Tenor and Alto

name in all the earth; Who has set Thy glo - ry a-

bove the heav'ns! We'll praise Thy ho - ly name for ev - er, ev - er-more.

CHORUS

O Lord, our Lord, how ex - cel-lent Thy name; O
We will praise Thy name for evermore, how ex-cel-lent Thy glo-ri-ous name;

Lord, our Lord, how ex - cel-lent Thy name.
We will praise Thy name for evermore, how ex - cel-lent Thy name. We'll praise and

O Lord, Our Lord, Concluded

We will praise Thy name for evermore, We will praise Thy name for
mag-ni-fy Thy name for ev-er-more, We'll

ev-er-more, We will laud and mag-ni-fy Thy name for evermore.
laud and mag-ni-fy Thy ho-ly name for evermore.

Soprano obligato

For ev - er, and ev - er, We will mag-ni-fy

We will praise Thy ho-ly name for ev-er, We will laud and mag-ni-fy Thy

ff   *rit.*

Thy name. A-men, A-men, A-men............

rit.

name for ev-er-more, For ev-er-more, for ev-er-more, A-men, and A-men.

449 Some Time We'll Understand

Maxwell N. Cornelius

James McGranahan

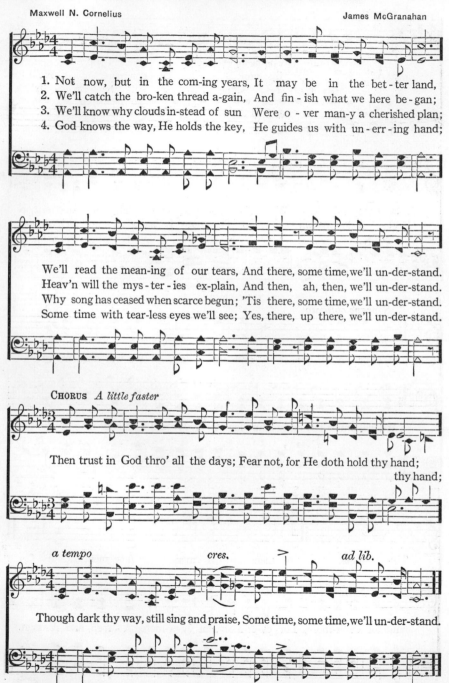

1. Not now, but in the com-ing years, It may be in the bet-ter land,
2. We'll catch the bro-ken thread a-gain, And fin-ish what we here be-gan;
3. We'll know why clouds in-stead of sun Were o-ver man-y a cherished plan;
4. God knows the way, He holds the key, He guides us with un-err-ing hand;

We'll read the mean-ing of our tears, And there, some time, we'll un-der-stand.
Heav'n will the mys-ter-ies ex-plain, And then, ah, then, we'll un-der-stand.
Why song has ceased when scarce begun; 'Tis there, some time, we'll un-der-stand.
Some time with tear-less eyes we'll see; Yes, there, up there, we'll un-der-stand.

CHORUS *A little faster*

Then trust in God thro' all the days; Fear not, for He doth hold thy hand;
thy hand;

a tempo　　　　　*cres.*　　　　*ad lib.*

Though dark thy way, still sing and praise, Some time, some time, we'll un-der-stand.

450 Fairest Lord Jesus

R. S. Willis, tr.

Arr. R. S. Willis

1. Fair - est Lord Je - sus! Ru - ler of all na - ture!
2. Fair are the mead - ows, Fair - er still the wood - lands,
3. Fair is the sun - shine, Fair - er still the moon - light,

O Thou of God and man the Son! Thee will I cher - ish,
Robed in the bloom-ing garb of spring; Je - sus is fair - er,
And all the twin - kling star - ry host: Je - sus shines bright-er,

Thee will I hon - or, Thou, my soul's glo - ry, joy, and crown.
Je - sus is pur - er, Who makes the woe - ful heart to sing.
Je - sus shines pur - er, Than all the an - gels heav'n can boast.

451 Holy, Holy, Holy Lord
(SANCTUS)

Ho - ly, ho - ly, ho - ly Lord, God of hosts, on high a - dored!

1

Who like me Thy praise should sing, O Al-might-y King!

2

dim.

Ho-ly, ho-ly, ho-ly.

452 Take Me Home, Father, Take Me Home

Vana R. Raye

L. O. Sanderson

1. When the sun of my life has gone down, And the shad-ows have
2. When my form is in-clined and I yield To the thorns of the
3. When the ones I have loved pass a-way; When I'm left in the

dens-er grown; When there's ought to re-mind of a fail-ing mind,
flesh I've known, And this tem-ple of clay on-ly in the way,
world a-lone, And there's none who can see an-y good for me,

CHORUS

Take me home, Fa-ther, take me home. Take me home, Fa-ther, take me

home! Leave me not in the world to roam! When I'm use-less be-

low, I would rath-er go— Take me home, Fa-ther, take me home.

TOPICAL INDEX

ACCOUNT

A charge to keep I have.. 287
Must we be to judgment
  brought 440
My idle words........... 309
Then be prepared........ 390
When the roll is called.... 361

ANCHOR

The haven of rest........ 267
We have an anchor....... 166

ASSURANCE

A mighty fortress is our
  God 433
A shelter in time of storm 327
Art thou weary.......... 226
Blessed assurance 153
Child of the King........ 345
Every cloud has a silver
  lining 341
He is able to deliver thee 149
How firm a foundation.. 88
I know that my Redeemer
  lives 2
I know whom I have
  believed 132
It is well with my soul.. 94
Jesus is mine............ 208
My hope is built on
  nothing less 177
Saved to the uttermost.... 283
That's enough for me.... 210
The haven of rest....... 267
The hollow of God's hand 175

ATONEMENT

Amazing grace 180
At the cross............. 7
Beneath the cross of Jesus 418
I gave my life for thee.. 198
Nailed to the cross...... 270
Nothing but the blood.... 59
Redeemed 338
Rock of ages........... 49
The old rugged cross.... 231
The way of the cross.... 249
There is a fountain...... 79
There is a green hill.... 5
Tho' your sins be as scarlet 293
What did he do........ 187
Why did my Saviour come
  to earth.............. 34

BAPTISM

A new creature.......... 32
O happy day............ 214
Only in Thee............ 243
Trust and obey.......... 1
Ye must be born again.... 401

BIBLE

Back to the Bible........ 346
Give me the Bible........ 232
My precious Bible........ 62
The precious book divine.. 16
'Tis the Bible 107
  (See "Word of God")

BLESSINGS

A blessing in prayer...... 295
Beauty for ashes.......... 100
Even me 379
O Thou fount of every
  blessing 70

Sweeter than all.......... 230
The Lord has been mindful 228
There shall be showers
  of blessings........... 29

BURDENS

After the shadows 381
Art thou weary.......... 226
Bring Christ your broken
  life 93
Cast thy burden on the
  Lord 27
Come, ye disconsolate 356
Does Jesus care.......... 238
Every cloud has a lining.. 341
God's hand is in it all.... 64
In the hour of trial...... 312
Light after darkness...... 333
Nobody knows but Jesus.. 352
O heart bowed down
  with sorrow........... 63
Oft in sorrow, oft in woe.. 442
Sometime we'll understand 449
Take me home, Father.. 450
The cross is not greater.. 263
The Master's touch...... 173

CHILDREN'S SONGS
Nos. 309-315

CHORUSES

Christ the Lord is risen
  today 306
Consider the lilies 14
Do you know the song.... 371
From every stormy wind.. 239
Hallelujah, praise Jehovah 143
Let every heart rejoice
  and sing 158
Lord's supper 307
O Lord our Lord........ 448
Peace be still............ 169
Praise the Lord.......... 10
Pray all the time........ 289
Sing on, ye joyful pilgrim 22
The heavens declare..... 343
The silver star.......... 388
Then be prepared........ 390
There is a sea........... 224
What did he do........ 187
Whispering hope 322

CHRIST

Christ for the world we
  sing 355
For Christ and the church. 417
He changes not 304
He keeps me singing...... 347
I will sing the wondrous
  story 204
Jesus, the very thought of
  Thee 431
More about Jesus........ 152
My Lord my truth my way 445
The great physician...... 151
We may not climb........ 114
Worthy art thou......... 25

Birth of Christ

Away in a manger...... 414
Do you know the song 371
Have you any room..... 199
It came upon a midnight 115
Joy to the world........ 378
O come, all ye faithful.. 233
Silent night 399
The silver star......... 388

Blood of Christ

Are you washed in
  the blood............ 181
I gave my life for thee 198
Nailed to the cross...... 270
Nothing but the blood.. 59
Rock of ages.......... 49
The cleansing wave.... 349
The gate ajar.......... 184
There is a fountain.... 79
There is power in the
  blood 354
What can wash away
  my sins 59

Cross of Christ

Am I a soldier of the
  cross 285
At the cross............ 7
Beneath the cross of
  Jesus 418
I am coming to the cross 176
In the cross of Christ.. 241
Jesus keep me near
  the cross 65
Must Jesus bear the cross 30
Nailed to the cross..... 270
Room at the cross...... 315
The old rugged cross.. 231
The way of the cross.... 249
There is a green hill... 5

Death of Christ

I gave my life for thee.. 198
Jesus paid it all 188
Low in the grave he lay. 119
My hope is built 177
What did he do........ 187
  (See also Blood, Cross)

Life of Christ

Break thou the bread.. 297
I love to tell the story 242
Seeking for me......... 51
Tell me the old, old
  story 280
Tell me the story of Jesus 24
We saw Thee not...... 247
Why did my Saviour
  come 34

Love of Christ

He loves me 179
I know I love Thee better 19
Immortal love forever
  full 53
Jesus, lover of my
  soul 145, 146
Jesus loves even me.... 206
O wonderful love...... 332
Somebody loves you.... 318
Sweeter as the years
  go by 261
There is a green hill.... 5
Why did my Saviour
  come 34
Wonderful love of Jesus 46
Wonderful story of love 72

Name of Christ

Am I a soldier of the
  cross 285
Blessed be the name.... 275
Glory to his name..... 142
He keeps me singing.... 347
How sweet the name of
  Jesus 47
O how I love Jesus.... 48
O Lord our Lord ...447, 448

Take the name of Jesus. 162
The great physician.... 151

Resurrection of Christ
A new creature........ 32
Christ, the Lord, is risen 306
I know that my
Redeemer lives 2
Low in the grave he lay 119
Tell me the story of
Jesus 24
We saw Thee not...... 247

Second Coming of Christ
Face to face........... 265
In the morning of joy.. 272
Must I empty handed go 6
The Lord's return..... 383
We'll work till Jesus
comes 86
Will Jesus find us
watching 45

CHRIST AS A —
Foundation:
How firm a foundation.. 88
My hope is built....... 177
The church's one
foundation 316
We have an anchor.... 166
(See also "Rock")

Fountain:
In the desert of sorrow.. 140
Jesus keep me near the
cross 65
O Thou Fount......... 70
The cleansing wave..... 349
There is a fountain.... 79
There's a fountain free.. 357

Friend:
Everybody's friend 330
I must tell Jesus....... 344
I've found a friend.... 66
Just such a friend is he. 387
No not one........... 4
The Lily of the valley. 139
What a friend we have.. 75

King:
Child of the King...... 345
Crowned with honor.... 351
O spread the tidings
'round 427
O worship the King.... 336
We shall see the King.. 217

Redeemer and Saviour:
A wonderful Saviour... 425
He is able to deliver thee 149
I know that my
Redeemer lives 2
I will sing of my
Redeemer 13
Is it for me........... 215
Jesus, lover of my soul. 145
My Gracious Redeemer.. 420
Saviour more than life.. 35
The great physician.... 151

Rock and refuge:
A shelter in time
of storm 327
He hideth my soul..... 425
He will hide me....... 296
Hiding in Thee........ 277
In the desert of sorrow. 140
Mighty rock whose
towering 99
Rock in the desert...... 251

Rock of ages........... 49
Shelter us under thy
wings 326
The rock that is higher. 223
There stands a rock.... 245

Shepherd:
Jesus the loving Shepherd 246
Saviour like a shepherd. 196
The Lord my Shepherd is 161
The Lord's my Shepherd 430

CHRISTIAN LIFE
A new creature.......... 32
A song, a beautiful song Preface
I am the vine.......... 78
Is that somebody you.... 133
Is your life a channel.... 89
Did you think to pray... 39
Fear not little flock...... 255
I'll live for Him........ 55
I'm not ashamed to own
my Lord 200
Live for Jesus.......... 160
More holiness give me.... 163
More like Jesus......... 252
O to be like Thee........ 273
Saviour divine, dwell in my
heart 260
Take my life, O Father,
mould it 443
Take time to be holy..... 419
The cross is not greater... 263
We shall be like Him.... 339
Where livest thou........ 385
Whiter than snow....... 389

CHURCH or KINGDOM
Fear not, little flock...... 255
For Christ and the church 417
I love Thy kingdom Lord. 178
I want to be a worker.... 258
In the kingdom......... 398
Sowing the seed of the
kingdom 182
The church of God...... 372
The church's one
foundation 316
The kingdoms of earth
pass away 342

CLOSING HYMNS
Abide with me........... 150
Be with me Lord........ 21
Blest be the tie that binds. 9
Doxology 119
God be with you........ 382
Let the words of my mouth 58
Now the day is over...... 386
O Lord watch over us.... 439
Our day of praise is done 311
Take the name of Jesus
with you 162

COMFORT AND
CONSOLATION
After the shadows....... 381
Always with us.......... 441
Beyond the sunset....... 301
Come ye disconsolate.... 356
Does Jesus care........ 238
God's hand is in it all.... 64
He changes not 304
Hold Thou my hand...... 300
I must tell Jesus........ 344
I'll never forsake my Lord 52
It pays to serve Jesus.... 362
Light after darkness..... 333
My Jesus as Thou wilt.... 446
Nobody knows but Jesus.. 352

O 'tis wonderful.......... 211
Sweeter than all.......... 230
The Lord has been mindful
of me 228
Thou thinkest, Lord, of
me 276
Sweet is the promise...... 159

CONSECRATION
Close to Thee........... 190
Give of your best to the
Master 323
I am Thine O Lord...... 172
I gave my life for Thee... 198
I know I love Thee
better Lord 19
I'll never forsake my Lord 52
Jesus calls us........... 185
Just as I am........... 50
More love to Thee, O
Christ 17
My Jesus, I love Thee.... 156
Nearer and nearer....... 213
Nearer to Jesus......... 423
Saviour to Thee we
humbly bow 365
Something for Jesus...... 192
Take my life and let it be. 44
Take the world but give
me Jesus 60
To Christ be true........ 69

DEPENDENCE
Back to the Bible for it all 346
Be with me, Lord....... 21
Break Thou the bread
of life 297
Cast thy burden on the
Lord 27
Closer to Thee.......... 334
Consider the lilies of the
field 14
Have Thine own way, Lord 393
He leadeth me.......... 38
Hold Thou my hand...... 300
Hold to God's unchanging
hand 227
I know whom I have
believed 132
I need Thee every hour.. 85
I'll never forsake my Lord 52
Jesus Saviour pilot me.... 325
Leading me 269
Leaning on the everlasting
arms 134
My Jesus as Thou wilt.. 446
Only in Thee........... 243
Pass me not 76
Saviour, breathe an
evening blessing 98
Shelter us under Thy wings 326
Tarry with me, O my
Saviour 87
Trust and obey......... 1
With Thee 375

DEVOTION
Beneath the cross of Jesus 418
Close to Thee........... 190
Faith of our fathers..... 20
For the beauty of the earth 434
Give me Jesus.......... 60
Have Thine own way..... 393
I am resolved........... 271
I surrender all......... 237
It is well with my soul.. 94
Jesus is mine.......... 208
Lord, we come before
Thee now 147
My faith looks up to Thee. 125
Nearer, my God, to Thee. 41

O love that will not let
  me go 376
Only in Thee 243

END OF LIFE
A song, a beautiful song Preface
Abide with me 150
After the shadows 381
Am I nearer to heaven ... 313
Crossing the bar 209
Gathering home 264
My latest sun is sinking fast 197
Only waiting 194
Shall we gather at the river 274
Take me home, Father ... 452
Tarry with me 87
The end of the way 363
There will be light 259
Till the sun goes down .. 436
We are going down the
  valley 422

FAITH AND TRUST
Faith is the victory 416
Faith of our fathers 20
I know whom I have
  believed 132
My faith looks up to Thee 125
O for a faith 253
'Tis so sweet to trust in
  Jesus 292
Trust and obey 1
What is your prospect 368

FELLOWSHIP
Be with me, Lord 21
Come closer, Lord, today .. 370
Hold to God's unchanging
  hand 227
How sweet, how heavenly. 168
Jesus is mine 208
Nearer and nearer 213
Nearer to Jesus 423
One blessed hour with Jesus 67
We are fellow-creatures ... 225
With Thee 375

FOLLOWING
Am I a soldier of the cross 285
Anywhere with Jesus 108
Follow on 248
Footprints of Jesus 279
He knows 384
Stepping in the light 353
Where he leads I'll follow. 189
Where he leads me I will
  follow 83
Who will follow Jesus 426

FORGIVENESS
Bring Christ your broken
  life 93
Dear Lord and Father
  of mankind 432
He is able to deliver thee. 149
Jesus saves 298
Only in Thee 243
There's a pardon full
  and sweet 364
When God forgives He
  forgets 360

FUNERAL
Asleep in Jesus 229
Be with me Lord 21
Crossing the bar 209
Does Jesus care 238
Face to face 265
God be with you 385
Never grow old 288
Only a shadow between ... 373

Safe in the arms of Jesus 221
Shall we meet 236
Some sweet day 130
There is a place of refuge. 250
We are going down the
  valley 422
We'll never say goodby 314
(See also, Future Life, Heaven)

FUTURE LIFE
By and by 305
Glory for me 400
Good morning in glory ... 367
He knows 384
I shall know him 421
In the Morning of Joy 272
Some blessed day 118
Some day we shall be
  satisfied 335
Sometime we'll understand 449
We shall be like him 339
We shall see the King
  someday 217
Welcome for me 391
When the roll is called
  up yonder 361
Where the gates swing
  outward never 256
(See also Heaven)

GETHSEMANE
Night with ebon pinion.. 131
'Tis midnight and on
  Olive's brow 57
When my love to Christ
  grows weak 266

GIVING
Give of your best to the
  Master 323
I gave my life for Thee .. 198
I love Thy kingdom, Lord 178
I surrender all 237
Jesus paid it all 188
None of self and all of
  Thee 340
Something for Jesus 192
Take my life and let it be 44
Take the world but give
  me Jesus 60

GOD
A Mighty Fortress is
  our God 433
Dear Lord and Father of
  mankind 432
God is love 31
God's hand is in it all 64
He is able to deliver thee. 149
Hold to God's unchanging
  hand 227
Holy, holy, holy, Lord God 101
The providence of God ... 329

GUIDANCE
Anywhere with Jesus 108
Guide me, O Thou great
  Jehovah 155
He leadeth me 38
I'll go where you want me
  to go 317
Lead, kindly light 299
Lead me gently home 171
Leading me 269
Saviour, lead me lest I stray 102
(See, also, Following)

HEAVEN
An empty mansion 377
Above the bright blue 170
Beautiful valley of Eden .. 254
Beautiful Zion 380
Beyond the sunset 301
Beyond this land of parting 116
Heaven holds all to me ... 123
Home over there 174
I'm going home 291
One sweetly solemn thought 337
Sometime, somehow,
  somewhere 320
Sweet by and by 154
The home up there 15
The unclouded day 96
There is a habitation 28
When we all get to heaven 37

HOLINESS: 71, 101, 163, 191

HOPE: 177, 322, 368. (See
  also Faith)

INVITATION
Almst persuaded 56
Are you coming to Jesus
  tonight 112
Are you washed in the
  blood 181
Bring Christ your broken
  life 93
Come to Jesus 193
Come to the feast 12
Come unto me 63
God is calling the prodigal 203
Hark! the gentle voice.... 73
Have you any room for
  Jesus 199
I am coming Lord 74
I am coming to the cross.. 176
I am resolved 271
Is thy heart right with God 201
Jesus, I come 121
Jesus is calling 126
Jesus is tenderly calling .. 157
Jesus now is calling thee.. 397
Jesus the loving Shepherd. 246
Jesus will give you rest.... 90
Just as I am 50
Let him in 11
O come to the Saviour . 331
O what will you do with
  Jesus 268
O why not tonight 26
Only a step 127
Room at the cross 315
Softly and tenderly 91
Soul, a Saviour thou art
  needing 262
There's a fountain free .. 357
There's a great day coming 23
There's a pardon full and
  sweet 364
There is a fountain 79
There is rest for the weary 428
Trust and obey 1
What shall it be 195
Where He leads me I will
  follow 83
While Jesus whispers 18
While we pray and while
  we plead 435
Who at the door is
  standing 82
Who will follow Jesus 426
Why do you wait 77
Why keep Jesus waiting .. 68
Will Jesus find us watching 45

JOY AND HAPPINESS
Every cloud has a silver
  lining 341
Heavenly sunlight 43
I'm happy with Jesus alone 358
Let us with a gladsome
  mind 424
O happy day........... 214
O 'tis wonderful.......... 211
Sunlight, sunlight 302
Sweeter as the years go by 261
Sweeter than all......... 230
There is sunshine in
  my soul............... 122

JUDGMENT
Must we be to the
  judgment brought 440
Then be prepared........ 390
There's a great day coming 23
When the roll is called... 361
Will Jesus find us waiting. 45

LORD'S SUPPER
Break Thou the bread
  of life 297
By Christ redeemed...... 205
Night with ebon pinion... 131
The Lord's Supper...... 207
The solemn feast........ 307
'Tis midnight and on
  Olive's brow 57
'Tis set, the feast divine... 104
When my love to Christ
  grows weak 266
(See, also, 41, 49, 50, 55, 71,
167, 188, 198, 213, 412, 431)

LOYALTY
For Christ and the church 417
I'll live for Him........ 55
I'll never forsake my Lord 52
Is that somebody you.... 133
More love to Thee, O Christ 17
O love that wilt not let
  me go 376
Oft in sorrow, oft in woe. 442
Stand up for Jesus....... 111
Take the world but give
  me Jesus 60
To Christ be loyal...... 69
True hearted, whole
  hearted 294

MEDITATION: 186, 244, 337,
350, 369, 373, 392, 431, 450.

MISSIONARY
Bring them in........... 144
Christ for the world...... 355
Far and near........... 189
From Greenland's icy
  mountains 321
I'll go where you want me 317
Is that somebody you.... 133
Let the lower lights be
  burning 110
Must I go and empty
  handed 6
O spread the tidings round 427
Ready to suffer.......... 394
Rescue the perishing...... 81
Seeking the lost......... 103
Send the light........... 202
The gospel is for all...... 61
The Master's touch....... 173
There is a sea.......... 224
Throw out the life line.. 129
Will you not tell it today. 109
Whosoever will may come. 113

NAME: (See Christ, name of)

PEACE: 92, 105, 164, 169, 290.

OBEDIENCE
A charge to keep I have.. 287
How happy are they..... 281
O happy day............ 214
True-hearted, whole-
  hearted 294
Trust and obey.......... 1

PRAISE
Amazing grace 180
Blessed assurance 153
Blessed be the name.... 275
Day is dying in the West.. 135
Doxology 120
For the beauty of the earth 434
Hallelujah, praise Jehovah 143
Holy, holy, holy.......... 101
Let every heart rejoice
  and sing 158
Let us with a gladsome
  mind 424
My gracious Redeemer... 420
O Thou fount of every
  blessing 70
Praise the Lord ye heavens 10
Revive us again......... 234
Standing on the promises. 104
Worthy art Thou........ 25

PRAYER
A blessing in prayer...... 295
Abide with me........... 150
Close to Thee........... 190
Closer to Thee........... 334
Did you think to pray?... 39
Dear Lord and Father.... 432
Even me 379
From every stormy wind.. 239
I am Thine, O Lord..... 172
I must tell Jesus......... 344
I need Thee every hour.. 85
I will pray.............. 117
Jesus meek and gentle.... 303
Let the words of my mouth 58
Lord, we come before
  Thee now 147
My God, my Father...... 444
My faith looks up to Thee 125
My Jesus, as Thou wilt.. 446
O Lord watch over us.... 439
Pray all the time........ 289
Remember me, O Mighty
  One 218
Saviour, breathe an
  evening blessing 98
Saviour, grant me rest
  and peace 164
Saviour, to Thee we
  humbly bow 365
Shelter us under Thy wings 326
Sweet hour of prayer.... 36
Tell it to Jesus alone.... 97
The garden of prayer.... 222
'Tis the blessed hour of
  prayer 54
What a friend we have
  in Jesus 75

PROVIDENCE
Consider the lilies....... 14
For me He careth........ 3
How firm a foundation... 88
God's hand is in it all.... 64
Sweet is the promise..... 159
The Lord has been mindful 228
The providence of God.... 329

SINGING: 8, 13, 22, 37, 158,
204, 347.

SPECIAL: (See Choruses)

SOWING AND REAPING
Bringing in the sheaves.. 80
Harvest time 141
Ho! reapers of life's harvest 124
Scattering precious seed... 374
Sowing the seed of the
  Kingdom 182

STORY: 24, 72, 152, 204, 242,
280.

SUBMISSION
Anywhere with Jesus..... 108
Have Thine own way, Lord 393
I surrender all........... 237
Let Him have His way
  with thee 84
My God, my Father, though
  I stray 444
My Jesus, as Thou wilt.. 446
None of self and all
  of Thee 340
Out of self and into Thee 438
Saviour, to Thee we
  humbly bow 365
Take my life and let it be 44
Take my life, O Father... 443

TEMPTATION: 42, 219, 312,
333, 344, 391.

WARFARE
A mighty fortress......... 433
Am I a soldier of the cross 285
Faith is the victory....... 416
My soul be on Thy guard 42
Oft in sorrow............ 442
Onward, Christian Soldiers 395
Stand up for Jesus........ 111
There's a royal banner.... 429
True-hearted, whole-
  hearted 294

WORD OF GOD
How firm a foundation.... 88
How shall the young secure 319
My Jesus as Thou wilt ... 446
My God, my Father, though
  I stray 444
O sacred word........... 324
Precious words 310
Standing on the promises. 104
The precious book divine. 16
Wonderful words of life... 212

WORK
(See, also, Bible)
Give of your best to
  the Master 323
I want to be a worker.... 258
It pays to serve Jesus.... 362
Till the sun goes down.. 436
To the work............. 40
We'll work till Jesus comes 86
Work for Jesus.......... 278
Work, for the night is
  coming 284

WORSHIP
Holy, holy, holy.......... 101
Jesus calls us............ 185
O worship the King....... 336
One blessed hour with
  Jesus 67
Saviour, to Thee we
  humbly bow 365
The Lord is in His holy
  temple 95
We assemble here to
  worship 128

GENERAL INDEX

•

TITLES IN Caps and Small Caps; first lines, lower case.

•

PAGE

A Blessing In Prayer............ 295
A Charge to Keep I Have........ 287
A Child's Evening Prayer........ 403
A Mighty Fortress Is Our God... 433
A New Creature................. 32
A ruler once came to Jesus.......... 401
A Shelter in the Time of Storm.. 327
A Song! A Beautiful Song.....Preface
A wonderful Saviour is Jesus........ 425
Abide With Me.................. 150
Above the Bright Blue.......... 170
After the life-paths we're treading... 259
After the midnight.............. 381
After the Shadows.............. 381
Again the Lord of Light and Life 167
Alas! and did my Saviour bleed...... 7
All praise to him who reigns above.. 275
All things are ready.............. 12
All Things Bright and Beautiful 415
All to Jesus I surrender........... 237
Almost Persuaded 56
Alone at Eve.................... 244
Always With Us 441
Am I A Soldier of the Cross...... 285
Am I Nearer to Heaven Today... 313
Amazing Grace 180
Amid the changing scenes below.... 304
Amid the trials which I meet...... 276
An Empty Mansion.............. 377
Angry Words 308
Anywhere With Jesus........... 108
Are You Coming to Jesus Tonight? 112
Are you sowing the seed?.......... 182
Are You Washed in the Blood?.. 181
Are you weary, are you heavy laden? 97
Arise, the master calls for thee...... 141
Art Thou Weary?.............. 226
Asleep in Jesus.................. 229
At the Cross.................... 7
Away in a Manger.............. 414

Back to the Bible for It All.... 346
Be With Me Lord................ 21
Be ye kind, ever kind............ 408
Beaulah Land 257
Beautiful Valley of Eden........ 254
Beautiful Zion, Built Above..... 380
Beauty for Ashes................ 100
Beneath the Cross of Jesus...... 418
Beyond the Sunset.............. 301
Beyond This Land of Parting.... 116
Blessed Assurance 153
Blessed Be the Name........... 275
Blest Be the Tie................ 9
Break Thou the Bread of Life... 297

PAGE

Brightly beams our Father's mercy.. 110
Bring Christ Your Broken Life.. 93
Bring Them In.................. 144
Bringing In the Sheaves.......... 80
Buried with Christ................ 32
By and By...................... 305
By Christ Redeemed............. 205

Cast Thy Burden on the Lord... 27
Child of the King.............. 345
Children, Obey Your Parents.... 406
Christ for the World We Sing... 355
Christ Receiveth Sinful Men..... 148
Christ the Lord is Risen Today.. 306
Christ will me his aid afford....... 230
Close to Thee.................. 190
Closer to Thee................. 334
Come Closer Lord Today........ 370
Come, let us all unite to sing........ 31
Come to Jesus.................. 193
Come to the Feast.............. 12
Come Unto Me.................. 63
Come, we that love the Lord........ 8
Come Ye Disconsolate........... 356
Come ye weary and oppressed 397
Consider the Lilies of the Field 14
Crossing the Bar................ 209
Crowned With Honor........... 351

Day is Dying in the West......... 135
Dear Lord and Father of
  Mankind 432
Did You Think to Pray?......... 39
Do You Know the Song?.......... 371
Do you unto others.............. 411
Does Jesus Care?................ 238
Down at the cross.............. 142
Down in the valley.............. 248
Doxology 120

Earth holds no treasure.......... 123
Encamped along the hills of light.... 416
Ere you left your room this morning 39
Even Me 379
Every Cloud Has a Silver Lining. 341
Everybody's Friend 330

Face to Face.................... 265
Fade, fade each earthly joy.......... 208
Fairest Lord Jesus.............. 450
Faith Is the Victory............ 416
Faith of Our Fathers........... 20
Far and Near................... 189
Far away in the depths.......... 290
Father, in the morning.......... 117
Fear Not, Little Flock.......... 255

	PAGE
FOLLOW ON	248
FOOTPRINTS OF JESUS	279
FOR CHRIST AND THE CHURCH	417
FOR ME HE CARETH	3
FOR THE BEAUTY OF THE EARTH	434
FROM EVERY STORMY WIND (WIlder)	239
FROM EVERY STORMY WIND (Retreat)	240
FROM GREENLAND'S ICY MOUNTAINS	321
GATHERING HOME	264
GIVE ME JESUS	60
GIVE ME THE BIBLE	232
GIVE OF YOUR BEST TO THE MASTER	323
GLORY FOR ME	400
GLORY TO HIS NAME	142
GOD BE WITH YOU	382
GOD IS CALLING THE PRODIGAL	203
GOD IS LOVE	31
God's family is his church	372
GOD'S HAND IS IN IT ALL	64
GOOD MORNING IN GLORY	367
GUIDE ME, O THOU GREAT JEHOVAH	155
HALLELUJAH! PRAISE JEHOVAH!	143
HARK! THE GENTLE VOICE	73
Hark! 'tis the Shepherd's voice	144
HARVEST TIME	141
Have thine affections been nailed?	201
HAVE THINE OWN WAY, LORD	393
HAVE YOU ANY ROOM FOR JESUS?	199
Have you been to Jesus?	181
HE CHANGES NOT	304
HE HIDETH MY SOUL	425
HE IS ABLE TO DELIVER THEE	149
HE KEEPS ME SINGING	347
HE LEADETH ME	38
HE KNOWS	384
HE LOVES ME	179
He may come at morning	383
HE WILL HIDE ME	296
Hear the sweet voice of Jesus	127
Hear the voice of Jesus say	278
HEAVEN HOLDS ALL TO ME	123
HEAVENLY SUNLIGHT	43
Here I labor and toil	377
HIDE ME, O MY SAVIOUR, HIDE ME	165
HIDING IN THEE	277
HIGHER GROUND	235
HO! REAPERS OF LIFE'S HARVEST	124
HOLD THOU MY HAND	300
HOLD TO GOD'S UNCHANGING HAND	227
HOLY, HOLY, HOLY	101
HOLY, HOLY, HOLY LORD	351
HOME OVER THERE	174
HOW FIRM A FOUNDATION	88
HOW HAPPY ARE THEY	281
How precious is the book divine	16
How shall I my Saviour set forth?	332
HOW SHALL THE YOUNG SECURE THEIR HEARTS?	319

	PAGE
HOW SWEET, HOW HEAVENLY IS THE SIGHT	168
HOW SWEET THE NAME OF JESUS	47
I AM BOUND FOR THE PROMISED LAND	137
I AM COMING, LORD	74
I AM COMING TO THE CROSS	176
I AM PRAYING FOR YOU	216
I AM RESOLVED	271
I am safe whatever may betide me	175
I am so glad that our Father	206
I AM THE VINE	78
I AM THINE, O LORD	172
I can hear my Saviour calling	83
I do not ask that I may know	269
I GAVE MY LIFE FOR THEE	198
I have a home in a fair summer land	373
I have a Saviour	216
I have found a friend in Jesus	139
I have heard of a land	288
I hear the Saviour say	188
I hear Thy welcome voice	74
I know every idle word	309
I KNOW I LOVE THEE BETTER, LORD	19
I know not what awaits me	384
I know not why God's wondrous grace	132
I KNOW THAT MY REDEEMER LIVES	2
I KNOW WHOM I HAVE BELIEVED	132
I LOVE THY KINGDOM, LORD	178
I LOVE TO TELL THE STORY	242
I must needs go home	249
I MUST TELL JESUS	344
I NEED THEE EVERY HOUR	85
I SHALL KNOW HIM	421
I SURRENDER ALL	237
I wandered in the shades of night	302
I WANT TO BE A WORKER	258
I want to be more like Jesus	252
I WILL PRAY	117
I WILL SING OF MY REDEEMER	13
I WILL SING THE WONDROUS STORY	204
I would be a ray of sunshine	413
I WOULD BE HOLY	412
I would like to think	Preface
I WOULD SHINE FOR JESUS	413
If the name of the Saviour	109
If you will come to Jesus	410
I'LL GO WHERE YOU WANT ME	317
I'M GOING HOME	291
I'LL LIVE FOR HIM	55
I'LL NEVER FORSAKE MY LORD	52
I'M HAPPY WITH JESUS ALONE	358
I'M NOT ASHAMED TO OWN MY LORD	200
I'm pressing on the upward way	235
I'VE FOUND A FRIEND	66
I've reached the land	257
IMMORTAL LOVE FOREVER FULL	53
IN THE CROSS OF CHRIST I GLORY	241
IN THE DESERT OF SORROW AND SIN	140
IN THE HOUR OF TRIAL	312
IN THE KINGDOM	398

In the Morning of Joy.......... 272
In the Shadow of His Wings...... 33
In vain in high and holy lays...... 46
Is It for Me?.................... 215
Is That Somebody You?.......... 133
Is Thy Heart Right With God?.. 201
Is Your Life a Channel of
  Blessing? 89
It Came Upon a Midnight Clear.. 115
It Is Well With My Soul........ 94
It may be far, it may be near........ 305
It may not be on the mountain's ... 317
It Pays to Serve Jesus............ 362

Jesus Bids Us Shine............... 405
Jesus born to bless the burdened.... 199
Jesus Calls Us.................... 185
Jesus, Friend of Children........ 407
Jesus, I Come.................... 121
Jesus Is Calling.................. 126
Jesus Is Mine..................... 208
Jesus Is Tenderly Calling........ 157
Jesus, Keep Me Near the Cross... 65
Jesus, Lover of My Soul (Martyn). 145
Jesus, Lover of My Soul (Refuge).. 146
Jesus Loves Even Me.............. 206
Jesus Loves Me.................... 402
Jesus, Meek and Gentle.......... 303
Jesus, my Saviour, to Bethlehem
  came 51
Jesus Now Is Calling............. 397
Jesus Paid It All................. 188
Jesus, royal heavenly friend......... 330
Jesus Saves 298
Jesus, Saviour, Pilot Me......... 325
Jesus, the Loving Shepherd...... 246
Jesus, the Very Thought of Thee 431
Jesus Will Give You Rest........ 90
Jesus, wilt thou guard the slumber?. 403
Joy to the World................. 378
Just a few more days............. 256
Just As I Am..................... 50
Just Such a Friend Is He........ 387

Lead, Kindly Light............... 299
Lead Me Gently Home, Father... 171
Leading Me 269
Leaning On the Everlasting Arms 134
Let Every Heart Rejoice and Sing 158
Let Him Have His Way With Thee 84
Let Him In....................... 11
Let the Lower Lights Be Burning 110
Let the Words of My Mouth.... 58
Let Us With a Gladsome Mind... 424
Light After Dark................. 333
Like a bird on the deep.......... 391
Like a star of the morning........ 62
Live for Jesus 160
Lord, I hear of showers of blessing.. 379
Lord, in thy mercy............... 260
Lord Jesus, I long to be perfectly
  whole 389

Lord, We Come Before Thee
  Now 147
Love Him, Love Him............... 401
Low in the Grave He Lay........ 119

Master, the tempest is raging....... 169
Mighty Rock Whose Towering
  Form 99
More About Jesus................. 152
More Holiness Give Me.......... 163
More Like Jesus.................. 252
More Love to Thee, O Christil.... 17
Must I Go and Empty Handed?... 6
Must Jesus Bear the Cross Alone? 30
Must We Be to the Judgment
  Brought? 440
My Faith Looks Up to Thee..... 125
My Father is rich in houses and land 345
My God, My Father, Though I
  Stray 444
My Gracious Redeemer I Love... 420
My heart is singing a glad new song 360
My heavenly home is bright and fair 291
My Hope Is Built On Nothing Less 177
My Idle Words.................... 309
My Jesus, as Thou Wilt.......... 446
My Jesus, I Love Thee............ 156
My Latest Sun Is Sinking Fast... 197
My life, my love I give to Thee..... 55
My Lord, My Truth, My Way.... 445
My Precious Bible............... 62
My Soul Be On Thy Guard...... 42
My soul in sad exile.............. 267

Nailed to the Cross............. 270
Nearer and Nearer............... 213
Nearer My God to Thee.......... 41
Nearer to Jesus.................. 423
Never Grow Old.................. 288
Night With Ebon Pinion.......... 131
No, Not One..................... 4
Nobody Knows But Jesus........ 352
None of Self and All of Thee.. 340
Not all earth's gold and silver....... 186
Not now, but in the coming years... 449
Nothing But the Blood.......... 59
Now the Day Is Over............. 386

O Come, All Ye Faithful........ 233
O Come to the Saviour.......... 331
O do not let the word depart........ 26
O For a Faith.................... 253
O For a Soul..................... 328
O Happy Day..................... 214
O heart bowed down with sorrow.. 63
O How I Love Jesus............... 48
O land of rest, for thee I sigh....... 86
O listen to our wondrous story...... 187
O Lord, Our Lord................. 447
O Lord, Our Lord (Chorus)....... 448
O Lord, Watch Over Us.......... 439

	PAGE
O love surpassing knowledge	210
O LOVE THAT WILL NOT LET ME GO	376
O now I see the crimson wave	349
O rock in the desert	251
O SACRED WORD	324
O safe to the rock	277
O sometimes the shadows are deep	223
O SPREAD THE TIDINGS ROUND	427
O the unsearchable riches	286
O the yesterday's moments	313
O they tell me of a home	96
O think of the home over there	174
O THOU FOUNT OF EVERY BLESSING	70
O TO BE LIKE THEE	273
O WHAT WILL YOU DO WITH JESUS?	268
O WHY NOT TONIGHT?	26
O WONDERFUL LOVE	332
O WORSHIP THE KING	336
Of Jesus' love that sought me	261
Of one the Lord has made the race	61
OFT IN SORROW, OFT IN WOE	442
Oh, the bitter pain and sorrow	340
OH, 'TIS WONDERFUL	211
On a hill far away	231
ON JORDAN'S STORMY BANKS (Evergreen Shore)	136
On Jordan's stormy banks (I am bound . . .)	137
On the brow of night	388
ON ZION'S GLORIOUS SUMMIT	369
ONE BLESSED HOUR WITH JESUS	67
ONE STEP AT A TIME	220
ONE SWEETLY SOLEMN THOUGHT	337
ONLY A SHADOW BETWEEN	373
ONLY A STEP	127
ONLY IN THEE	243
ONLY WAITING	194
ONWARD, CHRISTIAN SOLDIERS	395
OUR DAY OF PRAISE IS DONE	311
Out of my bondage	121
Out of sadness into gladness	438
OUT OF SELF AND INTO THEE	438
OUTSHINE THE SUN	410
PASS ME NOT	76
PEACE, BE STILL	169
PEACE, PERFECT PEACE	92
Praise God from whom all blessing flow	120
PRAISE THE LORD, YE HEAVENS ADORE HIM	10
PRAY ALL THE TIME	289
PRECIOUS WORDS	310
PURER IN HEART, O GOD	71
PURER YET AND PURER	191
REDEEMED	338
READY TO SUFFER	394
REMEMBER ME, O MIGHTY ONE	218
RESCUE THE PERISHING	81
REVIVE US AGAIN	234

	PAGE
ROCK IN THE DESERT	251
ROCK OF AGES	49
ROOM AT THE CROSS	315
SAFE IN THE ARMS OF JESUS	221
SAVED TO THE UTTERMOST	283
SAVIOUR, BREATHE AN EVENING BLESSING	98
SAVIOUR DIVINE, DWELL IN MY HEART	260
SAVIOUR, GRANT ME REST AND PEACE	164
SAVIOUR, LEAD ME LEST I STRAY	102
SAVIOUR, LIKE A SHEPHERD, LEAD US	196
SAVIOUR, MORE THAN LIFE	35
SAVIOUR, TEACH ME	348
Saviour, Thou callest and often	326
Saviour, Thy dying love	192
SAVIOUR, TO THEE WE HUMBLY BOW	365
SCATTERING PRECIOUS SEED	374
SEEKING FOR ME	51
SEEKING THE LOST	103
SEND THE LIGHT	202
SHALL WE GATHER AT THE RIVER?	274
SHALL WE MEET?	236
SHELTER US UNDER THY WINGS	326
SILENT NIGHT, HOLY NIGHT	399
Sing the wondrous love of Jesus	37
Sing them over again to me	212
SING ON, YE JOYFUL PILGRIMS	22
Sinners Jesus will receive	148
Soft as the voice of an angel	322
SOFTLY AND TENDERLY	91
SOME BLESSED DAY	118
SOME DAY WE SHALL BE SATISFIED	335
SOME SWEET DAY	130
SOMEBODY LOVES YOU, 'TIS JESUS	318
Some day in Jesus' name	118
SOMETHING FOR JESUS	192
Someone by faith has been born again	133
SOMETIME, SOMEHOW, SOMEWHERE	320
SOMETIME WE'LL UNDERSTAND	449
SOUL, A SAVIOUR THOU ART NEEDING	262
Soul burdened and straying	331
Sowing in the morning	80
SOWING THE SEED OF THE KINGDOM	182
STAND UP, STAND UP FOR JESUS	111
STANDING ON THE PROMISES	104
STEPPING IN THE LIGHT	353
SUNLIGHT, SUNLIGHT	302
Sunset and evening star	209
Sweet are the promises	183
SWEET BY AND BY	154
SWEET HOUR OF PRAYER	36
SWEET IS THE PROMISE	159
SWEETER AS THE YEARS GO BY	261
SWEETER THAN ALL	230
Sweetly, Lord, have we heard Thee calling	279
SWEET PEACE, THE GIFT OF GOD'S LOVE	105

PAGE

TAKE ME HOME, FATHER, TAKE ME
HOME 452
TAKE MY LIFE AND LET IT BE...... 44
TAKE MY LIFE, O FATHER, MOULD
IT 443
TAKE THE NAME OF JESUS WITH YOU 162
Take the world but give me Jesus.. 60
TAKE TIME TO BE HOLY.......... 419
TARRY WITH ME, O MY SAVIOUR... 87
TELL IT TO JESUS ALONE.......... 97
TELL ME THE OLD, OLD, STORY..... 280
TELL ME THE STORY OF JESUS..... 24
That dreadful night before his death 307
THAT'S ENOUGH FOR ME........... 210
THE CHURCH OF GOD.............. 372
THE CHURCH'S ONE FOUNDATION.. 316
THE CLEANSING WAVE............. 349
THE CROSS IS NOT GREATER........ 263
The cross that he gave may be heavy 263
THE END OF THE WAY............. 363
THE GARDEN OF PRAYER........... 222
THE GATE AJAR................... 184
THE GOLDEN RULE................ 411
THE GOSPEL IS FOR ALL........... 61
THE GREAT PHYSICIAN............. 151
THE HAVEN OF REST.............. 267
The head that once was crowned... 351
THE HEAVENS DECLARE THE GLORY. 343
THE HOLLOW OF GOD'S HAND...... 175
THE HOME UP THERE.............. 15
THE KINGDOMS OF EARTH PASS AWAY 342
THE LILY OF THE VALLEY.......... 139
The little flower that opens........ 415
THE LORD HAS BEEN MINDFUL
OF ME 228
THE LORD IS IN HIS HOLY TEMPLE 95
THE LORD IS OUR SALVATION...... 437
THE LORD IS WATCHING YOU...... 408
THE LORD, MY SHEPHERD IS........ 161
THE LORD'S MY SHEPHERD, I'LL
NOT WANT 430
The Lord's our rock................ 327
THE LORD'S RETURN.............. 383
THE LORD'S SUPPER............... 207
THE MASTER'S TOUCH............. 173
The mighty God, omniscient One.... 329
The night is fast passing........... 367
THE OLD RUGGED CROSS.......... 231
THE PRECIOUS BOOK DIVINE....... 16
THE PROVIDENCE OF GOD......... 329
THE ROCK THAT IS HIGHER THAN I 223
The sands have been washed....... 363
The service of Jesus true pleasure.. 362
THE SILVER STAR................. 388
THE SOLEMN FEAST............... 307
THE UNCLOUDED DAY............. 96
The voice of the Saviour says come.. 112
THE WAY OF THE CROSS
LEADS HOME 249

PAGE

The world has lost the right of
prayer 289
THEN BE PREPARED................ 390
There's a book which surpasses.... 107
There comes to my heart one sweet
strain 105
There is a city God hath made...... 390
THERE IS A FOUNTAIN.............. 79
There is a gate that stands ajar.... 184
THERE IS A GREEN HILL FAR AWAY 5
THERE IS A HABITATION............ 28
There is a name I love to hear...... 48
THERE IS A PLACE OF REFUGE 250
THERE IS A SEA................... 224
THERE IS POWER IN THE BLOOD... 354
THERE IS REST FOR THE WEARY.... 428
There is rest, sweet rest............ 295
THERE IS SUNSHINE IN MY SOUL.... 122
There is work enough to do........ 436
THERE SHALL BE SHOWERS OF
BLESSINGS 29
THERE STANDS A ROCK ON SHORES
OF TIME 245
There was One who was willing.... 270
THERE WILL BE LIGHT............. 259
There's a beautiful place called
heaven 170
There's a call comes ringing........ 202
THERE'S A FOUNTAIN FREE........ 357
There's a garden where Jesus is
waiting 222
THERE'S A GREAT DAY COMING..... 23
There's a land beyond the river.... 366
There's a land that is fairer........ 154
THERE'S A PARDON FULL AND SWEET 364
THERE'S A ROYAL BANNER.......... 429
There's a stranger at the door...... 11
THERE'S A WIDENESS IN GOD'S MERCY 396
There's many a heart that's weary.. 173
There's not a friend................ 4
There's nothing so precious........ 358
There's within my heart a melody...347
THINK ON THESE THINGS.......... 350
This is not our rest................ 15
Though my cross may be hard to
bear 52
THROW OUT THE LIFE LINE........ 129
THOU ART THE WAY.............. 282
Thou my everlasting portion........ 190
THOU THINKEST, LORD, OF ME...... 276
Though I thru the valley of shadow 228
Though the storm clouds rise above
us 341
Though the way we journey........ 217
Though you are helpless........... 318
THOUGH YOUR SINS BE AS SCARLET 293
TILL THE SUN GOES DOWN......... 436
Time is filled with swift transition. 227
'TIS SET, THE FEAST DIVINE........ 106
'TIS SO SWEET TO TRUST IN JESUS... 292

PAGE

'Tis the Bible................... 107
'Tis the Blessed Hour of Prayer. 54
'Tis Midnight and on Olive's
  Brow 57
'Tis the grandest theme............ 149
To Christ be loyal and be true...... 69
To Christ Be True............. 69
To the Work................. 40
True-hearted, Whole-hearted... 294
Trust and Obey................ 1
Trying to walk in the steps....... 353

Unsearchable Riches 286
Up to the bountiful Giver of life.. 264

Vainly we seek after men......... 346

Walking alone at eve............. 244
Walking in sunlight............... 43
We Are Fellow Creatures....... 225
We Are Going Down the Valley 422
We Assemble Here to Worship.. 128
We Have An Anchor............. 166
We have heard the joyful sound.... 298
We May Not Climb the Heavenly
  Steeps 114
We praise Thee, O God.......... 234
We Saw Thee Not............. 247
We Shall Be Like Him........... 339
We Shall See the King Some Day 217
We'll Never Say Goodby....... 314
We'll Work Till Jesus Comes.... 86
Welcome for Me............... 391
We're Marching to Zion........ 8
What a fellowship................. 134
What a Friend We Have In Jesus 75
What can wash away my sins?...... 59
What Did He Do?............. 187
What Is Your Prospect?......... 368
What Shall It Be?............. 195
What Shall It Profit?.......... 186
What Will Christ Do With Me?. 392
What will you do with Jesus?..... 195
Whatsoever is honest 350
When God Forgives He Forgets.. 360
When He Cometh............... 409
When I am lonely................ 387
When I Can Read My Title Clear 138
When I was far away and lost...... 211
When in his glory................ 400
When Jesus comes to reward....... 45
When Morning Lights the
  Eastern Skies 359
When my life work is ended........ 421
When My Love to Christ
  Grows Weak 266
When peace like a river........... 94
When skies are clear and friends
  are dear 64
When storms around are sweeping.. 218

PAGE

When the departure for worlds
  unknown 392
When the Roll Is Called
  Up Yonder 361
When the storms of life are raging.. 296
When the sun of my life has gone
  down 452
When the trumpet of the Lord..... 361
When the trumpet shall sound...... 272
When They Ring the Golden
  Bells 366
When We All Get to Heaven.... 37
When we meet in sweet communion 207
When we shall reach the more
  excellent 339
When we walk with the Lord....... 1
Where He Leads I'll Follow.... 183
Where He Leads Me I Will
  Follow 83
Where Livest Thou?............. 385
Where the Gates Swing
  Outward Never 256
While Jesus Whispers to You.... 18
While We Pray and While
  We Plead 435
Whispering Hope 322
Whiter Than Snow............. 389
Who at the Door Is Standing?... 82
Who Will Follow Jesus?........ 426
Whosoever heareth shout, shout
  the sound 113
Whosoever Will May Come...... 113
Why Did My Saviour Come to
  Earth? 34
Why did the Saviour heaven leave?.. 179
Why Keep Jesus Waiting?......... 68
Why Do You Wait?............. 77
Will Jesus Find Us Watching?.... 45
Will you come, will you come?...... 90
Will You Not Tell It Today?.... 109
Will your anchor hold?........... 166
With friends on earth we meet.... 314
With Thee 375
Wonderful Love of Jesus........ 46
Wonderful Peace 290
Wonderful Story of Love....... 72
Wonderful Words of Life....... 212
Work for Jesus................. 278
Work, for the Night Is Coming.. 284
Worthy Art Thou............... 25
Would you be free from the burden? 354
Would you live for Jesus?......... 84

Ye Must Be Born Again.......... 401
Yes, for me, for me He careth...... 3
Yield Not to Temptation........ 219